M000217175

Number Eight
The W. L. Moody, Jr., Natural History Series

Amphibians and Reptiles of Texas

Amphibians and Reptiles of Texas

WITH KEYS, TAXONOMIC SYNOPSES, BIBLIOGRAPHY, AND DISTRIBUTION MAPS

BY

James R. Dixon

TEXAS A&M UNIVERSITY PRESS

College Station

Copyright © 1987 by James R. Dixon
All rights reserved

Library of Congress Cataloging-in-Publication Data
Dixon, James Ray.
  Amphibians and reptiles of Texas.
  Bibliography: p.
  Includes index.
  1. Amphibians—Texas. 2. Reptiles—Texas.
I. Title.
QL653.T4D59 1987   597.6'09764   86-23036
ISBN 0-89096-293-6
ISBN 0-89096-358-4 pbk.

Manufactured in the United States of America
FIRST EDITION

Contents

Illustrations

Figures

Photographs   *following page* 56

Mole Salamander
Texas Blind Salamander
Black-spotted Newt
Mexican Burrowing Toad
Spotted Chirping Frog
Mexican Treefrog
Houston Toad
Pig Frog
Big Bend Mud Turtle
Cagle's Map Turtle
Reticulated Gecko
Mountain Short-horned Lizard
Mesquite Lizard
Worm Snake
Gray-checkered Whiptail

Acknowledgments

This work would never have been possible without the aid of colleagues, friends, and students. I am particularly pleased to acknowledge the aid of Ken King and David Kizirian, two students who suffered the hardships of surveying northwest Texas counties that possessed fewer than ten recorded species of amphibians and reptiles; they did an admirable job.

My thanks to those curators who responded to my plea for museum records: P. Alberch, W. Auffenberg, R. L. Bezy, B. C. Brown, S. D. Busak, J. Campbell, C. C. Carpenter, A. H. Chaney, C. J. Cole, W. W. Dalquest, W. G. Degenhardt, W. E. Duellman, N. Ford, J. Fouquette, T. Fritts, D. A. Gallagher, J. Green, H. W. Greene, S. Hammack, L. M. Hardy, W. R. Heyer, R. F. Inger, S. Kerr, A. G. Kluge, J. M. Legler, D. Lentz, A. E. Leviton, C. S. Lieb, E. A. Liner, C. J. McCoy, R. W. McDiarmid, H. Marx, E. V. Malnate, R. F. Martin, T. Maxwell, J. S. Mecham, E. Morgan, R. H. Mount, C. W. Myers, M. A. Nickerson, R. A. Nussbaum, W. J. Pyburn, F. Rainwater, J. Rosado, W. Seifert, N. J. Scott, J. F. Scudday, C. B. Smith, H. M. Smith, P. W. Smith, T. Uzzell, J. V. Vindum, W. J. Voss, D. B. Wake, R. G. Webb, J. W. Wright, G. Zug, and R. G. Zweifel.

Special thanks go to those colleageus and students who furnished specimen records, literature, and other courtesies: R. W. Axtell, R. J. Baldauf, D. Barker, P. M. Burchfield, C. T. Coody, R. H. Dean, C. H. Ernst, E. Farmer, G. W. Ferguson, T. Gallucci, M. Haiduk, C. Harrison, F. S. Hendricks, T. Hibbitts, J. B. Iverson, J. D. Johnson, J. Karges, B. Keeley, W. W. Lamar, W. L. McClure, H. D. McCrystal, E. J. Michaud, E. O. Moll, W. S. Parker, F. E. Potter, A. H. Price, H. Quinn, F. L. Rose, M. E. Seidel, J. W. Sites, D. Stine, S. Stone, R. A. Thomas, T. Vance, T. Vermersch, J. Ward, and J. E. Werler.

I am especially appreciative of Elinor Auffenberg, who donated her time to compile a list of Texas snake records from the Florida State Museum, and to Carl Lieb and Bill Lamar, who have never failed to respond to requests for information and other amenities.

I am forever in debt to Jerry Raun and Fred Gehlbach, who compiled the literature prior to 1967. They made my job much easier. I owe much to David Kizirian who scanned 95 percent of the 1967–1982 literature and provided subject categories.

R. W. Axtell, R. Conant, R. W. McDiarmid, E. V. Malnate, and F. E. Potter aided this project by solving problems of distribution and identification of various amphibian and reptile species.

Photographs and/or slides were donated by D. Barker, R. Bezy, J. T. Collins, the late I. H. Conant, W. G. Degenhardt, W. W. Lamar, C. M. Mather, A. Odum, J. F. Scudday, J. W. Sites, R. A. Thomas, L. J. Vitt, J. E. Werler, and J. W. Wright.

This manuscript was typed by Sally Kim, who devoted much of her time to correcting my errors, and I appreciate her patience and understanding.

I am forever thankful for my wife Mary, who had many lonely evenings while I worked on this project. Without her kindness and understanding this project would have never reached completion. She is gratefully acknowledged for some of the line drawings utilized in the keys, and kind permission for the use of others was given by Alan Chaney.

Amphibians and Reptiles of Texas

1
Introduction

This work began as an updating of the Texas herpetological literature following the pattern set by Raun and Gehlbach's 1972 treatise,
Amphibians and Reptiles in Texas. I later decided to revise Raun and
Gehlbach's work and received their approval to do so. I felt it necessary to
add keys to species and subspecies to make the work more usable as a
laboratory guide. A change in the style of literature citation used by Raun
and Gehlbach would have made their book and the present work incom-
patible, so I decided to insert all new literature citations directly into
their system by using decimal points.

Texas contains 204 species and 283 taxa of amphibians and reptiles.
These taxa are, to some extent, restricted to particular vegetation communities, soil types, or water sources. Although the various environments of the state appear to have their own particular herpetofauna, a
number of "generalists" tend to mask the uniqueness of some of these environments. Texas is situated at the junction of four major physiographic
divisions of North America. These are the Rocky Mountains, Great Plains,
Eastern Forests, and the Southwestern Deserts. Each of the latter divisions is further divided into biotic provinces. For a summary of these
provinces and their attendant herpetofauna, see Blair (74).

An analysis of species densities by counties (political units of un-
equal size) reveals more about resident herpetologists and intensive herpetofauna inventories than about the distribution of the amphibians and
reptiles in Texas. The highest number of recorded species occur in such
counties as Bexar, Brazos, Dallas, Harris, Hays, McLennan, Tarrant, and
Travis. Each of these counties contains a major state university and one or
more resident herpetologists. Other species-rich counties may be the result of incidental collection of species while in pursuit of more desirable
"target" species or of their diverse environments. For example, Bexar
County contains 97 amphibian and reptile species, the highest species
density in the state, and 48 percent of the total herpetofauna of Texas.
Bexar County also contains one of the most diverse environments of the
state, and several active herpetologists reside there.

All major museums of the United States and smaller museums in
Texas were asked to supply Texas records for their holdings of amphibians
and reptiles. About 90 percent responded with 12,389 county records and
more than 100,000 individual localities. Questionable identifications and
isolated distributional records were verified where possible either by vis-
iting the museum or by borrowing the material for examination.

The more than 12,300 species records for 254 Texas counties reveal that 49 species occur in 60 percent of all Texas counties, and 50 species occur in only 1.5 percent of all counties. The distribution of species suggests that 25 percent of the taxa are abundant, 25 percent rare, and 50 percent of average distribution. Salamanders comprise 4.2 percent of the total number of records, frogs and toads 22.9 percent, turtles 11.6 percent, lizards 20.3 percent, and snakes 41.0 percent. About 29 percent (3,612) of the 12,389 records have been accumulated during the past fifteen years.

County distribution maps are provided for all Texas species of amphibians and reptiles. Those species with limited distribution may be combined with other species belonging to the same family on a single map but with separate county segments (see Map 2). Questionable records are mentioned under *Comments*. Most of the questionable localities have correct identifications, but those individuals may have escaped from captivity, been improperly labeled as to locality, or been transported accidentally.

The Texas Herpetological Literature

About 1,800 scholarly publications concerning Texas amphibians and reptiles appeared between 1852 and 1980 (Figure 1). By the end of 1985, more than 2,000 publications on various aspects of the Texas herpetofauna had appeared. These include only a few popular articles, newspaper accounts, and reports to federal and state agencies. The Texas herpetological literature has increased 38 percent following the publication of Raun and Gehlbach's 1972 treatise. The first 115 years of Texas herpetological literature averaged only ten articles per year, while the subsequent 15 years averaged forty-eight articles per year.

Approximately 717 primary authors have utilized 292 publication resources. Seven of these, *Copeia* (239), *Herpetologica* (208), *Texas Journal of Science* (149), *Herp Review* (133), *Southwestern Naturalist* (116), *Catalogue of American Amphibians and Reptiles* (87), and *Journal of Herpetology* (63), contain about 50 percent of all published articles on Texas amphibians and reptiles. About 541 (27 percent) of all published articles are coauthored, with the bulk of coauthorship occurring after 1945 (Figure 2). The coauthorship rate has doubled since 1945, and of the 573 coauthors, 259 (45 percent) never appear as senior authors. There are about 719 primary authors, of which 439 appear only once, and 614 (85 percent) appear as authors fewer than five times. Of the 719 primary authors, 105 have published 1,070 (53 percent) of the total number of articles (Figure 3). Sixteen authors have published 20 or more articles on Texas herpetology. They make up only 2 percent of all authors, and 22 percent of all publications. Eight of the 16 authors are deceased, and

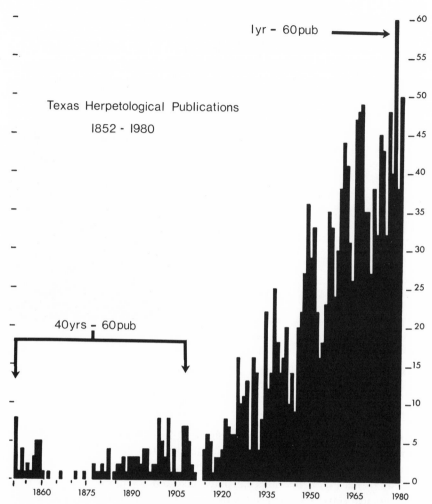

FIG. 1. The increase in publications on Texas herpetology from 1852 to 1980.

eight continue to publish on Texas herpetology. Those deceased, their Texas publications record, and their active period are J. Strecker (58) 1902–1935; W. F. Blair (39) 1949–1976; D. W. Tinkle (26) 1951–1979; E. D. Cope (25) 1859–1900; W. W. Milstead (25) 1951–1978; C. E. Burt (20) 1928–1938; and E. H. Taylor (20) 1931–1950. The current active authors and their publication records are H. M. Smith (65), J. R. Dixon (25), F. H. Gehlbach (24), B. C. Brown (23), R. W. Axtell (21), R. Conant (21), F. L. Rose (20), and C. T. McAllister (20).

Strecker, a resident of Texas, achieved a publication record of 58 articles in 22 years, while Cope, a nonresident, published 25 articles over

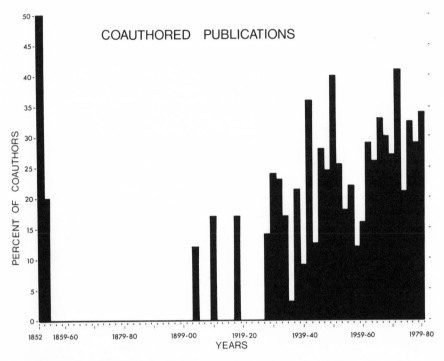

FIG. 2. The rate of coauthorship for Texas herpetological publications by individual authors from 1852 to 1980.

41 years. Resident herpetologists have a distinct advantage concerning knowledge of their local herpetofauna. Of active herpetologists, H. M. Smith's 65 published articles over a 52-year span (1933–1985) is a monument to his excellence as a herpetologist and his desire to create herpetological activity among his colleagues. Only the young herpetologists of today will have the opportunity to be as productive as H. M. Smith.

A Brief History of Texas Herpetology

Some of the early writers on Texas herpetology neither resided in nor visited Texas. Most of their material came from such early collectors of natural history lore as Spanish explorers, botanists, and survey engineers.

Spanish explorers during the period 1650–1700 recorded encounters with rattlesnakes in Texas. The French botanist, Jean Louis Berlandier, was probably the earliest science writer on amphibians and reptiles of Texas. Although Berlandier was French, he resided in Mexico and was one of the first scientists to write extensively on his Texas travels. Berlan-

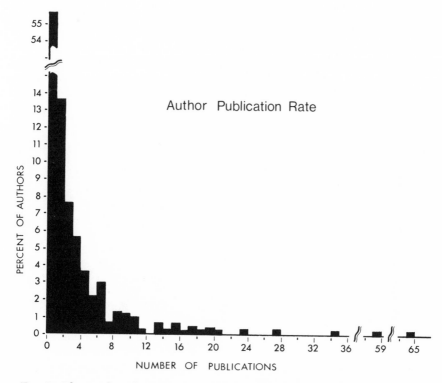

FIG. 3. The number of Texas herpetological publications by individual authors from 1852 to 1980.

dier (59.65) made several expeditions on horseback and on foot across the southern half of Texas between 1828 and 1834 (Figure 4). His major expeditions were from Laredo to Bexar (February 20, 1828, to March 1, 1828), from Bexar–San Felipe–Trinity and back to Bexar (April 13 to June 18, 1828), Aransas–Goliad several times (May, 1829), Bexar to Laredo (July 14–28, 1829), Bexar to Goliad (February 2–5, 1830), Matamoros to Goliad (April, 1834), Bexar–Eagle Pass–Laredo–Matamoros (June 10–July 28, 1834). On his first trip, he encountered the Texas tortoise and bullfrogs along the route, and as he crossed the Nueces River he encountered alligators and soft-shelled turtles and remarked how common *Trionyx* and *Rana* were around Bexar. Throughout Berlandier's trip to San Felipe, Trinity, and return trip to Bexar, he encountered box turtles, salamanders, western diamondback and timber rattlesnakes, *Rana* and alligators. Berlandier's trips between Copano Bay and Goliad were frequently dangerous because of his contact with timber rattlesnakes. On one of his trips during 1829 he encountered the Texas horned lizard for the first time. Occasionally Berlandier mentioned encounters with treefrogs, but he failed

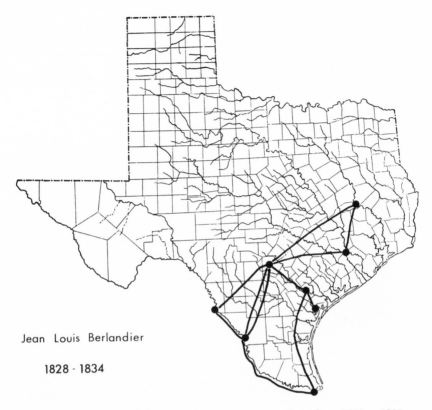

Jean Louis Berlandier

1828 - 1834

FIG. 4. Jean Louis Berlandier's exploration routes in Texas from 1828 to 1834.

to give the scientific names. Because of his general observations and collecting, his name is associated in the literature with the Texas tortoise, Rio Grande leopard frog, and many plant species.

John Bartlett and William Emory's boundary surveys of 1850–1854, and their subsequent collections of amphibians and reptiles, resulted in a partial list of Texas specimens through the publications of Baird and Girard (34–39; 402–404). Baird and Girard recorded a total of eighty-six species in the area between Indianola and El Paso.

Several noted herpetologists began describing Texas species following the field collections of Berlandier, Emory, Bartlett, and others. Among these were E. D. Cope, G. A. Boulenger, Louis Agassiz, Albert Gunther, Robert Kennicott, and Spencer F. Baird. By 1900, John Strecker had begun collecting in Texas, and by 1915 he had published the first definitive list, 163 species, of reptiles and amphibians for the state of Texas. By 1933, Strecker had accumulated the largest collection of Texas reptiles and amphibians, and he housed the collection at Baylor University. By the time of his death, Strecker had written 60 papers on the herpetofauna of Texas. Brown (162) produced the next major checklist of Texas amphibians and reptiles and recognized 182 species, followed by Raun and Gehlbach (770.3), who recognized 199 species. The most recent state list by Robert Thomas (1003.31) records 203 species.

The major herpetologists working with Texas species between Strecker's era and World War II were Laurence Klauber, Roger Conant, Charles Burt, Bryce Brown, Hobart Smith, Edward Taylor, Howard Gloyd, Stanley Mulaik, Karl P. Schmidt, Frank Blanchard, and Alan H. Wright. Only Brown and Smith actually resided in Texas.

Identification Keys

The dichotomous identification keys are arranged by major taxonomic groups, for example, salamanders, frogs and toads, turtles, lizards, and snakes. Various terms used in the keys are figured for the less serious student of herpetology, but the majority of the terms are standard terminology used by herpetologists.

The glossary is provided for those persons who may have difficulty in understanding the figures and terminology.

Distribution Maps

The maps are generally arranged alphabetically by species within phylogenetic family lineages. However, some species with restricted distributions (for example, Trans-Pecos, Balcones Escarpment, Marine, Semitropical) are consolidated into fifteen maps. These maps are arranged in a phylogenetic sequence where possible (see Maps 2, 5, 6, 8, 9, 11, 41, 62, 64, 66, 76, 91, 104, 127, 132).

Questionable county records are indicated by a dot with a question mark placed nearby. The questionable records may represent errors in identification, erroneous locality data, and/or an escaped pet that found its way into a museum or collection. A few records have a small x placed near the dot. These are intergrades, but the subspecies involved are unknown. Other zones of intergradation are marked with Y x Z to indicate which of the subspecies are involved in the contact zone. Where two or more subspecies are present on the same map, each has a letter designation and is listed in the caption.

2
Glossary

ADPRESSED LIMBS: Forelimb laid backward along the body and the hindlimb brought forward, with both limbs fully extended.

ALVEOLAR SURFACE: The crushing surface of the jaw just within the mouth of turtles.

ANAL PLATE: The terminal scale (plate) of the ventral series of snakes. It may be entire or divided by a diagonal suture near the midline; always lies below the anus.

AXILLARY SHIELD: An epidermal plate on the anterior edge of the bridge of turtles.

BICORNUATE TONGUE: A protuberant extension or "horn" on the posterior lateral edge of the tongue.

BONY SPINE: A row of bony spines covered with skin, immediately behind the head of some lizards.

BRIDGE: The part of the turtle's shell that connects the upper (carapace) and lower (plastron) bony parts. It may be composed of several sutured shields.

CANTHUS ROSTRALIS: The angle of the head from the eye to the nostril or tip of the snout.

CARAPACE: The dorsal part of a turtle shell, including the epidermal shields and the bony elements beneath them.

CHIN SHIELD: One or more pairs of enlarged, elongated scales between the mandibles of snakes.

COSTAL GROOVE: The vertical grooves along the sides of salamanders, usually between the limbs.

COSTAL SHIELD: A series of shields that cover the ribs and lie between the vertebrals and marginals on the turtle carapace.

CRANIAL CRESTS: Elevated bony ridges on the top of the head of bufonid toads; may have designated names according to their position on the head.

DERMAL RIDGE: An elevated (or folded) transverse layer of skin on the palate of some frogs.

DEWLAP: A vertical, laterally compressed fold of extensible skin on the throat of some iguanid lizards, particularly anoles.

DORSOLATERAL FOLD: An enlarged, granular, dorsolateral ridge than can extend to various lengths from behind the eye toward the hindlimb of ranid frogs.

EXTERNAL GILL: A respiratory organ usually located on the side of the neck of salamanders.

FEMORAL PORE: A relatively deep pit in the center or near the posterior edge of an enlarged scale or series of scales on the ventral surface of the thigh of some lizards.

FEMORAL WART: An external wart (poison gland) on the dorsal surface of the thigh of bufonid toads.

FRONTAL TROUGH: A depression that extends from the eyes to the snout and lies between the canthal ridges.

GILL RAKER: A bony or cartilaginous fingerlike process on the gill arch of larval salamanders.

GILL SLIT: A fissure or cleft in the side of the neck of salamanders that is associated with either internal or external gills.

GRANULAR SCALE: A surface texture of small, convex, nonoverlapping scales; a pebbled appearance.

GULAR FOLD: A transverse fold of skin across the throat, anterior to the forelimb insertion. In teiid lizards, this fold is called a mesoptychial fold.

GULAR SHIELD: The first pair of shields on the plastron of most turtles, but may be single or absent.

INGUINAL SHIELD: An epidermal shield on the posterior edge of the bridge of turtles.

INTERCALARY CARTILAGE: A segment of cartilage in the penultimate position of a hylid frog toe, and normally at right angles to the other elements.

INTERNASAL SCALE: Scales that lie between the nasals on the head of snakes and lizards.

INTERORBITAL BOSS: A round protuberance or knoblike process between the eyes of some amphibians.

INTERORBITAL DISTANCE: The horizontal distance between the eyes, normally measured from the middle of the eye.

INTERORBITAL SCALE: The scales that lie between the orbits on the dorsal surface of the head. The scales are frequently bounded on the outside by semicircular rows of scales that border the supraocular series of scales.

INTERPARIETAL SCALE: A head scale of a lizard that lies between the parietal scales.

INTERPECTORAL SUTURE: A suture between the third pair of plastron shields of a turtle.

KEELED SCALE: A ridgelike process on the carapace of turtles, or a ridge along the scales of some lizards and snakes.

LATERAL FOLD: A longitudinal fold of skin from the arm to the groin in certain lizards.

LENS RING: A dark area of pigmentation around the outer edge of the lens in the eye of some salamanders.

LICHEN-LIKE: A pattern of rounded but irregular peripheral branching of blotches in salamanders.

LOREAL SCALE: A rectangular or squarish scale on the side of the head between the nasal and preocular. Lizards may have one or many, but snakes normally have only one.

MARGINAL SHIELD: A shield in the outer series on the carapace of turtles, usually visible from above and below. It is characterized by its sharp angle, marking the edge of the carapace.

MESOPTYCHIAL FOLD: Synonymous with the gular fold, but the term is frequently applied to associated scales around the fold in teiid lizards.

METATARSAL TUBERCLE: A protuberance or horny projection on the basal part of the foot, generally near the heel in amphibians.

NASAL SCALE: A scale on the side of the head that includes the external naris (nostril) in most reptiles. It may be vertically divided through the nostril.

NASAL SEPTUM: A vertical segment of cartilage separating the two nasal passages. In some softshell turtles, the cartilage may have a horizontal ridge along the septum.

NASOLABIAL GROOVE: A groove extending from the nostril to the lip in some plethodontid salamanders.

NUCHAL SHEILD: A shield on the turtle carapace that precedes the vertebral shields along the midline.

PARIETAL SCALE: One or more scales covering the occiput in reptiles. In snakes, the parietals are paired and are the last pair of scales on the head.

PAROTOID GLAND: A swollen glandular area behind the eye on the head, that may extend onto the neck or shoulder. It is generally characterized by its shape and size.

PECTORAL GLAND: A small, often ill-defined gland on the chest of some spade-foot toads.

PLASTRON: The ventral part of the turtle shell, usually consisting of paired external shields with underlying bone.

POSTANTEBRACHIAL SCALE: Scales on the underside of the forelimb, usually toward the elbow. They are usually characterized in teiid lizards by their shape and size.

POSTFEMORAL POCKET: A fold or pocket of skin behind the insertion of the hindlimb of some lizards.

POSTLABIAL SCALE: A series of large or small scales lying posterior to and in line with the labial scales.

POSTMENTAL SCALE: A series of paried or unpaired scales lying along the midventral line immediately posterior to the mental scale.

POSTNASAL SCALE: A scale or series of scales lying behind the nasal scale and in front of the loreal scale.

POSTOCULAR SCALE: A scale or series of scales at the posterior edge of the orbit.

POSTORBITAL CRESTS: A cranial crest posterior to and perpendicular to the posterior edge of the orbit.

PREFRONTAL SHIELD: An epidermal shield or scale or series of shields or scales immediately anterior to the frontal.

PREMAXILLARY TEETH: Teeth associated with a pair of bones near the midline of the anterior angle of the upper jaw.

PREOCULAR SCALE: A scale or series of scales at the anterior edge of the orbit.

ROSTRAL SCALE: The scale at the tip of the snout.

SCALE ROWS: The dorsal scales of lizards and snakes, usually arranged in a continuous series of rows, with each scale clearly assignable to a sequence. These are normally counted in a particular fashion around the body to determine the number of rows between the ventrals in snakes, or around the entire body of some lizards.

SUBCAUDALS: Scales lying beneath the tail in reptiles. The scales may be single or divided in snakes.

SUBOCULAR SCALE: A scale or series of scales directly below the orbit.

SUPRALABIAL SCALE: A series of scales that are often enlarged and cover the upper lip.

SUPRANASAL SCALE: A scale or series of scales lying directly above the nasal scale and lateral to the internasal scale.

SUPRAOCULAR SCALE: A series of scales that lie on the dorsum of the orbit in lizards; a large scale that lies directly above the eye in snakes.

SUPRAORBITAL CRESTS: A cranial crest that lies between the eyes and parallels the canthus rostralis anteriorly.

TARSUS: The area of the hind foot between the digits and the articulation with the tibia/fibula.

TEMPORAL SCALE: A scale or series of scales behind the postoculars, below the parietal and above the supralabials.

TIBIAL WART: A wart of variable size on the lower legs of some toads.

TRUNK VERTEBRAE: The vertebrae lying between the pectoral and pelvic girdles.

TUBERCLE: A small to large rounded or triangular bump in the skin. It may be an enlarged and raised scale in lizards and snakes, or similar to warts in amphibians.

TYMPANUM: The membrane covering the external opening of the middle ear chamber.

VENTRAL SCALE: Any one of many large scales on the belly of a snake.

VERTEBRAL SHIELD: The midline dorsal row of shields on the carapace of turtles, normally preceded by the nuchal shield.

VOMERINE TEETH: Teeth lying on the vomer bone in the palate of amphibians.

WART: Any hard, cornified, raised structure on the skin of amphibians.

WEBBING: A thin membrane of skin connecting adjacent digits in frogs and toads.

WHORL: A symmetrical series of scales around a caudal segment of lizards.

3
Keys to the Amphibians and Reptiles of Texas

Salamanders

1. Hind limbs present 2
   Hind limbs absent ...... *Siren intermedia* (A), Lesser Siren.
   - A. Costal grooves (Figure 5) between legs and anus 34–36; olive gray above with scattered black spots; belly with numerous light spots ....
     .... *Siren i. nettingi*, Western Lesser Siren.
     Costal grooves between legs and anus 36–38; gray or brownish gray above with tiny black spots; belly gray
     .... *Siren i. texana*, Rio Grande Lesser Siren.

2. Hind toes four or five; body not eel-like 3
   Hind toes three; body eel-like ...... *Amphiuma tridactylum*,
   Three-toed Amphiuma.

3. Hind toes four 4
   Hind toes five 5

4. Aquatic salamanders with three pairs of external gills (Figure 5) .... *Necturus beyeri*, Gulf Coast Water Dog.
   Very small terrestrial salamander without external gills .....
   .... *Eurycea quadridigitata*, Dwarf Salamander.

5. Costal grooves absent or indistinct; top of head rough with numerous low ridges, including canthus rostralis 6
   Costal grooves well developed; top of head smooth, without ridges 7

6. Belly spots large, about size of eye; dorsum never reddish or with red spots .... *Notophthalmus meridionalis*,
   Black-spotted Newt.
   Belly spots small, smaller than eye; dorsum reddish, often with red spots ....
   ..... *Notophthalmus viridiscens louisianensis*, Central Newt.

NASOLABIAL GROOVE

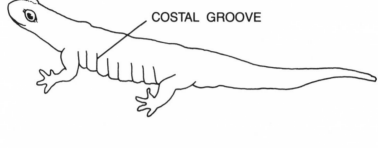

COSTAL GROOVE

EXTERNAL GILL

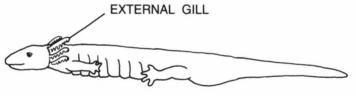

FIG. 5. Some key features of salamanders.

7. Nasolabial groove (Figure 5) present if external gills absent; if external gills present, then with three gill slits 8
    Nasolabial groove absent; if external gills present, then with four gill slits 16

8. Venter uniformly light; tail laterally compressed 9
    Venter solid black or black with light flecks; tail round in cross section . . . . *Plethodon glutinosus* (A), Slimy Salamander.
    A. Lower jaw and throat white in contrast to other body color . . . . . *Plethodon g. albagula,* White Throat Slimy Salamander.
    Lower jaw and throat only slightly lighter than body color . . . . . *Plethodon g. glutinosus,* Slimy Salamander.

9. External gills and three gill slits; no nasolabial groove 10
    External gills absent; nasolabial groove present . . . .
    . . . *Desmognathus auriculatus,* Southern Dusky Salamander.

10. Costal grooves 13 or more; eye diameter six or fewer times
    smaller than interorbital distance 13
    Costal grooves 12 or fewer; eye diameter ten or more times
    smaller than interorbital distance 11

11. Premaxillary teeth 40 or more; 13 trunk vertebrae 12
    Premaxillary teeth 33 or fewer; 14 trunk vertebrae .. *Eurycea
    tridentifera*, Comal Blind Salamander.

12. Adpressed limbs overlap one costal groove ..... *Typhlomolge
    robusta*, Blanco Blind Salamander.
    Adpressed limbs overlap five or more costal grooves ....
    .... *Typhlomolge rathbuni*, Texas Blind Salamander.

13. Eye lacking dark lens ring; body brownish yellow to white .. 14
    Eye with dark lens ring; body brown ....
    .... *Eurycea nana*, San Marcos Salamander.

14. Four or more costal grooves between adpressed limbs; pre-
    maxillary teeth 20 or fewer 15
    Three or fewer costal grooves between adpressed limbs; pre-
    maxillary teeth 25 or more ..... *Eurycea troglodytes*, Valdina
    Farms Salamander.

15. Eye diameter four to five times smaller than interorbital dis-
    tance; costal grooves 14 to 15, about four between adpressed
    limbs ...... *Eurycea latitans*, Cascade Caverns Salamander.
    Eye diameter two times smaller than interorbital distance; cos-
    tal grooves 15 to 17, about five to seven between adpressed
    limbs .... *Eurycea neotenes*, Texas Salamander.

16. External gills present or absent; if external gills present, then
    gill rakers also present 17
    External gills present, but without gill rakers ....
    .... *Desmognathus auriculatus* (larvae).

17. Body with small light flecks (at least laterally) or lichenlike
    markings, or totally dark 18
    Body with clearly defined spots, bars, or blotches 19

18. Costal grooves ten; head broad and flat, considerably wider
    than neck; body short and stout; tail also short ... *Ambystoma
    talpoideum*, Mole Salamander.
    Costal grooves 14; head not broad, little wider than neck; body

moderately slender . . . . . . *Ambystoma texanum*, Smallmouth Salamander.

19. Body with light yellow to orange markings   20
Body with light metallic white markings . . . .
. . . . *Ambystoma opacum*, Marbled Salamander.

20. Yellowish to orange round spots arranged in two rows dorsally
. . . . *Ambystoma maculatum*, Spotted Salamander.
Yellow blotches or bars extending onto sides and often onto belly . . . . *Ambystoma tigrinum* (A), Tiger Salamander.
    A. Light spots or blotches on body 15 to 58 (avg. 30) . . . .
. . . *Ambystoma t. tigrinum*, Eastern Tiger Salamander.
Light spots or blotches on body large, numbering 6 to 36 (avg. 17) . . . .
Ambystoma t. marvortium, Barred Tiger Salamander.

Frogs and Toads

1. Pupil of eye vertical; skin smooth; hind legs obviously modified for burrowing   2
Pupil of eye round or horizontal; hind limbs may or may not be modified for burrowing; if modified for burrowing, then skin warty   6

2. Tongue attached in front of mouth   3
Tongue attached in rear of mouth . . . . *Rhinophrynus dorsalis*, Mexican Burrowing Toad.

3. Pectoral glands absent   4
Pectoral glands present . . . . . . *Scaphiopus holbrooki hurteri*, Hurter's Spadefoot.

4. Interorbital boss absent   5
Interorbital boss present . . . . *Scaphiopus bombifrons*, Plains Spadefoot.

5. Pigmented edge of metatarsal tubercle (Figure 6) rounded, about as wide as long . . . .
. . . . *Scaphiopus multiplicatus*, New Mexico Spadefoot.
Pigmented edge of metatarsal tubercle elongate, about twice as long as wide . . . . . . *Scaphiopus couchi*, Couch's Spadefoot.

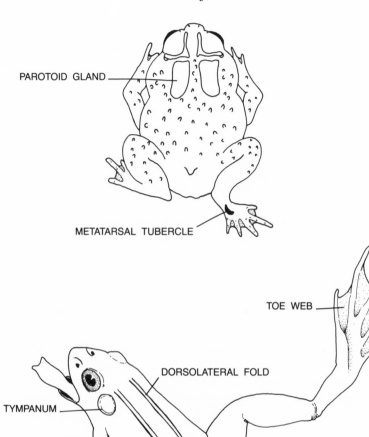

FIG. 6. Some key features of frogs and toads.

6. Tympanum (Figure 6) present 9
   Tympanum absent 7

7. One metatarsal tubercle; light middorsal line absent; no smooth
   dermal ridges across palate in front of pharynx 8
   Two metatarsal tubercles; light middorsal line present; two
   smooth dermal ridges across palate in front of pharynx . . . . .
   . . . . *Hypopachus variolosus*, Sheep Frog.

8. Belly immaculate cream (white) . . . . . *Gastrophryne olivacea*,
    Great Plains Narrowmouth Toad.
    Belly darkly mottled . . . .
    . . . . *Gastrophryne carolinensis*, Eastern Narrowmouth Toad.

9. Tongue bicornuate posteriorly   10
    Tongue not bicornuate posteriorly   18

10. Dorsolateral folds (Figure 6) absent   11
    Dorsolateral folds present   12

11. Distance from heel to knee about equal to distance from heel
    to first toe; corner of mouth to tip of snout equal to width of
    head at anterior edge of tympanum . . . .
    . . . . *Rana grylio*, Pig Frog.
    Distance from heel to knee about equal to distance from heel
    to second toe; corner of mouth to tip of snout about 25 percent
    greater than width of head at anterior edge of tympanum
    . . . . *Rana catesbeiana*, Bullfrog.

12. Dorsolateral fold extends entire length of body (may be bro-
    ken posteriorly); dorsal pattern of spots   13
    Dorsolateral fold extends two-thirds of body; general color
    brown . . . . *Rana clamitans clamitans*, Bronze Frog.

13. Spots between dorsolateral folds rounded; folds consistent in
    width throughout their length   14
    Spots between dorsolateral folds in two rectangular rows; folds
    much broader anteriorly than posteriorly . . . .
    . . . . *Rana palustris*, Pickerel Frog.

14. Dorsal spots without encircling white rings   15
    Dorsal spots enclosed by white rings . . . .
    . . . . *Rana areolata areolata*, Southern Crawfish Frog.

15. Dorsolateral folds continuous to hind limb insertion   16
    Dorsolateral folds interrupted posteriorly   17

16. Dorsal dark spots, usually with light border; posterior thigh
    pattern of discrete dark spots; tympanal light spot absent; dark
    snout spot usually present; vocal sacs not external . . . .
    . . . . *Rana pipiens*, Northern Leopard Frog.
    Dorsal dark spots without light borders; posterior thigh pat-

tern of dark reticulating lines; tympanal light spot present; dark snout spot usually absent; external vocal sacs . . . .
. . . . *Rana sphenocephala,* Southern Leopard Frog.

17. Well-defined whitish supralabial stripe from rear angle of jaw to near tip of snout; white tympanal and dark snout spots usually present; posterior thigh pattern of indistinct brownish, reticulating lines . . . . *Rana blairi,* Plains Leopard Frog. Supralabial white stripe, when present, not well defined anterior to eye; white tympanal and dark snout spots usually absent; posterior thigh pattern of heavy black reticulating lines . . . . *Rana berlandieri,* Rio Grande Leopard Frog.

18. Parotoid glands (Figure 7) and warty skin present   19
    Parotoid glands and warty skin absent   27

19. Parotoid glands triangular in shape, as long as head   20
    Parotoid glands not triangular in shape and not as long as head   21

20. Color brown to yellowish brown; adults greater than 84-mm snout-vent length . . . . *Bufo marinus,* Giant Toad. Color green to olive green; adults less than 60-mm snout-vent length . . . . *Bufo deblis* (A), Green Toad.
    A. Toes half webbed (Figure 6); nostrils at tip of snout
    . . . . *Bufo d. insidior,* Western Green Toad.

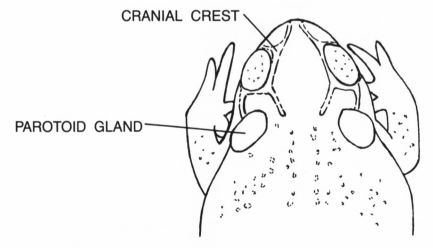

CRANIAL CREST

PAROTOID GLAND

FIG. 7. Cranial crests on a bufonid toad.

Toes one-third webbed; nostrils not at tip of snout . . .
. . . . *Bufo d. deblis*, Eastern Green Toad.

21. Parotoid glands circular or tear-shaped   22
    Parotoid glands elongate, from nearly two to more than three
    times as long as wide   23

22. Parotoid gland tear-shaped; cranial crests prominent (Figure 7)
    . . . . *Bufo valliceps valliceps*, Gulf Coast Toad.
    Parotoid gland circular; cranial crests absent or ill-defined
    . . . . *Bufo punctatus*, Red Spotted Toad.

23. Supraorbital crests parallel, not united into boss at the level of
    anterior margin of eyes   24
    Supraorbital crests united into boss at the level of anterior
    margin of eyes . . . . *Bufo cognatus*, Great Plains Toad.

24. Cranial crests prominent   25
    Cranial crests absent or ill-defined . . . .
    . . . . *Bufo speciosus*, Texas Toad.

25. Parotoid glands closest together at their midpoint   26
    Parotoid glands closest together anteriorly . . . .
    . . . . *Bufo woodhousei* (A), Woodhouse's Toad.
    A. Dark spots on chest absent, but a few dark spots may be
       present on throat of males . . . . B
       Dark spots present on chest . . . .
       . . . . *Bufo w. velatus*, East Texas Toad.
    B. Supraorbital crests thickened, often reducing the size
       of the frontal trough; frontal area elevated . . . .
       . . . . *Bufo w. woodhousei*, Woodhouse's Toad.
       Supraorbital crests narrow, separated by a normal frontal
       trough; frontal area not elevated . . . .
       . . . *Bufo w. australis*, Southwestern Woodhouse's Toad.

26. Femoral warts small and tibial warts large; postorbital and su-
    praorbital crests about equal in size . . . .
    . . . . . . *Bufo americanus charlesmithi*, Dwarf American Toad.
    Femoral and tibial warts about equal in size; postorbital crests
    conspicuously larger than supraorbital crests . . . .
    . . . . *Bufo houstonensis*, Houston Toad.

27. Toes with intercalary cartilage or bone present   28
    Toes without intercalary cartilage or bone   38

28. Toe pads greatly reduced in size, little wider than digits 29
    Toe pads large, distinctly wider than digits 32

29. Webs between toes poorly developed or reduced in size 30
    Webs between toes well developed, extending nearly to toe
    tips .... *Acris crepitans* (A), Cricket Frog.
       A. Throat pink in males; no well-defined dark bar on rear
          of thigh .... *Acris c. paludicola*, Coastal Cricket Frog.
          Throat dark gray to blackish in males; well-defined dark
          bar on rear of thigh .... B
       B. Dark bar with ragged edges on rear of thigh ....
          .... *Acris c. blanchardi*, Blanchard's Cricket Frog.
          Dark bar with smooth edges on rear of thigh ....
          .... *Acris c. crepitans*, Northern Cricket Frog.

30. Dorsal pattern of spots or blotches 31
    Dorsal pattern of three dark lines ....
    .... *Pseudacris triseriata feriarum*, Upland Chorus Frog.

31. A distinct uninterrupted dark line from eye to midbody on
    each side; broken lines or rows of spots dorsally ....
    .... *Pseudacris clarki*, Spotted Chorus Frog.
    No uninterrupted dark line from eye to midbody; body may be
    spotted, unicolored, or blotched ....
    .... *Pseudacris streckeri*, Strecker's Chorus Frog.

32. Tympanum much smaller than eye 33
    Tympanum about equal in size to eye ....
    .... *Smilisca baudinii*, Mexican Treefrog.

33. A black-bordered light spot below eye 34
    No black-bordered light spot below eye 35

34. The call represented by a low trill, about 25 pulses per second
    .... *Hyla versicolor*, Gray Treefrog.
    The call represented by a fast trill, about 50 pulses per second
    .... *Hyla chrysoscelis*, Cope's Gray Treefrog.

35. Dorsum uniform in color or with small darker spots or mark-
    ings 36
    Dorsum with a X-shaped pattern ....
    .... *Hyla crucifer crucifer*, Northern Spring Peeper.

36. Dorsum unicolor, or with only a few dark spots 37

Dorsum with many dark spots . . . .
. . . . *Hyla arenicolor*, Canyon Treefrog.

37. Diffuse white stripe from insertion of forelimb to hindlimb;
     adults usually less than 35-mm snout-vent length . . . .
     . . . . *Hyla squirella*, Squirrel Treefrog.
     Prominent white stripe from lips to midbody or slightly be-
     yond, seldom reaching hind limb insertion; adults bright
     green, usually more than 40-mm snouth-vent length . . . .
     . . . . *Hyla cinerea*, Green Treefrog.

38. Tips of digits expanded, frequently T-shaped   39
     Tips of digits not expanded . . . .
     . . . . *Leptodactylus fragilis*, White-lipped Frog.

39. Vomerine teeth absent   40
     Vomerine teeth present . . . .
     . . . . . . *Hylactophryne augusti latrans*, Eastern Barking Frog.

40. Dorsal markings of numerous irregular lines, spots, or blotches;
     forelimbs usually greater than foot with tarsus   41
     Dorsal markings of a few poorly defined spots; forelimbs usu-
     ally less than foot with tarsus . . . .
     . . . . *Syrrhophus cystignathoides campi*, Rio Grande Chirping
     Frog.

41. Dark bar present between eyes . . . .
     . . . . *Syrrhophus guttulatus*, Spotted Chirping Frog.
     Dark bar absent between eyes . . . .
     . . . . *Syrrhophus marnocki*, Cliff Chirping Frog.

Turtles

1. Carapace (Figure 8) covered with leathery skin   2
    Carapace covered with horny shields   4

2. Carapace flat, without longitudinal ridges; snout long and
    flexible   3
    Carapace rounded, with seven longitudinal ridges; snout never
    long and flexible . . . .
    . . . . . . *Dermochelys coriacea coriacea*, Atlantic Leatherback.

3. Horizontal ridge through nasal septum (Figure 9) present;

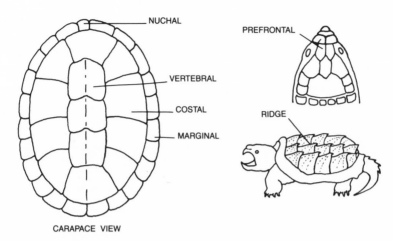

NUCHAL

PREFRONTAL

VERTEBRAL

COSTAL

RIDGE

MARGINAL

CARAPACE VIEW

FIG. 8. Key features of the carapace of a turtle shell; a snapping turtle showing ridges; a sea turtle head showing the prefrontal shields.

tubercles present along anterior edge of carapace . . . .
. . . . *Trionyx spiniferus* (A), Spiny Softshell.

   A. Pale rim around outer margin of carapace absent, or pale rim less than four times as wide posteriorly as laterally; light stripe behind eye not interrupted . . . . . . B
      Pale rim of carapace four or more times wider posteriorly than laterally; postocular stripe usually interrupted . . . . . . *Trionyx s. emoryi*, Texas Spiny Softshell

   B. Carapace with white tubercles; eye-like spots (ocelli) usually absent unless surrounding white tubercles . . . C
      White tubercles absent; dark spots and ocelli usually present. . . . .
      . . . . *Trionyx s. hartwegi*, Western Spiny Softshell.

   C. White tubercles more prevalent on the posterior part of the carapace; ocelli and black spots absent . . . .
      . . . . *Trionyx s. pallidus*, Pallid Spiny Softshell.
      Large tubercles more prevalent on the anterior part of the carapace; ocelli and black dots often present . . . . .
      Trionyx s. guadalupensis, Guadalupe Spiny Softshell.
Horizontal ridge through nasal septum absent; anterior edge of carapace smooth, lacking tubercles . . . .
      . . . . *Trionyx muticus muticus*, Midland Smooth Softshell.

4. Limbs modified into flippers; digits never visible   5
   Limbs normal; digits visible   8

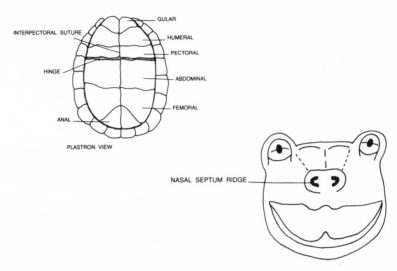

FIG. 9. Key features of the plastron of a turtle shell; a spiny softshell turtle showing the nasal septum ridge.

5. Four costal shields (Figure 8) on each side of carapace, first
    costal not touching nuchal shield 6
    Five or more costal shields on each side of carapace, first
    costal shield touching nuchal shield 7

6. Shields of carapace strongly overlapping; two pairs of prefron-
    tals (Figure 8) on head ....
    ..... *Eretmochelys imbricata imbricata*, Atlantic Hawksbill.
    Shields of carapace not overlapping; one pair of prefrontals on
    head .... *Chelonia mydas mydas*, Atlantic Green Turtle.

7. Three small bridge shields ....
    .... *Caretta caretta caretta*, Atlantic Loggerhead.
    Four small bridge shields ....
    .... *Lepidochelys kempi*, Atlantic Ridley.

8. Tail more than half the length of the plastron (Figure 9);
    bridge at least twice as long as wide 9
    Tail less than half the length of the plastron; bridge equal to or
    slightly longer than wide 10

9. Four shields between marginals and costals; three prominent
    ridges (Figure 8) on carapace ....

.... *Macroclemys temmincki*, Alligator Snapping Turtle.
Marginals in contact with costals along entire length of cara-
pace; no prominent ridges on carapace ....
. *Chelydra serpentina serpentina*, Common Snapping Turtle.

10. Ten marginals (Figure 8) on each side of carapace 11
    Eleven marginals on each side of carapace 15

11. Plastron with two hinges (Figure 9); plastron nearly fills space
    beneath carapace 12
    Plastron without hinges; plastron small, not nearly filling space
    beneath carapace 14

12. Ninth marginal roughly triangular with apex extending well
    above eighth marginal ....
    ...... *Kinosternon flavescens flavescens*, Yellow Mud Turtle.
    Ninth marginal not extending above eighth marginal 13

13. Interpectoral (Figure 9) suture less than half the greatest
    length of the pectoral shield ....
    Kinosternon subrubrum hippocrepis, Mississippi Mud Turtle.
    Interpectoral suture at least half the greatest length of the pec-
    toral shield ....
    .... *Kinosternon hirtipes murrayi*, Big Bend Mud Turtle.

14. Well-developed gular shield (Figure 9); head with two light
    stripes on dark background; carapace dark, without keels or
    weakly keeled .... *Sternotherus odoratus*, Stinkpot.
    Gular shield reduced in size or absent; head with dark spots
    on a light background; carapace tan, strongly keeled ....,
    .... *Sternotherus carinatus*, Razorback Musk Turtle.

15. Gular shield forked anteriorly; hind feet elephantine, with
    bony scales .... *Gopherus berlandieri*, Texas Tortoise.
    Gular shields normal; hind feet not elephantine 16

16. Plastron not hinged; carapace presents a low-arched profile . 18
    Plastron hinged; carapace presents highly arched profile 17

17. Carapace normally flattened on top; pattern on costals consist-
    ing of many yellow lines radiating downward on dark ground
    color .... *Terrapene ornata* (A), Western Box Turtle.
    A. Eleven to 14 yellow lines on the second costal that are

equal in length to half the width of the costal . . . .
. . . . *Terrapene ornata luteola*, Desert Box Turtle.
Five to eight yellow lines on the second costal . . . .
. . . . *Terrapene ornata ornata*, Ornate Box Turtle.
Carapace normally rounded on top; pattern on carapace normally consisting of dark flecks on a tan to straw background
. . . . *Terrapene carolina triunguis*, Three-toed Box Turtle.

18. Head and neck with light stripes, smooth scutes, rarely with concentric ridges; inguinals and axillaries large and well developed   19
Head and neck without stripes; head spotted or mottled; scutes with many concentric ridges; inguinals and axillaries small or absent . . . .
Malaclemys terrapin littoralis, Texas Diamondback Terrapin.

19. Head plus neck about equal to half the plastron length; no vertical stripes on posterior thighs   20
Head plus neck about equal to plastron length; vertical stripes on posterior thighs . . . .
. . . . *Deirochelys reticularia miaria*, Western Chicken Turtle.

20. Alveolar surface of upper jaw with a ridge or row of tubercles extending parallel to its margin   21
Alveolar surface of upper jaw smooth or undulating, not ridged
. . . .   25

21. First marginal extending beyond suture between first costal and first vertebral   22
First marginal not extending beyond suture between first costal and first vertebral . . . *Chrysemys picta* (A), Painted Turtle.
A. Bright red or yellow middorsal carapace stripe . . . .
. . . . *Chrysemys p. dorsalis*, Southern Painted Turtle.
Carapace marked but never with dorsal stripe . . . .
. . . . *Chrysemys p. belli*, Western Painted Turtle.

22. A wide and prominent yellow, orange, or red postocular stripe or blotch   23
Postorbital stripe always narrow, or absent; if present, always yellow   24

23. A large orange spot behind eye; carapace reticulated; plastron with an intricate central plastron pattern . . . .
. . . . *Trachemys gaigeae*, Big Bend Slider.

An elongate red bar behind eye (occasionally broken into two parts), carapace usually with light lines; plastron with paired, solid dark blotches . . . . *Trachemys scripta elegans*, Red-eared Slider.

24. Second costal with a light vertical or inverted Y-shaped mark; dark markings on plastron usually absent . . . .
. . . . *Pseudemys texana*, Texas River Cooter.
Second costal with a light C-shaped mark; pattern on plastron consisting of dark lines . . . .
. . . . *Pseudemys concinna* (A), River Cooter.
   A. Second costal with five distinct whorls of concentric black and yellow ocelli . . . .
. . . . *Pseudemys c. gorzugi*, Zug's River Cooter.
Second costal without whorls of concentric black and yellow ocelli . . . .
. . . . *Pseudemys c. metteri*, Metter's River Cooter.

25. Yellow stripe(s) reaching eye, one to nine   26
Light postorbital crescent mark extending anteriorly beneath eye, preventing stripes from reaching eye   27

26. One yellow or orange stripe terminating above eye; with a J-shaped mark behind eye . . . .
. . . . *Graptemys versa*, Texas Map Turtle.
Two or more light lines touching eye; light postorbital spot present . . . . *Graptemys pseudogeographica* (A), False Map Turtle.
   A. One to three lines reach eye; a light spot below eye
. . . . *Graptemys p. ouachitensis*, Ouachita Map Turtle.
Five to nine light lines reach eye; no light spot below eye . . . . . *Graptemys p. sabinensis*, Sabine Map Turtle.

27. Ventral surface of jaw with transverse cream lines . . . .
. . . . *Graptemys caglei*, Cagle's Map Turtle.
Ventral surface of jaw with longitudinal yellow stripe at symphysis of jaw . . . . . *Graptemys kohni*, Mississippi Map Turtle.

Lizards

1. Two pairs of legs   2
Legs absent . . . .
. . . . . *Ophisaurus attenuatus*, Western Slender Glass Lizard.

2. Movable eyelids present   4
    Movable eyelids absent   3

3. Digits slender, narrow through entire length . . . .
    . . . . *Cyrtodactylus scaber*, Rough-scaled Gecko.
    Digits short, dilated; claw portion arising above expanded pad
    . . . . *Hemidactylus turcicus*, Mediterranean Gecko.

4. Tail with all scales about equal in size   5
    Tail with whorls of enlarged scales separated by one complete
    and often one incomplete series of smaller scales . . . .
    . . . . *Ctenosaura pectinata*, Western Spiny-tailed Iguana.

5. Scales around body equal in size, smooth and shiny   6
    Scales around body unequal in size, not smooth or shiny   16

6. Supranasals (Figure 10) present; eyelids scaly   7
    Supranasals absent; lower eyelid with a transparent disk . . . .
    . . . . *Scincella lateralis*, Ground Skink.

7. Lateral scales parallel to dorsal rows; young not black; adults
    not light with dark-bordered scales   8
    Lateral scales not parallel to dorsal rows; young black; adults
    light with dark-bordered scales . . . .
    . . . . *Eumeces obsoletus*, Great Plains Skink.

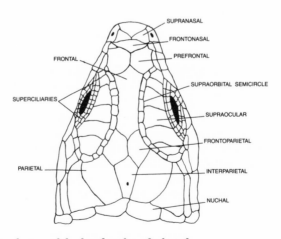

FIG. 10. Dorsal view of the head scales of a lizard.

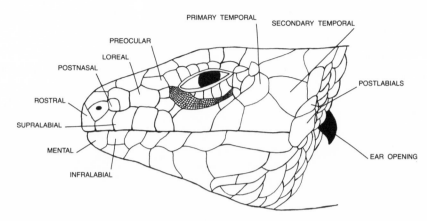

FIG. 11. Lateral view of the head scales of a lizard.

8. Dorsolateral light lines not involving only third scale row from
median line 9
Dorsolateral light lines absent or, if present, involving only
third scale row from median line ....
.... *Eumeces multivirgatus epipleurotus*, Variable Skink.

9. Dorsal light lines (dorsolateral or medial) not evident on either
neck or trunk 10
Dorsal light lines present on neck and/or trunk 12

10. Postnasal (Figure 11) present 11
Postnasal absent .... *Eumeces tetragrammus* (A),
Four-lined Skink.
    A. Dorsolateral light lines terminate near front leg ......
    .... *E. t. brevilineatus*, Short-lined Skink.
    Dorsolateral light lines terminate near hind leg ......
    .... *E. t. tetragrammus*, Four-lined Skink.

11. Postlabials (Figure 11) two, of relatively large size; four supralabials anterior to subocular, size never greater than 85-mm
snout-vent length ..... *Eumeces fasciatus*, Five-lined Skink.
Postlabials absent or, if one or two, of relatively small size; five
supralabials anterior to subocular; size frequently over 85-mm
snout-vent length ...... *Eumeces laticeps*, Broadhead Skink.

12. Postnasal present 15
Postnasal absent 13

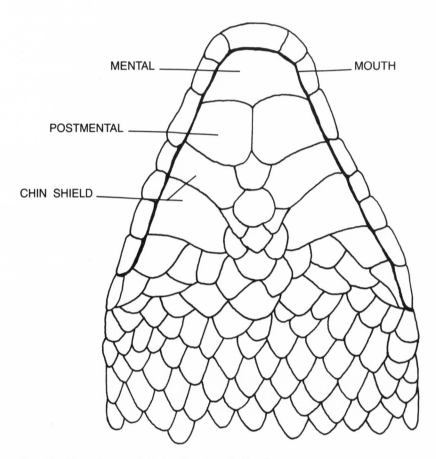

MENTAL

MOUTH

POSTMENTAL

CHIN SHIELD

FIG. 12. Ventral view of the head scales of a lizard.

13. Light lines absent on dorsal surface of head, body with or
     without a median light line   14
     A pair of light lines on top of head, usually visible posterior to
     nuchals, where they unite into a single line . . . .
     . . . . *Eumeces tetragrammus* (see 10), Four-lined Skink.

14. One postmental (Figure 12); limbs overlapping when adpressed
     except in very large females; dorsolateral light lines not edged
     medially with black . . . .
     . . . . *Eumeces anthracinus pluvialis*, Southern Coal Skink.
     Two postmentals; limbs not overlapping or touching except in
     young; dorsolateral light lines edged medially with black . . . .
     . . . . . *Eumeces septentrionalis obtusirostris*, Southern Prairie
                                                                Skink.

15. Postlabials two, of relatively large size; four supralabials anterior to subocular; dorsolateral light stripes involving third scale row from median line; lateral stripe passes directly through middle of ear, not directed toward upper anterior margin of ear; size not greater than 85-mm snout-vent length . . . .
. . . . *Eumeces fasciatus,* Five-lined Skink.
Postlabials absent or, if one or two, of relatively small size; five supralabials anterior to subocular; dorsolateral light stripes usually not involving third scale row from median line; lateral light stripe reaching anterior border of ear at its upper margin; size frequently over 85-mm snout-vent length . . . .
. . . . *Eumeces laticeps,* Broadhead Skink.

16. Lateral fold from head to hind leg absent   17
Lateral fold extending from head to hind leg; scales in fold much smaller than those above and below the fold . . . .
. . *Gerrhonotus liocephalus infernalis,* Texas Alligator Lizard.

17. Head covered with small granular scales (Figure 13)   18
Head covered with scales of different sizes   19

18. Dorsal tubercles present among the dorsal granules, most evident over the rump . . . .
. . . . *Coleonyx reticulatus,* Reticulated Gecko.
Dorsal tubercles absent . . . .
. . . . *Coleonyx brevis,* Texas Banded Gecko.

19. Belly scales rounded and smaller than, equal, or slightly larger than dorsal scales   20
Belly scales rectangular, much larger than dorsal scales   44

20. Femoral pores (Figure 13) present   22
Femoral pores absent   21

21. Dewlap pink; specimen green in life, but occasionally brown when cold, or mottled green and brown . . . .
. . . . *Anolis carolinensis,* Green Anole.
Dewlap orange red with median white border; specimen brown in life, never green; females with yellow middorsal stripe with dark brown half-moon circles along each side of the back . . . . *Anolis sagrei,* Brown Anole.

22. Head with bony spines or projecting ridge   23
Head without bony spines or projecting ridge   25

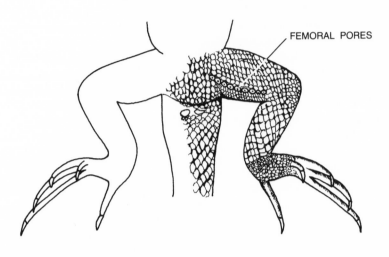

GRANULAR SCALES   SMOOTH SCALES   KEELED SCALES

FIG. 13. A dorsal view of various types of lizard and snake scales, and a ventral view of a male lizard showing femoral pores.

23. Sides of abdomen with one or two fringe-like rows of enlarged
     scales.. 24
     Sides of abdomen without fringe of enlarged scales ....
     .... *Phrynosoma modestum*, Roundtail Horned Lizard.

24. Sides of abdomen with one row of enlarged scales ....
     .. *Phrynosoma douglassi hernandesi*, Mountain Short-horned
                                                           Lizard.
     Sides of abdomen with two rows of enlarged scales ....
     .... *Phrynosoma cornutum*, Texas Horned Lizard.

25. Ear openings absent 26
     Ear openings present 29

26. Tail rounded, not flattened horizontally; without broad black ventral tail bands (small black spots may be present) 27
Tail flattened horizontally, with broad black transverse bands below .... *Cophosaurus texanus* (A), Greater Earless Lizard.
   A. Femoral pores 27 or fewer; orange or yellow dorsal spots absent .... *C. t. texanus*, Texas Earless Lizard.
     Femoral pores 28 or more; orange or yellow dorsal spots present .. *C. t. scitulus*, Southwestern Earless Lizard.

27. Spots absent on ventral side of tail 28
Spots present on ventral side of tail ....
.... *Holbrookia lacerata* (A), Spot-tailed Earless Lizard.
   A. Femoral pores 30 or more; four rows of dorsal blotches .... *H. l. subcaudalis*, Southern Earless Lizard.
     Femoral pores 28 or fewer; two rows of dorsal black blotches .... *H. l. lacerata*, Plateau Earless Lizard.

28. Scales keeled (Figure 13) ....
... *Holbrookia propinqua propinqua*, Keeled Earless Lizard.
Scales without keels ....
.... *Holbrookia maculata* (A), Lesser Earless Lizard.
   A. Four rows of dark dorsal blotches, or dorsal light spots present and dark blotches absent .... B
     Two rows of dark dorsal blotches; light spots absent ..
     .... *H. m. perspicua*, Eastern Earless Lizard.
   B. Dorsal blotches, if present, edged with white or blue .... *H. m. approximans*, Speckled Earless Lizard.
     Dorsal blotches present and not edged with white or blue ...... *H. m. maculata*, Northern Earless Lizard.

29. Transverse gular fold absent 34
Transverse gular fold present 30

30. Interparietal shield (Figure 10) much smaller than ear opening; nine or more supralabials (Figure 11) from rostral to below center of eye 31
Interparietal shield much larger than ear opening, fewer than nine supralabials from rostral to below center of eye 33

31. Black bands on neck absent 32
Black bands on neck number one or two ....
.... *Crotaphytus collaris* (A), Collared Lizard.
   A. Several of the interorbital scales fuse to form one row .... *C. c. collaris*, Eastern Collared Lizard.

Interorbital scales form two rows . . . .
. . . . *C. c. fuscus*, Chihuahuan Collared Lizard.

32. Head width equal to or greater than distance between ear and
     nostril . . . .
     . . . . *Crotaphytus reticulatus*, Reticulate Collared Lizard.
     Head width less than distance between ear and nostril . . . . .
     . . . . *Gambelia wislizeni wislizeni*, Longnose Leopard Lizard.

33. Three or more dorsal scale rows much larger than others; no
     scales between nasals and internasals . . . .
     . . . . *Urosaurus ornatus* (A), Tree Lizard.
     A. Central dorsal row of keeled scales less than one-half
         size of largest dorsal scales; large scales in even rows .
         . . . . *U. o. ornatus*, Eastern Tree Lizard.
         Central dorsal row of keeled scales more than one-half
         size of largest dorsal scales; large scales in uneven rows
         . . . . *U. o. schmidti*, Big Bend Tree Lizard.
     Dorsal scale rows equal in size; supranasals separating nasals
     from internasals . . . .
     . . *Uta stansburiana stejnegeri*, Desert Side-blotched Lizard.

34. Postfemoral dermal pocket absent; breeding males without
     pink belly patches   35
     Postfemoral dermal pocket present, breeding males with pink
     belly patches . . . .
     . . . . *Sceloporus variabilis marmoratus*, Rosebelly Lizard.

35. Lateral body scales large, overlapping; no rudimentary gular
     fold   36
     Lateral body scales small, granular, not overlapping; rudimen-
     tary granular gular fold on each side in front of shoulder
     . . . . *Sceloporus merriami* (A), Canyon Lizard.
     A. Dark bars present on throat and beneath tail . . . . B
         Dark bars absent on throat and beneath tail . . . .
         . . . . *S. m. merriami*, Merriam's Canyon Lizard.
     B. Paired dorsal spots squarish in shape . . . .
         . . . . *S. m. annulatus*, Big Bend Canyon Lizard.
         Paired dorsal spots "comma"-shaped . . . .
         . . . . *S. m. longipunctatus*, Presidio Canyon Lizard.

36. Supraoculars (Figure 10) small, in a single or double row, vari-
     able in number but all separated from median head scales by

one or two complete rows of small scales 37
Supraoculars very large, in a single row, usually five in number, and the last one or two not separated from the median head scales by a row of small scales as are the other supraoculars...
Sceloporus magister bimaculosus, Twin-spotted Spiny Lizard.

37. Broad black collar across neck and shoulders, bordered anteriorly and posteriorly by a light line 38
Distinct light-bordered black collar absent 39

38. Tail brightly banded toward tip; supraoculars usually in two regular rows; median head scales usually divided irregularly .... *Sceloporus poinsetti poinsetti*, Crevice Spiny Lizard.
Tail dimly banded; supraoculars large, irregular, one or two scales divided; median head scales usually not subdivided .... *Sceloporus cyanogenys*, Blue Spiny Lizard.

39. Scales on posterior surface of thigh very small, granular, not overlapping 40
Scales on posterior surface of thigh usually large, always keeled and overlapping 41

40. Lateral nuchal scales much smaller than and well differentiated from dorsal nuchal scales; gular region of males bluish, not reticulated ....
.... *Sceloporus grammicus microlepidotus*, Mesquite Lizard.
Lateral nuchal scales same size as dorsal nuchal scales; gular region of males never with two posteriolateral blue spots, but usually reticulated ....
.. *Sceloporus graciosus arenicolus*, Dunes Sagebrush Lizard.

41. Posterior surface of thigh nearly immaculate; body dorsolateral light lines distinct and dorsal dark bars absent in males 42
Posterior surface of thigh with a broad longitudinal dark line; poorly defined body dorsolateral light lines; dark dorsal crossbands visible in adult males 43

42. Dorsal scales 28 to 33, average about 30; supraoculars large .... *Sceloporus olivaceus*, Texas Spiny Lizard.
Dorsal scales 44 to 55, average about 50; supraoculars small .... *Sceloporus graciosus arenicolus*, Dunes Sagebrush Lizard.

43. Males without blue throat patches; vertical white shoulder mark with black anterior and posterior margins; dorsal scales 44 to 55, average about 50 . . . .
. . *Sceloporus graciosus arenicolus*, Dunes Sagebrush Lizard.
Males with blue throat patches (absent in *S. u. garmani*); vertical white shoulder mark without black edging; dorsal scales 35 to 47, average about 40 . . . .
. . . . *Sceloporus undulatus* (A), Eastern Fence Lizard.
   A. Female usually without distinct dorsolateral light lines; male with dark blue throat patches (not from Panhandle area) . . . . B
Both sexes with distinct dorsolateral light lines, male without blue throat patches (northern Panhandle area) . . . . *S. u. garmani*, Northern Prairie Lizard.
   B. Fine dark line between eyes; male with dark dorsal tail bars (east Texas) . . . .
. . . . *S. u. hyacinthinus*, Northern Fence Lizard.
Fine dark line between eyes usually absent; male usually without dark dorsal tail bars (west Texas) . . . .
. . . . *S. u. consobrinus*, Southern Prairie Lizard.

44. Dorsal pattern of alternating dark and light lines (stripes); dark stripes with even edges, never with light spots or bars in the dark fields   45
Dorsal pattern reticulated, with light and dark stripes and/or bars; if alternating light and dark stripes, then dark stripes (fields) invaded with white spots or bars   48

45. Scales bordering gular area enlarged and angular   46
Scales bordering gular fold granular . . . . *Cnemidophorus inornatus heptagrammus*, Trans-Pecos Striped Whiptail.

46. Postantebrachial scales moderately enlarged and angular   47
Postantebrachial scales granular . . . .
. . . . . . *Cnemidophorus sexlineatus*, Six-lined Racerunner (A).
   A. Usually six light stripes; scales around body 89 to 110, average about 95 . . . .
. . . . *C. s. sexlineatus*, Six-lined Racerunner.
Usually seven light stripes; scales around body 62 to 89, average about 77 . . . .
. . . . *C. s. viridis*, Prairie-lined Racerunner.

47. Usually six light stripes; ventral surface of tail greenish, no faint light spots in dark fields (El Paso area) . . . .
. . . . . *Cnemidophorus uniparens*, Desert Grassland Whiptail.
Usually seven light stripes; ventral surface of tail pinkish or whitish, faint light spots occasionally in the dark fields (Laredo, south along Rio Grande) . . . .
. . . . . . *Cnemidophorus laredoensis*, Laredo Striped Whiptail.

48. Postantebrachial scales distinctly enlarged, larger than first su-
pralabial 49
Postantebrachial scales similar in size to surrounding scales, or slightly enlarged, never larger than first supralabial 51

49. Dorsolateral light lines interrupted with white spots that ei-
ther join the light lines or are superimposed on them 50
Dorsolateral light lines straight, with light spots often in the dark fields between the light lines . . . .
. . . . *Cnemidophorus gularis gularis*, Texas Spotted Whiptail.

50. Dorsal pattern of distinct, straight dorsal light lines, though often with white spots superimposed on them, but not obscur-
ing the light lines; gular region immaculate . . . .
. . *Cnemidophorus exsanguis*, Chihuahuan Spotted Whiptail.
Dorsal pattern of light lines that tend to become broken and/ or obscure posteriorly; light spots often merging with light lines; gular region orange with black flecks . . . .
. . *Cnemidophorus septemvittatus*, Plateau Spotted Whiptail.

51. Scales along mesoptychial fold (gular fold) conspicuously larger than adjacent gular scales 52
Scales along mesoptychial fold not conspicuously larger than adjacent gular scales 53

52. Dorsal pattern of six to seven light lines joined by transverse crossbars to form a checkerboard pattern; dorsal pattern ap-
pearing to have more dark areas than light . . . .
. . *Cnemidophorus tesselatus*, Colorado Checkered Whiptail.
Dorsal pattern of eight or more light lines joined by transverse bars, often giving the appearance of more bars than lines; dor-
sal pattern appears to have more light than dark areas
. . . . *Cnemidophorus dixoni*, Gray-checkered Whiptail.

53. Lateral midbody color pattern of light and dark stripes, dorsolateral light stripes zig-zag; dark fields with light spots ...... *Cnemidophorus neomexicanus*, New Mexico Whiptail. Lateral midbody color pattern reticulated and, if lines present, with lateral light crossbars joining light dorsal lines .... *Cnemidophorus marmoratus*, Marbled Whiptail.

Snakes

1. No elongate transverse ventral scales; dorsal scales about same size as ventrals 2
   Ventral scales (Figure 14) transversely elongate; dorsal scales much smaller than ventrals 3

2. Supraoculars absent .... *Leptotyphlops humilis segregus*, Trans-Pecos Blind Snake. Supraoculars present .... *Leptotyphlops dulcis* (A), Texas Blind Snake.
   A. One supraocular shield .... *L. d. dulcis*, Plains Blind Snake. Two supraocular shields .... *L. d. dissectus*, New Mexico Blind Snake.

3. A loreal pit (Figure 15) located between eye and nostril 4
   No loreal pit between eye and nostril 13

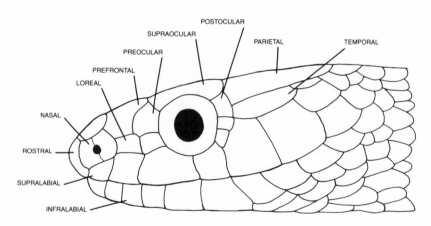

FIG. 14. Lateral view of the head scales of a snake.

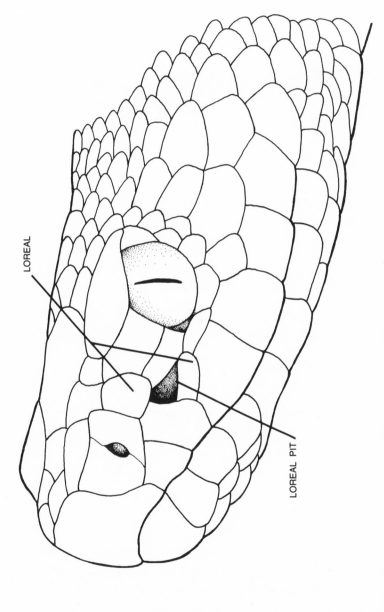

LOREAL

LOREAL PIT

Fig. 15. Lateral view of a copperhead showing the position of the loreal pit.

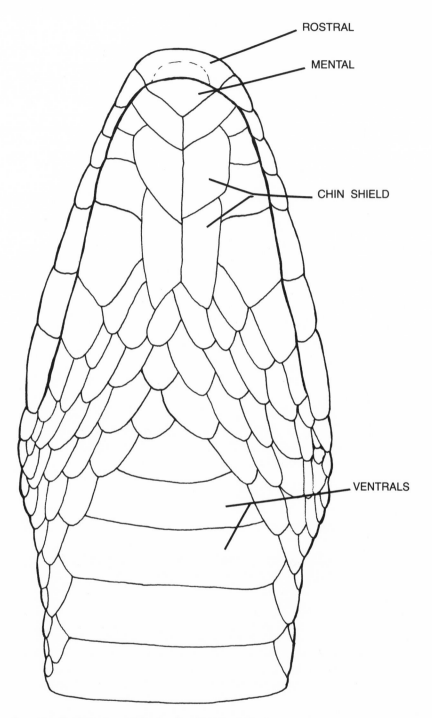

ROSTRAL

MENTAL

CHIN SHIELD

VENTRALS

FIG. 16. Ventral view of the head scales of a snake.

4. Rattle or large horny button present on end of tail 5
   No rattle or button on end of tail 12

5. Nine large symmetrical head plates 6
   Small head scales only 7

6. Upper preocular (Figure 16) in contact with postnasal ......
   .... *Sistrurus catenatus* (A), Massasauga.
      A. Midbody scale rows normally 25; venter light with
        darker markings...............................
        .... *S. c. tergemminus*, Western Massasauga.
        Midbody scale rows normally 23; venter white or nearly
        so .... *S. c. edwardsi*, Desert Massasauga.
   Upper preocular not in contact with postnasal ....
   ... *Sistrurus miliarius streckeri*, Western Pigmy Rattlesnake.

7. Upper preocular divided vertically, anterior portion being
   somewhat higher than the posterior and curved over the canthus rostralis in front of the supraocular shield; dorsal pattern
   of widely separated crossbars..........................
   .... *Crotalus lepidus* (A), Rock Rattlesnake.
      A. Single spot on occiput; body strongly banded with dark;
        no dark facial stripe ....
        .... *C. l. klauberi*, Banded Rock Rattlesnake.
        Two spots on occiput; body mottled or faded; dark
        stripe from eye to corner of mouth ....
        .... *C. l. lepidus*, Mottled Rock Rattlesnake.
   Upper preocular usually not divided vertically, or if divided,
   anterior portion not noticeably higher than the posterior and
   not curved over canthus rostralis in front of supraocular 8

8. Anterior body pattern consisting of blotches which grade into
   rings on the posterior portion of the body and tail ....
   .... *Crotalus viridis viridis*, Prairie Rattlesnake.
   Pattern not as above 9

9. Dorsal pattern on tail of alternating dark and light rings, in
   sharp contrast with posterior body pattern 10
   Dorsal pattern on tail never of alternating dark and light rings
   in contrast with posterior body rings 11

10. Dark and light tail rings about equal in width; interocular
    scales small...

.... *Crotalus atrox*, Western Diamondback Rattlesnake.
Dark rings on tail narrower than light rings; interocular scales
large compared with those at rear of head . . . .
.... *Crotalus scutulatus scutulatus*, Mojave Rattlesnake.

11. Anterior dorsal pattern consisting of chevron-shaped bars
    . . . . *Crotalus horridus*, Timber Rattlesnake.
    Anterior dorsal pattern consisting of an interconnected chain
    of dark blotches with light centers . . . .
    .... *Crotalus molossus molossus*, Blacktail Rattlesnake.

12. Loreal scale (Figure 16) present; maximum of 23 dorsal scale
    rows . . . . *Agkistrodon contortrix* (A), Copperhead.
    A. Dark dorsal markings usually broad (six to eight scale
       rows) at middorsum and seldom interrupted or offset;
       usually continuous with dark ventral markings . . . . . B
       Dorsal dark markings usually narrow at midbody and
       often interrupted or offset; may or may not be continu-
       ous with ventral dark markings . . . .
       . . . . *A. c. contortrix*, Southern Copperhead.
    B. Venter usually heavily mottled with dark color; sub-
       caudals in males usually 57 or more, females usually 52
       or more . . . *A. c. pictigaster*, Trans-Pecos Copperhead.
       Venter usually uniform tan or orangish pink, with or
       without a few dark markings; subcaudals in males usu-
       ally 54 or fewer, females usually 52 or fewer . . . .
       . . . . *A. c. laticinctus*, Broad-banded Copperhead.
    Loreal scale absent; maximum of 25 dorsal scale rows
    . . . . *Agkistrodon piscivorus leucostoma*,
                                              Western Cottonmouth.

13. Permanently erect fangs present at anterior end of maxillae;
    red, yellow, and black dorsal rings extend across belly
    . . . . *Micrurus fulvius tenere*, Texas Coral Snake.
    No permanently erect fangs at anterior end of maxillae; red,
    yellow, and/or black dorsal rings, if present, do not extend
    across belly   14

14. Prefrontals (Figure 17) more than two . . . .
    . . . . *Pituophis melanoleucus* (A), Pine Snake.
    A. Body blotches usually 40 or fewer; dark blotches usually
       obscuring ground color of neck and frequently fused . .

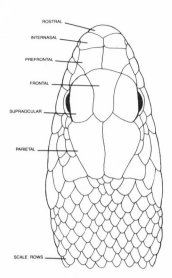

FIG. 17.   Dorsal view of the head scales of a snake.

.... *P. m. ruthveni*, Louisiana Pine Snake.
Body blotches usually 46 or more; dark blotches usually
distinct throughout .... B

   B.   Rostral scale much higher than wide, raised well above
        nearby scales; blotches contrasting on each end of body,
        less distinct in the middle ...... *P. m. sayi*, Bullsnake.
        Rostral scale broad, little or not raised above the sur-
        rounding scales; anterior dorsal blotches brown, uncon-
        nected to other blotches; posterior blotches black . . . .
        .... *P. m. affinis*, Sonoran Gopher Snake.
Prefrontals two   15

15.   Subcaudals (Figure 18) mostly single ....
      .... *Rhinocheilus lecontei tessellatus*, Texas Longnose Snake.
      Subcaudals all or mostly divided   16

16.   Loreal absent   17
      Loreal present   25

17.   Dorsal scale rows around midbody at least two more than just
      anterior to vent   18
      Dorsal scale rows around midbody same as just anterior to
      vent..   19

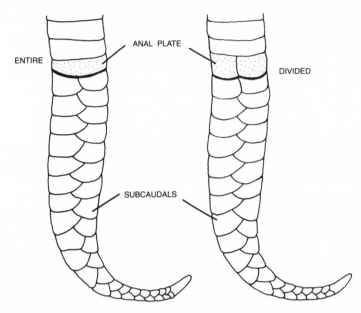

Fɪɢ. 18. Ventral view of the anal plate and tail of a snake, showing divided and entire anal plate and divided subcaudals.

18. Prefrontals in contact, separating rostral from frontal . . . .
. . . . *Gyalopion canum,* Western Hooknose Snake.
Prefrontals not in contact; rostral contacts frontal . . . .
. . . . *Ficimia streckeri,* Mexican Hooknose Snake.

19. Scales keeled 20
Scales smooth 21

20. Dorsal scale rows 15 . . . .
Storeria occipitomaculata obscura, Florida Redbelly Snake.
Dorsal scale rows 17 . . . . . *Storeria dekayi* (A), Brown Snake.
   A. Anterior temporal scale (Figure 16) immaculate, dark markings on sixth and seventh supralabials . . . .
   . . . . *S. d. texana,* Texas Brown Snake.
   Anterior temporal scale with horizontal dark line through the long axis of scale, no dark markings on sixth and seventh supralabial . . . .
   . . . . *S. d. limnetes,* Marsh Brown Snake.

21. Dark head cap absent or, if present, with rear edge concave; supralabials usually six . . . . *Tantilla gracilis,* Flathead Snake.

Dark head cap present; rear edge straight or convex; supralabials usually seven 22

22. Black head cap with straight or slightly convex posterior margin, extending three scales posterior to parietals along middorsal line, usually followed by pale border 23
Black head cap more or less V-shaped, extending four to seven scales beyond the parietals along the middorsal line; black cap may or may not be interrupted by a white nuchal collar 24

23. Usually two postoculars (Figure 16); mental usually touching anterior pair of chin shields ....
...... *Tantilla hobartsmithi*, Southwestern Blackhead Snake.
Usually one postocular; mental usually separated from anterior pair of chin shields ....
.... *Tantilla atriceps*, Mexican Blackhead Snake.

24. Black cap extending below angle of mouth, normally with a black-bordered, white nuchal collar (may be incomplete or absent); ventrals 161–81 ....
.... *Tantilla rubra* (A), Big Bend Blackhead Snake.
  A. White nuchal collar interrupted middorsally or absent
   .... *T. r. cucullata*, Blackhood Snake.
   White nuchal collar always complete ....
   .... *T. r. diabola*, Devil's River Blackhead Snake.
Black cap not extending below angle of mouth; white black-bordered collar absent; ventrals 130–61 ....
.... *Tantilla nigriceps* (A), Plains Blackhead Snake.
  A. Ventrals usually 146 or more ....
   .... *T. n. nigriceps*, Texas Blackhead Snake.
   Ventrals usually 146 or fewer ....
   .... *T. n. fumiceps*, Plains Blackhead Snake.

25. Loreals two ....
..... *Trimorphodon biscutatus vilkinsoni*, Texas Lyre Snake.
Loreal one 26

26. Preoculars (Figure 16) absent; loreal entering orbit 27
Preoculars present; loreal not entering orbit 30

27. Dorsal scale rows 19 ....
.... *Farancia abacura reinwardti*, Western Mud Snake.
Dorsal scale rows less than 19 28

28. Dorsal scale rows 13 . . . .
    . . . . *Carphophis amoenus vermis*, Western Worm Snake.
    Dorsal scale rows 17   29

29. Postocular single; five supralabials; scales strongly keeled . . .
    . . . . *Virginia striatula*, Rough Earth Snake.
    Postoculars two; six supralabials; scales weakly keeled or
    smooth . . . . *Virginia valeriae elegans*, Western Earth Snake.

30. Anal plate (Figure 18) entire   31
    Anal plate divided   43

31. Dorsal scales keeled   32
    Dorsal scales smooth   37

32. Belly with two median parallel rows of dark spots . . . .
    . . . . *Tropidoclonion lineatum* (A), Lined Snake.
       A. Ventrals 144 or more . . . .
          . . . . *T. l. annectens*, Central Lined Snake.
          Ventrals 143 or fewer . . . . B
       B. Subcaudals of males usually 41 or more, females 34 or
          more . . . . *T. l. mertensi*, New Mexico Lined Snake.
          Subcaudals of males usually 40 or fewer, females 34 or
          fewer . . . . *T. l. texanum*, Texas Lined Snake.
    Belly without two median parallel rows of dark spots   33

33. Lateral stripe anteriorly involving fourth scale row   34
    Lateral stripe anteriorly not involving fourth scale row, or ab-
    sent   35

34. Tail less than 27 percent of total length; supralabials and belly
    with some dark markings . . . .
    . . . *Thamnophis radix haydeni*, Western Plains Garter Snake.
    Tail more than 27 percent of total length; supralabials and
    belly without dark markings . . . .
    . . . . *Thamnophis proximus* (A), Western Ribbon Snake.
       A. Dorsum black; ventral stripe orange and usually nar-
          row; dark ventrolateral stripes absent . . . .
          . . . . *T. p. proximus*, Western Ribbon Snake.
          Dorsum olive gray or some shade of brown . . . . B
       B. Vertebral stripe bright red, of median width; ventro-
          lateral stripes narrow or absent . . . .
          . . . . *T. p. rubrilineatus*, Redstripe Ribbon Snake.

Vertebral stripe orange, grayish tan, or some shade of gold C

C. Vertebral stripe orange, of median width; dorsum olive gray; lateral stripe frequently reduced posteriorly; narrow ventrolateral stripe usually present . . . .

. . . . *T. p. diabolicus*, Arid Land Ribbon Snake.

Vertebral stripe usually some shade of gold and usually broad; dorsum olive-brown; lateral stripe rarely reduced; ventrolateral stripe usually absent . . . .·. .

. . . . *T. p. orarius*, Gulf Coast Ribbon Snake.

35. Lateral stripe anteriorly only on third dorsal scale row . . . . .

. . . . *Thamnophis marcianus marcianus*, Checkered Garter Snake.

Lateral stripe anteriorly on second and third dorsal scale rows   36

36. Supralabials (Figure 16) eight-eight; light crescent-shaped mark on side of head behind mouth; a pair of large black lateral neck spots that may unite behind head . . . .

. . . . *Thamnophis cyrtopsis* (A), Blackneck Garter Snake.

A. Top of head gray; ventrals in males usually 164–78 (171), females 157–70 (167) . . . .

. . . . . *T. c. cyrtopsis*, Western Blackneck Garter Snake.

Top of head black; ventrals in males 157–64 (160), females 148–65 (157) . . . .

. . . . . *T. c. ocellatus*, Eastern Blackneck Garter Snake.

Supralabials seven-seven; no light crescent-shaped marks behind mouth; no lateral black spots united behind head . . . . .

. . . . *Thamnophis sirtalis* (A), Common Garter Snake.

A. Vertebral stripe orange . . . .

. . . . *T. s. annectens*, Texas Garter Snake.

Vertebral stripe yellow or tan . . . . B

B. Vertebral stripe bright yellow, bordered by a continuous black line that is irregular below . . . .

. . . . *T. s. dorsalis*, New Mexico Garter Snake.

Vertebral stripe yellow or tan, bordered by a series of dark spots C

C. Dark dorsal pattern without red interspaces; lateral light stripe, if present, occupying only two scale rows

. . . . *T. s. sirtalis*, Eastern Garter Snake.

Dark dorsal pattern with red interspaces; lateral light stripe occupying four scale rows . . . .

. . . . *T. s. parietalis*, Red-sided Garter Snake.

37. Dorsal scale rows 17; dorsum solid black . . . .
      . . . . *Drymarchon corais erebennus*, Texas Indigo Snake.
      Dorsal scale rows 19 or more; some dorsal pattern present . .   38

38. Dorsal scale rows 19 . . . .
      . . . . *Cemophora coccinea* (A), Scarlet Snake.
         A. Supralabials usually six; red dorsal blotches black-edged
             ventrally . . . . *C. c. copei*, Northern Scarlet Snake.
             Supralabials usually seven, red dorsal blotches not
             black-edged ventrally . . . .
             . . . . *C. c. lineri*, Texas Scarlet Snake.
      Dorsal scale rows 21 or more   39

39. Dorsal scale rows 29 or more; dorsal pattern consisting of a se-
      ries of spots or blotches accompanied by an immaculate ven-
      ter; preoculars two . . . . . . *Arizona elegans* (A), Glossy Snake.
         A. Dark dorsal body blotches usually 60 or more; midbody
             scale rows usually 27 or fewer . . . .
             . . . . *A. e. philipi*, Painted Desert Glossy Snake.
             Dark dorsal body blotches usually 59 or fewer; midbody
             scale rows usually 29 or more . . . . B
         B. Ventrals of males 207–25 (215), females 217–31 (225)
             . . . . *A. e. arenicola*, Texas Glossy Snake.
             Ventrals of males 197–219 (206), females 208–27 (216)
             . . . . *A. e. elegans*, Kansas Glossy Snake.
      Dorsal scale rows 27 or fewer; dorsal pattern, if consisting of a
      series of spots or blotches, accompanied by a blotched venter;
      preoculars single   40

40. Dorsal pattern of narrow black crossbands, alternate bands
      being mixed or split with red or a pattern of alternating black-
      bordered red saddles and white-bordered gray saddles . . . . . .
      . . . . *Lampropeltis alterna*, Gray-banded Kingsnake.
      Dorsal pattern not as above   41

41. Dorsal pattern of small yellow and black spots or obscure black
      blotches with yellow borders . . . .
      . . . . *Lampropeltis getulus* (A), Common Kingsnake.
         A. Maximum number of dorsal scale rows 21 or fewer . . .
             . . . . *L. g. holbrooki*, Speckled Kingsnake.
             Maximum number of dorsal scale rows 23 or more . . .
             . . . . *L. g. splendida*, Desert Kingsnake.
      Dorsal pattern consisting of red, black, and yellow rings or
      dark-bordered blotches   42

42. Dorsal pattern consisting of a series of dark-bordered blotches
..... *Lampropeltis calligaster calligaster*, Prairie Kingsnake.
Dorsal pattern consisting of red, black and yellow to white
rings .... *Lampropeltis triangulum* (A), Milk Snake.
  A. Red rings complete around body ....
  .... *L. t. gentilis*, Central Plains Milk Snake.
  Red rings interrupted by black ventrally .... B
  B. Head and snout black; first few red rings interrupted by
  black ventrally . . . *L. t. annulata*, Mexican Milk Snake.
  Pattern not as above C
  C. Red rings usually 20 or more; ventral black margin of
  red ring forming a distinct border ....
  .... *L. t. celaenops*, New Mexico Milk Snake.
  Red rings usually fewer than 20; ventral black margin of
  red ring forming an irregular border ....
  .... *L. t. amaura*, Louisiana Milk Snake.

43. Dorsal scales keeled 44
Dorsal scales smooth 58

44. Dorsum unicolored (green in life); fewer than 145 ventrals
.... *Opheodrys aestivus* (A), Rough Green Snake.
  A. Subcaudals of males usually 127 or fewer, females 121
  or fewer..
  .... *O. a. majalis*, Western Rough Green Snake.
  Subcaudals of males usually 128 or more, females 122 or
  more .... *O. a. aestivus*, Eastern Rough Green snake.
Dorsum with some pattern; more than 145 ventrals 45

45. Rostral scale (Figure 16) turned up 46
Rostral scale normal, not turned up 47

46. Prefrontals separated by small scales; underside of tail not
lighter than belly....................................
.... *Heterodon nasicus* (A), Western Hognose Snake.
  A. Median body blotches of males usually 35 or more, fe-
  males 40 or more ....
  .... *H. n. nasicus*, Plains Hognose Snake.
  Median body blotches of males usually 32 or fewer, fe-
  males 37 or fewer .... B
  B. Two to six small scales posterior to rostral plate ......
  .... *H. n. kennerlyi*, Mexican Hognose Snake.
  Nine or more small scales posterior to rostral plate ...
  .... *H. n. gloydi*, Dusky Hognose Snake.

Prefrontals in contact; underside of tail lighter than belly . . .
. . . . *Heterodon platyrhinos*, Eastern Hognose Snake.

47. Dorsal scale rows 19   48
    Dorsal scale rows greater than 19   49

48. Belly with median dark line on posterior section; dorsum distinctly striped . . . *Regina grahami*, Graham's Crayfish Snake.
    Belly with two rows of dark spots; dorsal stripes absent or indistinct . . . . *Regina rigida sinicola*, Gulf Crayfish Snake.

49. Subocular scales present   50
    Subocular scales absent   51

50. Dorsal pattern consisting of a series of dark H-shaped markings on a light ground color . . . .
    . . . . *Elaphe subocularis*, Trans-Pecos Rat Snake.
    Dorsal pattern mottled green . . . .
    . . . . *Nerodia cyclopion*, Green Water Snake.

51. Ventrals 160 or less   52
    Ventrals 190 or more   56

52. Middorsal pattern consisting of a series of light dark-bordered diamond-shaped or chainlike markings . . . .
    Nerodia rhombifera rhombifera, Diamondback Water Snake.
    Middorsal pattern never a series of light, dark-bordered diamond-shaped or chainlike markings   53

53. Belly plain yellow or orange, or with dark markings confined to anterolateral margins of ventrals . . . .
    . . . . *Nerodia erythrogaster* (A), Plainbelly Water Snake.
       A. Dorsum of adults normally unpatterned; juveniles show pale crossbands middorsally . . . .
          . . . . *N. e. flavigaster*, Yellowbelly Water Snake.
          Dorsum of adults normally patterned (blotches); juvenile pattern similar to adult . . . .
          . . . . *N. e. transversa*, Blotched Water Snake.
    Belly with distinct dark spots or blotches   54

54. Dorsum with a double row of 50 or more spots and a row of lateral spots; belly with a row of spots down each side . . . . . .
    . . . . *Nerodia harteri* (A), Harter's Water Snake.

    A. Dorsal spots prominent; dark belly spots pronounced
.................*N. h. harteri*, Brazos Water Snake.
Dorsal spots faded; dark belly spots obscure or absent
.........*N. h. paucimaculata*, Concho Water Snake.
Dorsum striped or consisting of 30 or fewer crossbands; belly
strongly blotched or with two broad stripes   55

55. Dark stripe from eye to angle of jaw absent; anterior body with
a few bands; remainder of pattern a series of blotches that may
be uniform in color ....
.........*Nerodia sipedon pleuralis*, Midland Water Snake.
Dark stripe from eye to angle of jaw, dorsum banded through-
out ....*Nerodia fasciata* (A), Southern Water Snake.
    A. Dorsum with one median and two lateral dark stripes
..........*N. f. clarki*, Gulf Salt Marsh Water Snake.
Dorsum lacking stripes; body banded ....B
    B. Body bands usually fewer than 17 and irregular in shape
.........*N. f. confluens*, Broad-banded Water Snake.
Body bands usually 19 or more and irregular in shape
.............*N. f. pictiventris*, Florida Water Snake.

56. Postorbital stripe crossing near margin of mouth, occasionally
extending onto neck................................
...........*Elaphe guttata emoryi*, Great Plains Rat Snake.
Postorbital stripe, when present, stopping above rear margin
of mouth, never crossing or extending down neck   57

57. Dorsum with four dark stripes, frequently obscure; paraver-
tebral stripes most distinct but occasionally absent; young with
more than 47 dark crossbands on body ....
......................*Elaphe bairdi*, Baird's Rat Snake.
Dorsum with dark blotches, occasionally obscure; head frequently slate or black; young with fewer than 40 well-defined
dark blotches.......................................
............*Elaphe obsoleta lindheimeri*, Texas Rat Snake.

58. Dorsal scale rows (Figure 17) anterior to vent same as those at
midbody......................................   59
Dorsal scale rows anterior to vent at least two less than those
at midbody......................................   60

59. Dorsum tan or ringed................................
.........*Sonora semiannulata* (A), Western Ground Snake.

A. Scale rows typically 15-15-15, occasionally 15-14-14. . .
.... *S. s. semiannulata*, Western Ground Snake.
Scale rows typically 15-13-13, occasionally 15-14-13 . . .
.... *S. s. taylori*, South Texas Ground Snake.
Dorsum green in life, unicolored ....
.... *Opheodrys vernalis blanchardi*,
Western Smooth Green Snake.

60. Dorsal scale rows 19 or more 61
    Dorsal scale rows less than 19 63

61. Dorsum striped ....
    .... *Coniophanes imperialis imperialis*, Black-striped Snake.
    Dorsum not striped 62

62. Dorsal pattern consisting of large blotches with no alternating
    spots on sides .... *Leptodeira septentrionalis septentrionalis*,
    Northern Cat-eyed Snake.
    Dorsal pattern consisting of one or two small blotches; series
    of smaller alternating spots on sides ....
    .... *Hypsiglena torquata jani*, Texas Night Snake.

63. Rostral much enlarged, with free edges 64
    Rostral normal, no free edges 65

64. Posterior chin shields (Fig. 16) in contact or separated by one
    scale; supralabials usually eight ....
    ...... *Salvadora grahamiae* (A), Mountain Patchnose Snake.
    A. A narrow dark line on third scale row ....
    .... *S. g. lineata*, Texas Patchnose Snake.
    No narrow dark line on third or fourth scale rows ....
    .... *S. g. grahamiae*, Mountain Patchnose Snake.
    Posterior genials separated by two or three scales; supralabials
    usually nine ....
    ....;... *Salvadora deserticola*, Big Bend Patchnose Snake.

65. Preoculars single ....
    .. *Drymobius margaritiferus margaritiferus*, Speckled Racer.
    Preoculars two 66

66. Anterior temporals single; lower preocular not particularly
    small or wedged between adjacent supralabials ....
    .... *Diadophis punctatus* (A), Ringneck Snake.
    A. Light nuchal collar normally absent ....

.... *D. p. regalis*, Regal Ringneck Snake.
Light nuchal collar normally present .... B

B. Dorsal scale rows 17 anteriorly; dark belly spots scattered .... *D. p. arnyi*, Prairie Ringneck Snake.
Dorsal scale rows 15 anteriorly; dark belly spots arranged in more or less transverse pairs ....
.... *D. p. stictogenys*, Mississippi Ringneck Snake.
Anterior temporals usually two or three; lower preocular small
and wedged between adjacent supralabials 67

67. Dorsal scales just anterior to vent 15 ....
.... *Coluber constrictor* (A), Racer.

A. Dorsum black to tan with few to many individual scales of odd colors .... B
Dorsum usually uniform in color, from gray to black C

B. Dorsum blue, black, or olive ....
.... *C. c. anthicus*, Buttermilk Racer.
Dorsum tan .... *C. c. etheridgei*, Tan Racer.

C. Dorsum black; chin and throat white ....
.... *C. c. priapus*, Southern Black Racer.
Dorsum greenish or bluish .... D

D. Supralabials normally seven ....
.... *C. c. flaviventris*, Eastern Yellowbelly Racer.
Supralabials normally eight .... E

E. Maxillary teeth 15 to 19; young with dorsal blotches anteriorly; adult with entire body olive to grayish green; belly cream to orange-yellow ....
.... *C. c. mormon*, Western Yellowbelly Racer.
Maxillary teeth 13 to 14; young with narrow crossbands anteriorly; adults with middorsal area of body green or grayish green; sides of body lighter in color; belly usually light yellow to greenish yellow ....
.... *C. c. oaxaca*, Mexican Racer.
Dorsal scales just anterior to vent 11, 12, or 13 68

68. Dorsal scale rows 15; usually well-defined longitudinal light
stripes ...... *Masticophis taeniatus* (A), Striped Whipsnake.

A. No distinct lateral light lines in young or adults ......
.... *M. t. ruthveni*, Ruthven's Whipsnake.
Distinct lateral light lines present .... B

B. Lateral light lines broken anteriorly ....
.... *M. t. girardi*, Central Texas Whipsnake.
Lateral light lines not broken anteriorly C

C. Dorsolateral light stripe involving fifth scale row; five

stripes laterally . . . .
. . . . *M. t. taeniatus*, Desert Striped Whipsnake.
Dorsolateral light stripe not involving fifth scale row;
two to three stripes laterally . . . .
. . . . *M. t. schotti*, Schott's Whipsnake.
Dorsal scale rows 17; no well-defined longitudinal light stripes
. . . . *Masticophis flagellum* (A), Coachwhip.
A. Color of anterior body similar to posterior body; juve-
niles with anterior dark bands separated by three scale
rows of light scales . . . .
. . . . *M. f. testaceus*, Western Coachwhip.
Color of anterior part of body much lighter than pos-
terior part; juveniles with anterior bands separated by
one to two scale rows of light scales . . . .
. . . . *M. f. flagellum*, Eastern Coachwhip.

Ambystoma talpoideum, the Mole Salamander (Map 2). Photograph by L. J. Vitt.

Typhlomolge rathbuni, the Texas Blind Salamander (Map 6). Photograph by J. T. Collins.

Notophthalmus meridionalis, the Black-spotted Newt (Map 9). Photograph by D. G. Barker.

Rhinophrynus dorsalis, the Mexican Burrowing Toad (Map 9). Photograph courtesy of Los Angeles County Museum of Natural History.

Syrrhophus guttilatus, the Spotted Chirping Frog (Map 41). Photograph by W. W. Lamar.

Smilisca baudini, the Mexican Treefrog (Map 9). Photograph by D. G. Barker.

Bufo houstonensis, the Houston Toad (Map 28). Photograph by J. W. Sites.

Rana grylio, the Pig Frog (Map 8). Photograph by L. J. Vitt.

Kinosternon hirtipes, the Big Bend Mud Turtle (Map 41). Photograph by J. F. Scudday.

Graptemys caglei, Cagle's Map Turtle (Map 49). Photograph by D. G. Barker.

Coleonyx reticulatus, the Reticulated Gecko (Map 76). Photograph by J. T. Collins.

Phrynosoma douglassi, the Mountain Short-horned Lizard (Map 76). Photograph courtesy of Los Angeles County Museum of Natural History.

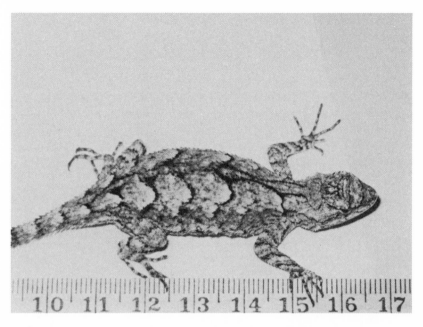

Sceloporus grammicus, the Mesquite Lizard (Map 64). Photograph by J. W. Sites.

Carphophis amoenus vermis, the Worm Snake (Map 66). Photograph by J. T. Collins.

Cnemidophorus dixoni, the Gray Checkered Whiptail (Map 91). Photograph by I. H. Conant.

Cemophora coccinea, the Scarlet Snake (Map 102). Photograph by J. E. Werler.

Cnemidophorus uniparens, the Desert Grassland Whiptail (Map 91). Photograph courtesy of Los Angeles County Museum of Natural History.

Coniophanes imperialis, the Black-striped Snake (Map 104). Photograph by J. E. Werler.

Drymobius margaritiferus, the Speckled Racer (Map 104). Photograph by J. Darling and J. E. Werler.

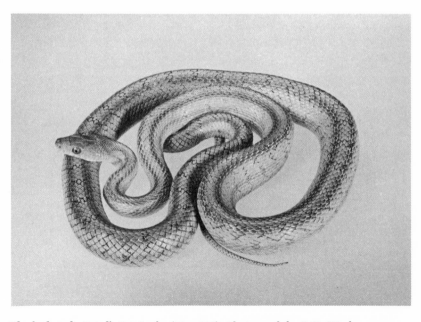

Elaphe bairdi, Baird's Rat Snake (Map 107). Photograph by J. E. Werler.

Nerodia sipedon pleuralis, the Midland Water Snake (Map 127). Photograph by J. T. Collins.

Opheodrys vernalis, the Smooth Green Snake (Map 127). Photograph by J. T. Collins.

Tantilla rubra diabola, the Devil's River Blackhead Snake (Map 132). Photograph by A. Odum.

Thamnophis radix, the Plains Garter Snake (Map 142). Photograph by J. T. Collins.

Trimorphodon biscutatus vilkinsoni, the Texas Lyre Snake (Map 132). Photograph by I. H. Conant.

4
Species Accounts

There are few publications that deal with all or major groups of species in Texas. These will not be found under each species, but are included here for general reference: Behler and King (59.5), Blair (72.5), Cagle (203.1), Chaney (214.9), Conant (230.12), Kiester (545.4), Raun and Gehlbach (770.3), Rogers (786.12), Tennant (1003.25, 1003.26), Thomas (1003.3, 1003.31), Wright and Wright (1095.1). Two book reviews are also worthy of mention: Conant (230.11) and Kroll (573.31).

Readers interested in the publications concerning fossil amphibians and reptiles of Texas may wish to examine the following list. About half of the citations do not appear in the text because they are extinct Cretaceous fossils, or more recent extinct species: 9.17, 13.12, 14, 59.7, 121.5, 143.51, 144.01, 145, 148.01, 216, 216.2, 278, 322.1, 334, 353.9, 353.91, 394.4, 400, 458, 458.2, 467, 468, 469, 470, 470.4, 480, 484.5, 489, 490, 491, 492, 493, 494, 495, 495.01, 495.02, 495.03, 495.04, 495.05, 495.08, 573.8, 579.2, 609.5, 614, 625.5, 639, 649, 660, 661, 661.1, 681.3, 718.1, 720.4, 721, 746.1, 770.2, 786.2, 786.21, 818, 821, 821.1, 821.2, 904.6, 910, 1006.5, 1006.51, 1008, 1009, 1045.22, 1045.23, 1056, 1084.1, 1101.

Class Amphibia

Order Caudata
Suborder Trachystomata
Family Sirenidae
Genus *Siren* Linnaeus
Systema Naturae 1766, 12(2), addenda (unpaged)
Siren intermedia
Lesser Siren (Map 1)

Siren intermedia Le Conte 1827. *J. Acad. Nat. Sci. Philadelphia* 1827 (1) 5:322.

REFERENCES: 9.16, 13, 29, 37, 63, 74, 144.01, 162, 171, 194, 211, 223, 228, 250, 289, 383, 394.2, 394.5, 395.1, 424, 425, 443, 480.2, 496, 585.2, 614.4, 614.41, 614.42, 614.6, 615, 710, 714, 726, 736, 753.4, 784.1, 809, 814, 858, 913, 914, 928, 932, 947, 962, 1042.11, 1092, 1098.

SUBSPECIES: *nettingi* Goin 1942, *Ann. Carnegie Mus.* 29:211; *texana* Goin 1957, *Herpetologica* 13:37.

COMMENTS: Gehlbach and others (394.2, 394.5, 395.1) describe the cocoon, aestivation, population ecology, and acoustic behavior of the Texas population of *S. i. nettingi*. The museum record for Dickens County is probably an escapee.

Suborder Salamandroidea
Family Ambystomatidae
Genus *Ambystoma* Tschudi
Mem. Soc. Sci. Nat. Neuchatel 1838, 2:92
Ambystoma maculatum
Spotted Salamander (Map 2)

Lacerta maculata Shaw 1802. *General Zool.* 3(1):304.
Ambystoma maculatum: Stejneger 1902. *Proc. Biol. Soc. Washington* 15: 239.
    REFERENCES: 5.32, 52, 63, 74, 162, 194, 228, 383, 480.2, 753.4, 786, 809, 858, 865, 947, 968, 1009.1, 1092.

Ambystoma opacum
Marbled Salamander (Map 2)

Salamandra opaca Gravenhorst 1807. *Vergl. Übersicht Zool. Syst.* 1807: 431.
Ambystoma opacum: Baird 1849. *J. Acad. Nat. Sci. Philadelphia* (2)1:283.
    REFERENCES: 5.31, 52, 63, 74, 162, 194, 228, 240, 251, 325, 480.2, 573.4, 622.232, 643.6, 753.4, 786, 786.05, 809, 858, 912, 914, 915, 928, 947, 968, 1009.1, 1092, 1098.
    FOSSIL RECORD: Scurry County (786.05).
    COMMENTS: The Wichita County (194) and McLennan County (915) records are erroneous, as is a museum record for Brown County.

Ambystoma talpoideum
Mole Salamander (Map 2)

Salamandra talpoidea Holbrook 1838. *N. Amer. Herp.* 3:117.
Ambystoma talpoideum: Gray 1850. *Cat. Batr. Grad. Brit. Mus.* 1850:36.
    REFERENCES: 9.16, 52, 74, 625, 753.4, 786, 858, 1009.1.
    COMMENTS: Recent museum records indicate that this species is more widespread than formerly believed.

Ambystoma texanum
Smallmouth Salamander (Map 3)

Salamandra texana Matthes 1855. *Allg. Deutsche Naturh. Zeitschr.* 1855 (n.s.) 1:266.

Ambystoma texanum: Baird 1859. *U.S. and Mex. Bound. Surv.* 2(2):29.
REFERENCES: 5.3, 63, 74, 122, 162, 175, 194, 220.14, 228, 240, 251, 383, 454.1, 463, 464, 480.2, 490, 491, 492, 495.05, 515, 701.22, 726, 753.4, 764, 765, 786, 809, 821.1, 858, 865, 885.5, 912, 913, 914, 915, 918, 920, 928, 932, 942, 947, 952, 956, 966, 993, 1009.1, 1042.11, 1092.
FOSSIL RECORD: Denton, Hardeman, and Harris counties (490, 491, 492, 495.05, 821.1).

Ambystoma tigrinum
Tiger Salamander (Map 4)

Salamandra tigrina Green 1825. *J. Acad. Nat. Sci. Philadelphia* (2) 5:116.
Ambystoma tigrinum: Baird 1849. *J. Acad. Nat. Sci. Philadelphia* (2) 1:284.
REFERENCES: 26.12, 37, 63, 74, 149.7, 162, 194, 214.5, 223, 228, 251, 253, 293.3, 330, 330.91, 383, 393.01, 407, 444, 451.5, 451.51, 454.1, 480, 480.2, 490, 495, 495.03, 495.04, 495.05, 521, 529.5, 529.52, 543.1, 587.1, 613, 622.233, 622.24, 630.3, 634, 642.06, 662, 665, 683.2, 726, 732.1, 732.2, 732.21, 753.4, 786, 786.32, 786.33, 786.4, 786.41, 786.42, 786.45, 786.5, 809, 816.3, 858, 862.5, 870, 871, 883, 885, 914, 918, 922, 932, 942, 947, 951, 952, 967, 1000, 1009.1, 1042.11, 1048.4, 1085.21, 1092, 1098.
FOSSIL RECORD: Delta, Knox, Llano, and Lubbock counties (480, 490, 495, 495.03, 495.04, 495.05).
SUBSPECIES: *tigrinum, marvortium* Baird 1850, *J. Acad. Nat. Sci. Philadelphia* (2) 1:284; and possibly *nebulosum* Hallowell 1852, *Proc. Acad. Nat. Sci. Philadelphia* 6:209, near El Paso.
COMMENTS: This species and its associated taxa have been widely introduced in Texas as fish bait; thus the status of subspecies within the state may never be resolved. Additionally, Hurricane Beulah in 1967 spread predatory fish into tiger salamander ponds in the Texas Coastal Bend, and these populations are now extirpated.

Family Amphiumidae
Genus *Amphiuma* Garden
in Smith, *Correspondence of Linneaus* 1821, 1:333.
Amphiuma tridactylum
Three-toed Amphiuma (Map 2)

Amphiuma tridactylum Cuvier 1827. *Mem. Mus. Nat. Hist. Paris* 14:708.
REFERENCES: 40, 63, 74, 162, 194, 228, 273, 480.2, 482, 492, 495.05, 753.4, 794.32, 794.33, 796, 809, 821.1, 858, 949, 968, 1092.
FOSSIL RECORD: Harris County (492, 495.05, 821.1).

Family Plethodontidæ
Genus *Desmognathus* Baird
J. Acad. Nat. Sci. Philadelphia 1850 (2) 1:282.
Desmognathus auriculatus
Southern Dusky Salamander (Map 5)

Salamandra auriculata Holbrook 1838. *N. Amer. Herp.* 3:115.
Desmognathus auriculatus: Baird 1850. *J. Acad. Nat. Sci. Philadelphia* (2)
1:286.
REFERENCES: 63, 74, 162, 175, 194, 228, 232.9, 295, 326, 438, 598,
633.5, 753.4, 799, 809, 816.8, 858, 1041, 1049, 1092.
COMMENTS: Although Raun and Gehlbach (770.3) give the McLennan County record as erroneous, it and Seifert and Wuerch's (816.8)
record for Dallas County are correctly identified. These records may be
the result of the larvae of this species being used as fish bait.

Genus *Eurycea* Rafinesque
Kentucky Gazette, Lexington, 1822 (n.s.) 1(9):3
Eurycea latitans
Cascade Caverns Salamander (Map 6)

Eurycea latitans Smith and Potter 1946. *Herpetologica* 3(4):105.
REFERENCES: 5.11, 42, 44, 45, 45.1, 74, 162, 167.01, 223, 228, 274,
646, 667, 667.1, 677, 708, 743, 775.1, 778.1, 786, 809, 846, 858, 863,
976.24, 1044, 1049.
COMMENTS: Milstead's (646) record for Kerr County is thought to be
erroneous (45).

Eurycea nana
San Marcos Salamander (Map 6)

Eurycea nana Bishop 1941. *Occ. Papers Mus. Zool. Univ. Michigan*
451:6.
REFERENCES: 5.11, 9.16, 42, 45, 45.1, 56.2, 62, 63, 74, 144.01, 162,
167.02, 228, 274, 361.22, 615, 617, 630, 667, 667.1, 725, 743, 786, 809,
818.1, 846, 858, 863, 873, 976.21, 976.22.
COMMENTS: S. Sweet (personal communication) has taken *E. nana*
from Comal County.

Eurycea neotenes
Texas Salamander (Map 6)

Eurycea neotenes Bishop and Wright 1937. *Proc. Biol. Soc. Washington*
50:142.

REFERENCES: 5.11, 9.16, 45, 45.1, 56, 56.2, 62, 63, 65, 74, 144.01, 162, 167.03, 170.7, 175, 194, 223, 228, 274, 454.1, 615, 630, 667, 667.1, 700, 743, 786, 809, 818.1, 858, 863, 976.21, 976.22, 976.23, 976.24, 1049, 1092.

COMMENTS: Sweet (976.23) is the most recent comprehensive work on the taxonomy and distribution of *E. neotenes.*

Eurycea quadridigitata
Dwarf Salamander (Map 5)

Salamandra quadridigitata Holbrook 1842. *N. Amer. Herp.* 5:65.
Eurycea quadridigitata: Dunn 1923. *Proc. New England Zool. Club* 7:40.
REFERENCES: 63, 74, 162, 326, 595, 622.232, 671, 672.1, 726, 786, 809, 858, 865, 947, 1049, 1092.
COMMENTS: A museum record for Tarrant County is erroneous.

Eurycea tridentifera
Comal Blind Salamander (Map 6)

Eurycea tridentifera Mitchell and Reddell 1965. *Texas J. Sci.* 17(1):14.
REFERENCES: 5.11, 9.16, 144.01, 667, 667.1, 774, 775.1, 778.1, 976.2, 976.24, 1049.

Eurycea troglodytes
Valdina Farms Salamander (Map 6)

Eurycea troglodytes Baker 1957. *Texas J. Sci.* 9(3):329.
REFERENCES: 5.11, 9.16, 42, 43, 45, 45.1, 144.01, 228, 617, 667, 667.1, 708, 775.1, 778.1, 786, 976.24, 1044, 1049.

Genus *Plethodon* Tschudi
Mem. Soc. Sci. Nat. Neuchatel 1838:92
Plethodon glutinosus
Slimy Salamander (Map 7)

Salamandra glutinosa Green 1818. *J. Acad. Nat. Sci. Philadelphia* (1) 1:357.
Plethodon glutinosus: Tschudi 1838. *Mem. Soc. Sci. Nat. Neuchatel* 1838:58.
REFERENCES: 45, 63, 74, 86.1, 99, 144.01, 162, 194, 228, 229, 251, 258, 325, 326, 436, 451.5, 451.51, 454.1, 481, 495.02, 495.05, 529.5, 615,

618, 630, 679, 725, 774, 775.1, 778, 809, 858, 873, 912, 914, 915, 947, 964, 967, 1049, 1092, 1098.

FOSSIL RECORD: Kendall County (495.02, 495.05).

SUBSPECIES: *glutinosus: albagula* Grobman 1944, *Ann. N.Y. Acad. Sci.* 45:283.

COMMENTS: Raun and Gehlbach (770.3) questioned records of this species from McLennan, Walker, and Upshur counties. The Upshur County specimens have been examined and are *P. glutinosus glutinosus* and represent the only known Texas field-collected specimens of the taxon. The cave records (775) for Mason and San Saba counties are questionable.

Genus *Typhlomolge* Stejneger
Proc. U.S. Natl. Mus. 1896, 18:620
Typhlomolge rathbuni
Texas Blind Salamander (Map 6)

Typhlomolge rathbuni Stejneger 1896. *Proc. U.S. Natl. Mus.* 18:620.

REFERENCES: 5, 5.11, 42, 43, 44, 45, 58, 63, 66, 74, 136, 144, 144.01, 146, 162, 223, 228, 274, 318, 323, 325, 326, 342, 343, 344, 345, 346, 347, 350, 353, 383, 386, 427, 475, 476, 484, 545.7, 603.2, 667, 667.1, 676, 678, 679, 680, 682, 708, 711, 732, 743, 775.1, 778.1, 809, 818.1, 846, 858, 863, 890, 907, 914, 977, 1036, 1037, 1038, 1039, 1040, 1044, 1049, 1084, 1092.

Typhlomolge robusta
Blanco Blind Salamander (Map 6)

Typhlomolge robusta Potter and Sweet 1981. *Copeia* 1981(1):70.

REFERENCES: 5.11, 603.2, 738.3.

COMMENTS: I do not accept Potter and Sweet's (738.3) arguments that Longley (603.2) is the author of this species. Longley's endangered species report on *T. rathbuni* is not primary literature and is not duplicated in such a manner that each copy is identical to the next, nor did he suggest that it was a new species description. His references to the species name came from an unpublished thesis of Potter, and in every case, Longley ascribed the name to Potter. Longley did not designate a type species, nor give a diagnosis or description, *sensu stricto*. In the spirit of the 1984 revised Code of Zoological Nomenclature, Potter and Sweet are the authors of the name *robusta*.

Family Proteidae
Genus *Necturus* Rafinesque
Blainville's J. Phys. 1819, 88:417
Necturus beyeri
Gulf Coast Water Dog (Map 8)

Necturus beyeri Viosca 1937. *Copeia* 1937(2):123.
REFERENCES: 5.11, 74, 144.01, 162, 228, 471, 753.4, 796, 809.
COMMENTS: The Montgomery County museum record is from the San Jacinto River system and is the first record west of the Trinity River basin.

Family Salamandridae
Genus *Notophthalmus* Rafinesque
Ann. Nat. Lexington 1820 (1):5
Notophthalmus meridionalis
Black-spotted Newt (Map 9)

Diemictylus miniatus meridionalis Cope 1880. *Bull. U.S. Natl. Mus.* 17:30.
Notophthalmus meridionalis: Smith 1953. *Herpetologica* 9(2):98.
REFERENCES: 9.16, 63, 74, 86.1, 99, 128, 130, 144.01, 162, 194, 228, 250, 251, 325, 383, 463, 464, 642.03, 642.04, 786, 809, 858, 870, 913, 926, 967, 1000, 1092.
SUBSPECIES: *meridionalis* (see above).
COMMENTS: Raun and Gehlbach (770.3) state that the Falls County (926) and Bexar County (162) records are erroneous. The Victoria County (913) record may represent *N. viridescens,* and the Duval County record is unverified. This species has become endangered in Texas because pesticides and herbicides have been used throughout its area of distribution in Texas.

Notophthalmus viridescens
Red-spotted Newt (Map 10)

Triturus viridescens Rafinesque 1820. *Amer. Nat. Lexington* (1):5.
Notophthalmus viridescens: Smith 1953. *Herpetologica* 9(2):98.
REFERENCES: 63, 74, 99, 162, 163, 175, 228, 451.5, 451.51, 622.232, 622.24, 642.01, 643.6, 726, 753.4, 786, 809, 858, 865, 913, 914, 915, 928, 947, 968, 1092, 1098.
SUBSPECIES: *louisianensis* Wolterstorff 1914, *Abh. Mus. Nat. Magdeburg* 2:283.
COMMENTS: The Hays County and Travis County records (162) have not been verified, nor has a museum record for Duval County.

Order Anura
Suborder Opisthocoela
Family Rhinophrynidae
Genus *Rhinophrynus* Dumeril and Bibron
Erpetol. Gen. 1841, 8:757
Rhinophrynus dorsalis
Mexican Burrowing Toad (Map 9)

Rhinophrynus dorsalis Dumeril and Bibron 1841. *Erpetol. Gen.* 8:
758–60.

REFERENCES: 5.1, 9.16, 379.1, 513, 786.

COMMENTS: Specimens of this species have not been found in Texas
during the past fifteen years.

Suborder Anomalocoela
Family Pelobatidae
Genus *Scaphiopus* Holbrook
N. Amer. Herp. 1836, 1:85
Scaphiopus bombifrons
Plains Spadefoot (Map 12)

Scaphiopus bombifrons Cope 1863. *Proc. Acad. Nat. Sci. Philadelphia*
15:53.

REFERENCES: 5.1, 20, 26.12, 27, 79, 98, 100.04, 142, 162, 170.2,
217, 228, 239, 251, 253, 297, 377.2, 379.11, 451.5, 451.51, 499, 500, 501,
529.51, 614.11, 619, 622.233, 642.06, 683.2, 732.32, 753.4, 801.5, 809,
816.3, 858, 883, 885, 914, 922, 979, 1048, 1054, 1054.12, 1093.

COMMENTS: There is a curious gap in the distribution of the Plains
Spadefoot Toad (see Map 12) that cannot be explained by current paleon-
tological theories.

Scaphiopus couchi
Couch's Spadefoot (Map 13)

Scaphiopus couchi Baird 1854. *Proc. Acad. Nat. Sci. Philadelphia* 7:62.

REFERENCES: 5.1, 15.1, 20, 21, 27, 53.3, 74, 79, 98, 99, 100.04,
162, 217, 228, 251, 254, 297, 390, 442, 451.5, 451.51, 454.1, 495.03, 497,
509.21, 513, 519, 521, 529.35, 529.51, 533, 545.62, 587.5, 588.21, 588.39,
619, 622.233, 642.06, 662, 665, 683.2, 714, 753.4, 782, 786, 809, 816.3,
858, 865, 870, 883, 885, 912, 913, 914, 915, 917, 918, 924, 945, 947, 951,
952, 956, 967, 977.21, 979, 1000, 1021, 1042.12, 1050.11, 1053, 1054,
1054.11, 1054.2, 1055.41, 1064, 1072.1, 1075, 1085.21, 1088, 1092, 1093,
1098, 1101.

FOSSIL RECORD: Edwards County (495.03).

Scaphiopus holbrooki
Eastern Spadefoot (Map 14)

Rana holbrooki Harlan 1835. *Med. Phys. Res.* 1835:105.
Scaphiopus holbrooki: Baird 1859. *Expl. Surv. R. R. Miss. Pacific* (4):12.
REFERENCES: 5.1, 15.1, 20, 27, 73, 74, 79, 88, 89, 99, 100.04, 162, 217, 228, 297, 438.41, 442, 454.1, 515, 529.51, 614.11, 619, 622.233, 622.24, 714, 753.4, 765, 770, 782, 786, 809, 829, 858, 865, 913, 914, 917, 923, 965, 979, 1051, 1052, 1054.1, 1054.12, 1072.2, 1072.21, 1075, 1092, 1093.
SUBSPECIES: *hurteri* Strecker 1910, *Proc. Biol. Soc. Washington* 23:116.

Scaphiopus multiplicatus
New Mexico Spadefoot (Map 15)

Scaphiopus multiplicatus Cope 1863. *Proc. Acad. Nat. Sci. Philadelphia* 15:52.
REFERENCES: 5.1, 21, 74, 79, 98, 100.04, 162, 170.2, 217, 228, 297, 377.2, 387, 442, 451.5, 451.51, 499, 501, 521, 533, 614.11, 622.233, 662, 665, 683.2, 753.4, 809, 816.3, 858, 870, 883, 885, 914, 917, 951, 967, 979, 1021, 1054, 1054.12, 1055.41, 1072.1, 1085.21, 1092, 1093.
COMMENTS: Brown's (170.2) review of the relationships between *S. hammondi* populations of California and populations east of California has shown that size, call structure, color, breeding season, and other natural history information suggest two species are involved. Brown restricted *S. hammondi* to the isolated California population and used the name *S. multiplicatus* for all remaining populations that were once considered *S. hammondi.* I tentatively follow Brown, but further work may show that the two taxa are conspecific, as suggested by Behler and King (59.5).

Suborder Procoela
Family Leptodactylidae
Genus *Hylactophryne* Lynch
Univ. Kansas Publ. Nat. Hist. 1968, 17:511
Hylactophryne augusti
Barking Frog (Map 16)

Hylodes augusti Duges 1879. In Brocchi, *Bull. Soc. Philos. Paris* (7) 3:21.
Hylactophryne augusti: Lynch 1968. *Univ. Kansas Publ. Nat. Hist.* 17:511.
REFERENCES: 21, 74, 133, 162, 223, 228, 243, 251, 297, 360, 379, 394, 454.1, 495.05, 514, 516, 533, 618, 639, 656, 683.2, 709, 731, 774, 775.1, 778, 780, 786, 809, 816, 816.5, 858, 870, 871, 882, 885, 912, 914,

915, 924, 947, 957, 964, 967, 1000, 1042, 1092, 1093, 1098, 1102, 1105, 1106.1

FOSSIL RECORD: Bexar County (495.05, 639).

SUBSPECIES: *latrans* Cope 1880, *Bull. U.S. Natl. Mus.* 17:25.

COMMENTS: This species shows a continuous distribution along the Balcones Escarpment, but is widely scattered through isolated localities elsewhere.

Leptodactylus fragilis
White-lipped Frog (Map 9)

Cystignathus fragilis Brocchi 1877. *Bull. Soc. Philos. Paris* (7) 1:182.

Leptodactylus fragilis: Heyer 1978. *Nat. Hist. Mus. Los Angeles Co.* 29:46.

REFERENCES: 5.1, 9.16, 74, 162, 228, 286, 379, 478.2, 478.21, 691, 809, 858, 870, 988, 1000, 1089, 1092, 1093.

COMMENTS: This frog may be extirpated from Texas through the continuous dispersal of organophosphate chemicals in the Rio Grande Valley.

Genus *Syrrhophus* Cope
Amer. Nat. 1878, 12:243
Syrrhophus cystignathoides
Rio Grande Chirping Frog (Map 17)

Phyllobates cystignathoides Cope 1877. *Proc. Amer. Philos. Soc.* 17:89.

Syrrhophus cystignathoides: Cope 1879. *Proc. Amer. Philos. Soc.* 18:268.

REFERENCES: 9.16, 74, 162, 223, 228, 616.2, 683.2, 809, 858, 870, 871, 893, 1000, 1091, 1092, 1093.

SUBSPECIES: *campi* Stejneger 1915, *Proc. Biol. Soc. Washington* 28:131.

COMMENTS: Rio Grande Chirping Frogs have been accidentally introduced into Houston and San Antonio via the potted plant trade from nurseries in the Rio Grande Valley.

Syrrhophus guttilatus
Spotted Chirping Frog (Map 41)

Malachylodes guttilatus Cope 1879. *Proc. Amer. Philos. Soc.* 18:264.

Syrrhophus guttilatus: Boulenger 1888. *Proc. Zool. Soc. London* 2:204.

REFERENCES: 9.16, 21, 162, 228, 290.2, 292, 521, 615, 656, 665, 725, 809, 811, 1093.

COMMENTS: There are calls reported of this species from the east side of the Davis Mountains, Jeff Davis County (King, personal communication).

Syrrhophus marnocki
Cliff Chirping Frog (Map 18)

Syrrhophus marnocki Cope 1878. *Amer. Nat.* 12:253.

REFERENCES: 41, 51, 74, 162, 228, 244, 251, 274, 297, 379, 394, 454.1, 480, 495.03, 495.05, 497.2, 516, 517, 610, 613, 618, 655, 660, 662, 676, 679, 683.2, 775.1, 778, 780, 809, 858, 865, 914, 956, 957, 967, 1008, 1033, 1034, 1055.41, 1092, 1093.

FOSSIL RECORD: Edwards, Foard, and Knox counties (480, 495.03, 495.05, 610, 1008).

COMMENTS: King (personal communication) and a field party from Texas Christian University heard calls of this species in Castle Gap County Park, Upton County.

Family Hylidae
Genus *Acris* Dumeril and Bibron
Erpetol. Gen. 1841, 8:506
Acris crepitans
Northern Cricket Frog (Map 19)

Acris crepitans: Baird 1854. *Proc. Acad. Nat. Sci. Philadelphia* 7:59.

REFERENCES: 5.1, 21, 33, 59.2, 74, 76, 84, 85, 92, 100.04, 113.7, 122, 139, 146, 162, 175, 195, 196, 202, 204.1, 216, 223, 228, 230.14, 251, 253, 277.4, 297, 329, 336, 451.5, 451.51, 454.1, 480, 489, 490, 491, 495.05, 509.2, 511, 515, 547, 588.21, 588.39, 592, 597, 601, 610, 611, 613, 615, 622.17, 622.21, 622.232, 642.06, 655, 656, 662, 683.2, 687.5, 706, 714, 726, 736, 749, 751, 752, 753, 753.4, 753.6, 765, 775.1, 809, 816.12, 858, 865, 870, 873, 882, 885, 907, 912, 913, 914, 915, 918, 919, 922, 924, 927, 928, 930, 932, 944, 951, 952, 956, 957, 964, 965, 966, 967, 968, 1063.1, 1072.2, 1072.21, 1092, 1093, 1098.

FOSSIL RECORD: Denton, Foard, Hardeman, Knox, and Lubbock counties (216, 480, 489, 490, 491, 495.05, 610).

SUBSPECIES: *crepitans; blanchardi* Harper 1947, *Proc. Biol. Soc. Washington* 60:39; *paludicola* Burger, Smith and Smith 1949, *J. Tenn. Acad. Sci.* 24(2):131.

COMMENTS: There is no recent evidence that *Acris gryllus* occurs in Texas.

Genus *Hyla* Laurenti
Syn. Rept. 1768:32
Hyla arenicolor
Canyon Treefrog (Map 41)

Hyla arenicolor Cope 1866. *J. Acad. Nat. Sci. Philadelphia* (2) 6:84.

REFERENCES: 5.1, 26.12, 74, 85, 86.1, 87, 99, 127, 130, 162, 330.91, 332.02, 387, 521, 522.1, 533, 648, 665, 683.2, 700, 732.3, 732.31, 785, 809, 811, 821.3, 858, 870, 871, 883, 885, 914, 1000, 1045.21, 1055.41, 1092, 1093.

COMMENTS: The El Paso, Texas, locality of *H. arenicolor* is represented by the cotypes of *H. copii* Boulenger (127). R. W. Webb (personal communication) suggests that *H. arenicolor* is currently unknown in El Paso County. The cotypes of *H. copii* may not have been taken at El Paso, but shipped from there. Thus, El Paso became the type locality by error, a common problem of early herpetological records from the western United States.

Hyla chrysoscelis
Cope's Gray Treefrog (Map 20)

Hyla femoralis chrysoscelis Cope 1880. *Bull. U.S. Natl. Mus.* 17:29.
Hyla chrysoscelis: Johnson 1966. *Texas J. Sci.* 18(4):361.

REFERENCES: 5.1, 85, 98, 99, 212.7, 372.1, 399.2, 438.41, 454.1, 523, 525, 526, 588.21, 588.39, 593, 614.11, 617.5, 622.233, 732.31, 732.33, 753.5, 753.51, 753.61, 753.64.

COMMENTS: *Hyla chrysoscelis* is frequently confused with *H. versicolor* because they are essentially identical in appearance. Much of the current literature includes one or both species as if they were one. Most museums maintain only one container labeled *chrysoscelis/versicolor.* Since pulse rate and/or blood cells and karyology are the only ways to separate the species, both species are still confused throughout their distribution. Map 20 shows a composite distribution of both species.

Hyla cinerea
Green Treefrog (Map 21)

Calamita cinereus Schneider 1799. *Hist. Amphib.* 1:174.
Hyla cinerea: Garman 1891. *Bull. Illinois St. Lab. Nat. Hist.* 3:189.

REFERENCES: 5.1, 53.3, 61, 74, 85, 86.1, 87, 139, 162, 175, 204.1, 228, 230.13, 251, 293.6, 297, 299, 405, 450, 454.1, 464, 522.1, 529.51, 543, 588.21, 592, 601, 614.11, 643.6, 683.1, 687.5, 714, 726, 732.31, 736, 753, 753.4, 765, 809, 858, 862.5, 865, 912, 913, 914, 915, 918, 924, 928, 932, 935, 956, 964, 965, 966, 968, 969, 985, 1042.11, 1092, 1093, 1098.

COMMENTS: The Real County record questioned by Raun and Gehlbach (770.3) is probably valid.

Hyla crucifer
Spring Peeper (Map 5)

Hyla crucifer Wied 1838. *Reise Nord Amer.* 1B(5):275.
REFERENCES: 5.1, 74, 87, 162, 204.1, 228, 406, 529.51, 595, 638, 714, 726, 753.4, 809, 858, 865, 1093.

Hyla squirella
Squirrel Treefrog (Map 22)

Hyla squirella Sonnini and Latreille 1802. *Hist. Nat. Rept.* 2:181.
REFERENCES: 5.1, 74, 86.1, 87, 90, 162, 228, 297, 405, 463, 588.21, 592, 614.43, 622.232, 622.24, 687.5, 702, 732.31, 736, 753, 753.4, 809, 858, 913, 914, 967, 968, 1092, 1093.
COMMENTS: The Bexar County record (914, 967) is erroneous, but the Bowie County record (968) is probably valid.

Hyla versicolor
Gray Treefrog (Map 20)

Hyla versicolor Le Conte 1825. *Ann. Lyc. Nat. Hist. N.Y.* 1:281.
REFERENCES: 5.1, 74, 85, 87, 98, 99, 122, 162, 195, 205.11, 212.7, 216, 223, 228, 251, 293.6, 297, 372.1, 381, 495.03, 495.05, 523, 525, 526, 542, 588.21, 592, 593, 610, 611, 614.11, 617.5, 632.233, 726, 732.31, 732.33, 736, 750, 753, 753.5, 753.51, 753.61, 753.64, 809, 856, 858, 865, 912, 914, 915, 922, 923, 928, 932, 947, 964, 967, 968, 1042.11, 1072.2, 1072.21, 1092, 1093.
FOSSIL RECORD: Edwards, Foard, and Lubbock counties (495.03, 495.05, 610, 611).
COMMENTS: See comments for *Hyla chrysoscelis* concerning identification of this species.

Genus *Pseudacris* Fitzinger
Syst. Rept. 1843:31
Pseudacris clarki
Spotted Chorus Frog (Map 23)

Helocaetes clarki Baird 1854. *Proc. Acad. Nat. Sci. Philadelphia* 7:60.
Pseudacris clarki: Smith 1934. *Amer. Midl. Nat.* 15:462.
REFERENCES: 5.1, 20, 30, 74, 92, 94, 98, 122, 162, 189, 204.1,

205.11, 216, 220.14, 228, 253, 333, 438.41, 454.1, 495.04, 495.05, 515, 519, 522.1, 529.51, 536, 588.39, 591, 592, 594, 605, 610, 616.2, 622.232, 638, 644, 701.25, 726, 732.31, 765, 809, 850, 858, 865, 912, 914, 951, 952, 1021, 1072.1, 1072.21, 1092, 1093, 1098.

FOSSIL RECORD: Foard and Lubbock counties (495.04, 495.05, 610).

Pseudacris streckeri
Strecker's Chorus Frog (Map 24)

Pseudacris streckeri Wright and Wright 1933. *Handbk. Frogs and Toads* 1:102.

REFERENCES: 5.1, 20, 26.21, 74, 85, 86.1, 92, 94, 98, 102, 122, 133, 162, 189, 228, 230.15, 251, 297, 381, 438.41, 454.1, 494, 495, 495.05, 498, 515, 519, 522.1, 588.21, 592, 594, 611, 622.18, 638, 640, 642, 643.6, 726, 753.4, 753.6, 765, 786, 809, 858, 865, 874.5, 914, 930, 934, 952, 956, 965, 966, 967, 968, 1062, 1072.2,, 1072.21, 1092, 1093.

FOSSIL RECORD: Hardeman and Llano counties (495.05, 611).

SUBSPECIES: *streckeri* (see above).

Pseudacris triseriata
Striped Chorus Frog (Map 25)

Hyla triseriata Wied 1838. *Reise Nord Amer.* 1(4):249.
Pseudacris triseriata: Schwartz 1957. *Amer. Mus. Novitates* 1838:11.

REFERENCES: 5.1, 74, 85, 98, 122, 162, 182, 189, 228, 463, 464, 536, 590, 600, 605, 625, 638, 644, 726, 753.4, 809, 850, 858, 865, 876, 885, 913, 914, 915, 918, 924, 967, 968, 1042.11, 1072.2, 1072.21, 1092, 1093.

SUBSPECIES: *feriarum* Baird 1854, Proc. Acad. Nat. Sci. Philadelphia 7:60.

COMMENTS: The Bexar County (967) and Burnet County (914, 967) records of this species probably represent *P. clarki*, but identifications have not been verified.

Genus *Smilisca* Cope
Proc. Acad. Nat. Sci. Philadelphia 1865, 17:194
Smilisca baudinii
Mexican Treefrog (Map 9)

Hyla baudinii Dumeril and Bibron 1841. *Erpetol. Gen.* 8:564.
Smilisca baudinii: Cope 1875. *Bull. U.S. Natl. Mus.* 1:31.

REFERENCES: 5.1, 30, 74, 87, 162, 223, 228, 238, 251, 297, 320.11,

320.12, 387, 533, 699.5, 753, 786, 809, 858, 870, 871, 913, 914, 967, 1092, 1093, 1098.

COMMENTS: The Bexar County (967) and Refugio County (913) records are correct identifications, but probably represent accidental introductions, via tropical plants transported from the Rio Grande Valley.

Family Bufonidae
Genus *Bufo* Laurenti
Syn. Rept. 1768:25
Bufo americanus
American Toad (Map 8)

Bufo americanus Holbrook 1836. *N. Amer. Herpetol.* 1:75.
REFERENCES: 5.1, 162, 170.31, 249, 625, 1084.1.
FOSSIL RECORD: Lubbock County (1084.1).
SUBSPECIES: *charlesmithi* Bragg 1954, *Wassman J. Biol.* 12:247.
COMMENTS: The American toad is more widespread than formerly believed. Further distributional data is needed to clarify the relationships between the Houston toad and the American toad.

Bufo cognatus
Great Plains Toad (Map 26)

Bufo cognatus Say 1823. In *Long's Exped. Rocky Mts.* 2:190.
REFERENCES: 5.1, 9.4, 74, 82, 100.01, 140, 162, 213.5, 228, 253, 390, 443.03, 451.5, 451.51, 491, 495.04, 495.05, 521, 533, 614.13, 620, 622.233, 639, 642.06, 683.2, 786.1, 786.11, 809, 816.3, 858, 865, 870, 882, 883, 885, 914, 922, 965, 1000, 1085.21, 1092, 1093.
FOSSIL RECORD: Bexar, Hardeman, and Lubbock counties (491, 495.04, 495.05, 639).
COMMENTS: Some of the fossil records may represent *Bufo speciosus* (495.05).

Bufo debilis
Green Toad (Map 27)

Bufo debilis Girard 1854. *Proc. Acad. Nat. Sci. Philadelphia* 7:87.
REFERENCES: 5.1, 21, 74, 82, 85, 88, 93, 98, 100.01, 118, 130, 162, 213.5, 228, 250, 251, 253, 254, 297, 454.1, 513, 515, 521, 529.51, 533, 588.21, 588.39, 614.11, 616.2, 620, 642.06, 665, 683.2, 765, 800, 802, 809, 811, 858, 870, 882, 883, 885, 912, 913, 914, 915, 917, 918, 924, 935, 941, 944, 945, 952, 956, 965, 967, 993, 1000, 1001, 1055.41, 1085.21, 1092, 1093.

SUBSPECIES: *debilis; insidior* Girard 1854, *Proc. Acad. Nat. Sci. Philadelphia* 7:88.

Bufo houstonensis
Houston Toad (Map 28)

Bufo houstonensis Sanders 1953. *Herpetologica* 9(1):26.
REFERENCES: 5.1, 9.1, 9.11, 9.12, 9.13, 9.2, 82, 85, 86.1, 88, 96, 96.1, 98, 99, 100.01, 113.80, 113.81, 141, 170.3, 170.32, 170.33, 170.35, 170.36, 170.37, 170.38, 223, 228, 320.1, 340.5, 361.2, 394.1, 426.4, 443.01, 443.03, 443.3, 482.6, 495.4, 529.1, 541, 587, 588.2, 588.21, 617.7, 620, 625.41, 630, 725.1, 753.12, 797, 798, 873, 1004.5, 1008.1, 1071.5.
COMMENTS: Much has been written about this toad since it was placed on the endangered species list in 1971. It is threatened by extinction through urbanization of its habitat and habitat alteration through lignite coal mining operations.

Bufo marinus
Giant Toad (Map 11)

Rana marina Linnaeus 1758. *Sys. Nat.* 1:211.
Bufo marinus Schneider 1799. *Hist. Amphib.* 1:219.
REFERENCES: 5.1, 9.16, 9.18, 27, 70, 74, 82, 85, 100.01, 162, 228, 451.5, 451.51, 513, 529.52, 588.3, 620, 683.2, 809, 858, 1000, 1001, 1002, 1093, 1100.2.
COMMENTS: The natural history of native populations of this species was recently documented (1100.2).

Bufo punctatus
Red-spotted Toad (Map 29)

Bufo punctatus Baird and Girard 1852. *Proc. Acad. Nat. Sci. Philadelphia* 6:173.
REFERENCES: 5.1, 21, 35, 50, 53.3, 70, 82, 88, 93, 97, 98, 100.01, 162, 223, 228, 250, 251, 253, 297, 394, 402, 454.1, 521, 529.5, 533, 587.5, 588.21, 614.11, 620, 622.233, 625.2, 642.06, 648, 662, 665, 683.2, 700, 775.1, 809, 811, 816.3, 822, 858, 865, 870, 871, 883, 885, 914, 915, 917, 918, 919, 924, 927, 930, 935, 938, 952, 956, 964, 965, 966, 967, 1000, 1021, 1055.41, 1085.21, 1088, 1092, 1093, 1098.
COMMENTS: The Brazos County record (50) is an accidental introduction via upstream flooding of the Brazos River. The Duval County and Starr County records (250, 533) are valid.

Bufo speciosus
Texas Toad (Map 30)

Bufo speciosus Girard 1854. *Proc. Acad. Nat. Sci. Philadelphia* 7:85.

REFERENCES: 5.1, 20, 21, 26.12, 53, 74, 82, 88, 93, 98, 100.01, 117, 162, 195, 196, 205.11, 213.5, 223, 228, 248, 251, 253, 297, 390, 394, 394.4, 402, 443.03, 451.5, 451.51, 454.1, 458.2, 491,, 495.05, 507, 513, 515, 521, 533, 588.2, 588.21, 588.39, 613, 614.11, 614.13, 620, 522.232, 634, 639, 642.06, 662, 665, 683.1, 683.2, 726, 753, 753.4, 765, 775.1, 782, 786.11, 809, 818, 851, 865, 870, 871, 883, 885, 913, 914, 915, 917, 918, 924, 930, 935, 945, 951, 956, 967, 1000, 1055.41, 1072.2, 1072.21, 1075, 1085.21, 1088, 1092, 1093, 1098.

FOSSIL RECORD: Bexar, Culberson, Hardeman, and Lubbock counties (394.4, 458.2, 491, 495.05, 639). Some fossil records are confused with *B. cognatus* (495.05).

Bufo valliceps
Gulf Coast Toad (Map 31)

Bufo valliceps Wiegmann 1833. *Isis* 26(7):657.

REFERENCES: 5.1, 15, 20, 32, 37, 43, 49, 53.3, 67, 74, 76, 81, 82, 83, 88, 89, 91, 92, 93, 94, 97, 98, 100, 100.01, 100.4, 162, 170.3, 170.32, 170.34, 170.6, 195, 204.4, 204.41, 205.11, 213.5, 220.13, 220.14, 223, 223.3, 228, 230.14, 248, 250, 251, 297, 372.7, 387, 390, 402, 405, 438.4, 438.41, 438.42, 438.43, 443.03, 454.1, 463, 482.6, 487, 497.2, 498, 513, 533, 573.32, 587.5, 588.21, 588.22, 614.11, 614.13, 618, 620, 656, 662, 679, 683.1, 683.2, 687.5, 701.5, 718, 726, 736, 737, 738, 738.1, 753.4, 765, 775.1, 777, 778, 782, 786, 797.1, 798, 809, 818, 858, 865, 870, 907, 912, 913, 914, 915, 917, 918, 924, 928, 930, 932, 939, 942, 944, 956, 966, 967, 1000, 1005, 1006, 1033, 1034, 1062, 1072.2, 1072.21, 1075, 1088, 1092, 1093, 1098.

SUBSPECIES: *valliceps* (see 738.1).

COMMENTS: There are museum records of this species for Brewster and El Paso counties. The El Paso County record represents an accidental introduction.

Bufo woodhousei
Woodhouse's Toad (Map 32)

Bufo woodhousei Girard 1854. *Proc. Acad. Nat. Sci. Philadelphia* 7:86.

REFERENCES: 5.1, 20, 25, 26.12, 46, 47, 53, 67, 68, 74, 81, 82, 83, 88, 92, 93, 95, 96, 98, 99, 100.01, 100.04, 122, 139, 143, 162, 170.3, 170.31, 170.32, 170.34, 170.37, 170.6, 195, 196, 204.4, 213.5, 223, 228, 230.14, 251, 253, 297, 330.91, 438.41, 440, 443.01, 443.03, 451.5, 451.51,

454.1, 474, 482.6, 489, 490, 495.03, 495.05, 507, 542, 587, 588.2, 588.21, 588.39, 601, 614.11, 614.13, 620, 622.232, 630, 633, 639, 665, 681.3, 682.3, 701.24, 718, 726, 753.4, 765, 797.1, 798, 803, 809, 811, 816.3, 858, 870, 873, 883, 885, 912, 913, 914, 915, 917, 918, 919, 924, 927, 928, 932, 944, 951, 952, 956, 966, 967, 968, 998, 1000, 1006, 1034, 1042.4, 1055.41, 1072.2, 1072.21, 1084.1, 1085.21, 1092, 1093.

FOSSIL RECORD: Bexar, Denton, Edwards, Foard, and Lubbock counties (489, 490, 495.03, 495.05, 639, 681.3, 1034.1).

SUBSPECIES: *woodhousei; australis* Shannon and Lowe 1955, *Herpetologica* 11(3):185; *velatus* Bragg and Sanders 1951, *Wassman J. Biol.* 9:366.

COMMENTS: There appears to be an isolated population of Woodhouse's toads in southern Texas. Raun and Gehlbach (770.3) suggested that a record from Webb County (162) was questionable, but in light of additional distributional records, it is probably valid.

Suborder Diplasiocoela
Family Ranidae
Genus *Rana* Linnaeus
Sys. Nat. 1758, 1:210
Rana areolata
Crawfish Frog (Map 33)

Rana areolata Baird and Girard 1852. *Proc. Acad. Nat. Sci. Philadelphia* 6:173.

REFERENCES: 5.1, 37, 86.1, 137, 162, 195, 223, 228, 251, 265.8, 285, 297, 426, 437, 456, 463, 464, 621, 624.1, 625, 630.2, 736, 753.4, 809, 816.54, 865, 914, 1062, 1092, 1093, 1098.

SUBSPECIES: *areolata* (see above).

Rana berlandieri
Rio Grande Leopard Frog (Map 34)

Rana berlandieri Baird 1859. *U.S. and Mex. Bound. Surv.* 2:27.

REFERENCES: 8, 21, 33, 55, 59.65, 61, 74, 76, 92, 94, 137, 162, 195, 196, 223, 228, 250, 265.8, 315, 388.6, 394, 394.4, 454.1, 458.2, 482.41, 482.42, 495, 495.05, 509.21, 521, 547, 573.05, 588.22, 594.1, 613, 622, 622.233, 639, 642.06, 642.2, 648, 662, 664, 683, 683.2, 687, 712.2, 712.3, 714, 718.2, 732.7, 770, 775.1, 777, 778, 778.1, 782, 794.2, 794.31, 809, 811, 818, 858, 865, 882, 883, 907, 913, 914, 915, 918, 924, 930, 944, 956, 957, 964, 966, 967, 985, 1001, 1055.41, 1085.21, 1092, 1093.

FOSSIL RECORD: Bexar and Llano counties (495.05).

COMMENTS: Some *Rana berlandieri* literature references may be included under the name *Rana pipiens*.

Rana blairi
Plains Leopard Frog (Map 35)

Rana blairi Mecham, Littlejohn, Oldham, Brown, and Brown 1973. *Occ. Papers Mus. Texas Tech Univ.* 18:3.

REFERENCES: 74, 162, 196, 253, 259, 480, 482.41, 489, 491, 495.04, 495.05, 509.2, 594.1, 613, 622.233, 642.05, 642.2, 732.7, 753.4, 786.44, 816.3, 865, 883, 922, 951, 952, 1092, 1093.

FOSSIL RECORD: Foard, Hardeman, and Lubbock counties (495.04, 495.05).

COMMENTS: See comments under *Rana pipiens*.

Rana catesbeiana
Bullfrog (Map 36)

Rana catesbeiana Shaw 1802. *Gen. Zool.* 3:106.

REFERENCES: 5.1, 33, 74, 76, 84, 91, 92, 94, 122, 123.5, 139, 162, 170.34, 175, 195, 220.13, 228, 297, 426.2, 464, 487.7, 490, 494, 495, 495.05, 497.2, 509.2, 512, 514, 529.5, 529.51, 547, 569, 587.5, 588.21, 601, 609.5, 613, 616.2, 622.233, 622.24, 626.5, 639, 642.06, 663, 683.2, 687.5, 701.26, 701.28, 701.3, 714, 721, 726, 736, 753.4, 765, 770, 809, 858, 862.5, 865, 870, 883, 885, 912, 913, 914, 915, 918, 927, 928, 930, 932, 944, 947, 951, 952, 956, 957, 966, 967, 968, 977.41, 985, 1000, 1042.11, 1085.21, 1092, 1093.

FOSSIL RECORD: Bexar, Delta, Llano, and San Patricio counties (490, 494, 495, 495.05, 609.5, 721).

COMMENTS: Natural distribution of this species is difficult to define because of widespread introduction into waters as a food resource.

Rana clamitans
Green Frog (Map 37)

Rana clamitans Latreille 1802. In Sonnini and Latreille, *Hist. Nat. Rept.* 2:157.

REFERENCES: 5.1, 39. 74, 99, 162, 228, 464, 601, 630.2, 635, 714, 726, 736, 753.4, 809, 865, 885, 904.8, 943, 968, 1084.1, 1092, 1093.

FOSSIL RECORD: Lubbock County (1084.1).

SUBSPECIES: *clamitans* (see above).

Rana grylio
Pig Frog (Map 8)

Rana grylio Stejneger 1901. *Proc. U.S. Natl. Mus.* 24:212.
REFERENCES: 5.1, 74, 86.1, 162, 228, 601, 624.11, 809.
COMMENTS: The pig frog is common in extreme southeast Texas.

Rana palustris
Pickerel Frog (Map 8)

Rana palustris Le Conte 1825. *Ann. Lyc. Nat. Hist. N.Y.* 1(2):282.
REFERENCES: 5.1, 74, 162, 228, 271, 295, 463, 588.21, 595, 622.232,
625, 718.2, 802.3, 802.31, 809, 855, 865, 1093.
COMMENTS: Pace (718.2) discusses the relationships of pickerel
frogs to leopard frogs. Schaaf and Smith (802.3) discuss the distribution of
pickerel frogs in Texas.

Rana pipiens Schreber
Northern Leopard Frog (Map 41)

Rana pipiens Schreber 1782. *Der Naturforscher* 18:185.
REFERENCES: 74, 162, 196, 228, 811.14, 882, 883, 1093.
COMMENTS: *Rana pipiens* occurs only in the Rio Grande Valley of
the greater El Paso area, south to Fort Hancock. It is known to be relatively common along the Rio Grande in New Mexico and probably reaches
its southern limit near the Quitman Mountains in extreme southern Hud-
speth County, Texas.

Prior to Mecham et al. (642.2), Pace (718.2), and Hillis (582.41) publications on the *Rana pipiens* complex in Texas, most references recorded
only *Rana pipiens*, its subspecies, or synonyms, as the Texas leopard frog.
A careful examination of localities mentioned in the earlier references
allowed me to place the majority of the literature with one or more of the
species (*berlandieri, blairi, pipiens, sphenocephala*) currently recognized
in Texas. Only a few references could not be placed with any degree of
certainty with the currently recognized species, and these are: 251, 297,
390, 463, 490, 506, 621, 675, 912, 1098.

Rana sphenocephala
Southern Leopard Frog (Map 38)

Rana sphenocephala Cope 1886. *Proc. Amer. Philos. Soc.* 23:517.
REFERENCES: 20, 74, 76, 92, 137, 139, 162, 195, 220.13, 220.14,

228, 265.8, 277.4, 438.44, 451.5, 451.51, 454.1, 464, 482.42, 492, 497.2, 573.05, 594.1, 595, 601, 622, 622.233, 642.2, 683, 687.5, 712.2, 712.3, 718.2, 726, 736, 753.4, 764.5, 765, 794.2, 794.31, 809, 821.1, 865, 883, 914, 915, 928, 932, 947, 968, 1042.11, 1072.2, 1072.21, 1092, 1093.

FOSSIL RECORD: Harris County (492, 821.1).

COMMENTS: See comments under *Rana pipiens*.

Family Microhylidae
Genus *Gastrophryne* Fitzinger
Syst. Rept. 1843:33
Gastrophryne carolinensis
Eastern Narrowmouth Toad (Map 39)

Engystoma carolinensis Holbrook 1836. *N. Amer. Herpetol.* 1:83.
Gastrophryne carolinensis: Stejneger 1910. *Proc. Biol. Soc. Washington* 23:166.

REFERENCES: 5.1, 74, 78, 80, 85, 86.1, 99, 162, 193, 228, 251, 297, 390, 451.5, 451.51, 463, 472, 542, 687.5, 704.2, 704.21, 704.23, 704.24, 719, 726, 736, 753.4, 765, 809, 858, 865, 892, 913, 914, 920, 921, 928, 932, 941, 968, 1000, 1042.11, 1092, 1093.

COMMENTS: Raun and Gehlbach's (770.3) Cooke County record for this species is erroneous. This specimen has been reidentified as *G. olivacea*, as have specimens identified as *G. carolinensis* from other midwestern Texas counties in museum collections.

Gastrophryne olivacea
Great Plains Narrowmouth Toad (Map 40)

Engystoma olivaceum Hallowell 1856. *Proc. Acad. Nat. Sci. Philadelphia* 8:252.
Gastrophryne olivacea: Smith 1933. *Copeia* 1933(4):217.

REFERENCES: 5.1, 20, 21, 26, 26.12, 53.3, 61, 74, 78, 80, 85, 92, 94, 99, 113.85, 122, 162, 193, 205.11, 220.14, 223, 228, 250, 251, 297, 364, 404, 405, 451.5, 451.51, 454.1, 472, 473, 490, 495.05, 497, 513, 515, 521, 588.21, 588.39, 589, 622.21, 622.22, 622.232, 622.24, 662, 665, 667, 683.2, 687.5, 701.23, 704.2, 704.22, 704.23, 704.24, 719, 726, 753, 753.4, 765, 809, 822, 823, 858, 865, 870, 883, 885, 907, 912, 914, 917, 921, 923, 924, 935, 944, 952, 956, 966, 967, 1001, 1021, 1055.41, 1072.2, 1072.21, 1076, 1088, 1092, 1093.

FOSSIL RECORD: Denton County (490, 495.05).

Genus *Hypopachus* Kerferstein
Nachr. Ges. Wiss. Gottingen 1867:351
Hypopachus variolosus
Sheep Frog (Map No. 11)

Engystoma variolosum Cope 1866. *Proc. Acad. Nat. Sci. Philadelphia* 18:131.
Hypopachus variolosus: Cope 1869(1871). *Proc. Amer. Philos. Soc.* 11:166.
REFERENCES: 5.1, 74, 162, 193, 223, 228, 250, 251, 297, 529.5, 529.51, 693, 699, 704.24, 704.25, 782, 809, 858, 870, 871, 914, 996, 1000, 1076, 1088, 1092, 1093.
COMMENTS: The most recent revisionary work concerning this species is that of Nelson (704.25).

Class Reptilia

Order Crocodilia
Family Crocodilidae
Genus *Alligator* Cuvier
Ann. Mus. Hist. Nat. Paris 1807, 10:25
Alligator mississippiensis
American Alligator (Map 63)

Crocodylus mississippiensis Daudin 1803. *Hist. Nat. Rept.* 2:412.
Alligator mississippiensis: Gray 1831. *Syn. Rept.* 1:62.
REFERENCES: 9.22, 59.65, 61.3, 139.6, 162, 228, 230.13, 264.5, 334, 374, 377.23, 429, 439, 454.1, 492, 495.04, 495.05, 526.2, 609.5, 634, 674, 687.5, 726, 781, 786.6, 809, 821, 821.1, 821.2, 822.1, 822.11, 822.2, 822.3, 822.4, 822.5, 862.5, 913, 923, 928, 932, 947, 956, 959, 967, 974.5, 1098.
FOSSIL RECORD: Dallas, Harris, Lubbock, McLennan, Orange, and San Patricio counties (334, 492, 495.04, 495.05, 609.5, 821, 821.1, 821.2).
COMMENTS: Because of federal and state protection during the past fifteen years, the alligator has made a remarkable recovery from its status as endangered. It was once extirpated from the majority of its natural range, but has now reestablished itself in many of those areas. The alligator has been removed from the endangered species list in the state, and is now being hunted on a limited basis under strict control of the Texas Parks and Wildlife Department.

Order Testudinata
Suborder Cryptodeira
Family Chelydridae
Genus *Chelydra* Schweigger
Kongisberg. Arch. Naturg. Math. 1812, 1:292
Chelydra serpentina
Snapping Turtle (Map 42)

Testudo serpentina Linnaeus 1758. *Syst. Nat.* 1:199.
Chelydra serpentina: Schweigger 1812. *Konigsberg. Arch. Naturg. Math.* 1:292.
REFERENCES: 2, 74, 122, 162, 168, 195, 212, 228, 230.14, 311, 353.6, 353.7, 353.8, 380, 439, 464, 491, 495.05, 506, 529.5, 529.51, 545.52, 576.06, 588.6, 622.24, 642.06, 683.2, 687.5, 714, 726, 734, 753.4, 765, 820, 865, 872, 883, 885, 912, 913, 915, 925, 928, 930, 932, 947, 952, 956, 964, 967, 968, 973, 1042.12.
FOSSIL RECORD: Hardeman County (491, 495.05).
SUBSPECIES: *serpentina* (see above).

Genus *Macroclemys* Gray
Cat. Shield. Rept. Brit. Mus. 1855, 1:48
Macroclemys temmincki
Alligator Snapping Turtle (Map 5)

Chelonura temminckii Troost 1835. In Harlan, *Med. Phys. Res.* 1835:158.
Macroclemys temmincki: Gray 1855. *Cat. Shield Rept. Brit. Mus.* 1:48.
REFERENCES: 162, 170.4, 228, 241, 311, 439, 468, 736, 753.4, 932, 947, 967.
FOSSIL RECORD: Brazos County (468).
COMMENTS: This species is becoming rare in Texas because it is being exploited as a food resource.

Family Kinosternidae
Genus *Kinosternon* Spix
Test. Brasil 1824:17
Kinosternon flavescens
Yellow Mud Turtle (Map 43)

Platyhyra flavescens Agassiz 1857. *Contro. Nat. Hist. U.S.* 1:430.
Kinosternon flavescens: Stone 1903. *Proc. Acad. Nat. Sci. Philadelphia* 55:540.
REFERENCES: 4, 21, 26.12, 74, 149.42, 155, 162, 212, 223, 228, 230.15, 230.2, 250, 253, 277.8, 311, 359.4, 372.8, 380, 451.5, 451.51,

454.1, 495.6, 510.31, 510.32, 521, 529.51, 576.01, 576.02, 576.05, 576.06, 587.5, 602.5, 611.2, 642.06, 665, 683.2, 726, 734, 736.2, 747.1, 747.12, 765, 775.1, 809, 811, 816.3, 816.4, 858, 865, 871, 872, 883, 885, 907, 912, 915, 918, 919, 922, 942, 951, 952, 956, 964, 966, 1055.41, 1085.21.

SUBSPECIES: *flavescens* (see above).

COMMENTS: Controversy concerning subspecies of this taxon has not been settled (495.6, 510.31, 510.32).

Kinosternon hirtipes
Mexican Mud Turtle (Map 41)

Cinosternon hirtipes Wagler 1830. *Nat. Syst. Amphib.* 1830:137.
Kinosternon hirtipes: Iverson 1981. *Tulane Stud. Zool. Bot.* 23(1):44.

REFERENCES: 9.16, 162, 212, 223, 230.14, 230.2, 408, 510.5, 510.51, 585, 683.2, 725, 809, 858, 872, 883.

SUBSPECIES: *murrayi* Glass and Hartweg 1951, *Copeia* 1951(1):50.

COMMENTS: The systematics of this species was recently completed by Iverson (510.5).

Kinosternon subrubrum
Eastern Mud Turtle (Map 44)

Testudo subrubra Lacepede 1788. *Hist. Nat. Quad. Ovip. Serp., Method.* 1:168–619.
Kinosternon subrubrum: Stejneger and Barbour 1917. *Checklist N. Amer. Amphib. Rept.* 1917:112.

REFERENCES: 14, 122, 149.42, 162, 212, 228, 230.15, 311, 353.7, 353.8, 359.4, 451.5, 451.51, 454.1, 464, 510.3, 529.5, 545.5, 576.02, 622.232, 687.5, 714, 726, 734, 753.4, 765, 793, 809, 858, 865, 912, 913, 915, 928, 942, 947, 956, 967, 968.

SUBSPECIES: *hippocrepis* Gray 1856, *Proc. Zool. Soc. London* 1856: 198.

COMMENTS: A museum record of this species for Parmer County is probably in error.

Genus *Sternotherus* Gray
Ann. Philos. (n.s.) 1825, 10:211
Sternotherus carinatus
Razorback Musk Turtle (Map 45)

Aromochelys carinatus Gray 1855. *Proc. Zool. Soc. London* 1855:199.
Sternotherus carinatus: Stejneger 1923. *Proc. U.S. Natl. Mus.* 62(6):2.

REFERENCES: 162, 212, 228, 353.7, 353.8, 464, 510.33, 545.51, 714, 726, 734, 753.4, 809, 858, 861, 925, 928, 930, 932, 967, 1011, 1024, 1042.12, 1098.

COMMENTS: I follow Conant (230.12) and Ernst and Barbour (353.6) in the spelling of the generic name.

Sternotherus odoratus
Stinkpot (Map 46)

Testudo odorata Latreille 1801. *Hist. Nat. Rept.* 1:122.
Sternothaerus odoratus: Bell 1825. *Zool. J.* 2:307.

REFERENCES: 4, 162, 178.01, 212, 223, 228, 230.14, 230.2, 353.7, 439, 450, 451.51, 454.1, 490, 495.05, 529.5, 545.5, 588.6, 622.232, 622.233, 622.24, 630.2, 681, 734, 753.4, 765, 767, 784.5, 809, 858, 865, 907, 915, 918, 956, 967, 1013, 1042.12, 1062.

FOSSIL RECORD: Denton County (490, 495.05).

COMMENTS: The Presidio County record is erroneous (162, 681).

Family Emydidae
Genus *Chrysemys* Gray
Cat. Tort. Brit. Mus. 1844:27
Chrysemys picta
Painted Turtle (Map 47)

Testudo picta Schneider 1783. *Naturg. Schildkr.* 1783:348.
Chrysemys picta: Gray 1856. *Cat. Shield Rept. Brit. Mus.* 1:32.

REFERENCES: 26.12, 64, 212, 228, 230.14, 322.1, 353.5, 353.6, 451.51, 470, 495.05, 642.06, 656, 683.2, 734, 809, 858, 872, 883, 885, 1056.

SUBSPECIES: *belli* Gray 1831, *Syn. Rept.* 1831:31; *dorsalis* Agassiz 1857, *Contr. Nat. Hist. U.S.* 1:440.

FOSSIL RECORD: Brazos and Lubbock counties (322.1, 470, 495.05).

COMMENTS: Texas museum records of specimens of *Chrysemys p. belli* are relatively few. There are no museum records of *Chrysemys p. dorsalis* from Texas, but reliable wildlife biologists have either examined, photographed, and released specimens of this taxon back to the wild from Caddo Lake (Marion/Harrison counties) and Toledo Bend Reservoir (Shelby County).

Genus *Deirochelys* Agassiz
Contr. Nat. Hist. U.S. 1857, 1:441
Deirochelys reticularia
Chicken Turtle (Map 48)

Testudo reticularia Latreille 1802. *Hist. Nat. Rept.* 1:124.
Deirochelys reticularia: Gray 1870. *Suppl. Cat. Shield Rept. Brit. Mus.*
1870:39.
REFERENCES: 14, 122, 162, 212, 228, 311, 353.6, 439, 451.5,
451.51, 714, 726, 734, 753.4, 809, 812, 858, 865, 873, 1042.12, 1100.1.
SUBSPECIES: *miaria* Schwartz 1956. *Field Zool.* 34:486.

Genus *Graptemys* Agassiz
Contr. Nat. Hist. U.S. 1857, 1:436
Graptemys caglei
Cagle's Map Turtle (Map 49)

Graptemys caglei Haynes and McKown 1974. *Tulane Stud. Zool. Bot.*
18(4):143.
REFERENCES: 59.8, 230.12, 470.2, 470.3.
COMMENTS: This species is restricted to the waters of the Guadalupe River basin.

Graptemys kohni
Mississippi Map Turtle (Map 50)

Malacoclemmys kohnni Baur 1890. *Science* (1)16:263.
Graptemys kohni: Cagle 1953. *Occ. Papers Mus. Zool. Univ. Michigan*
546:16.
REFERENCES: 59.8, 162, 203, 228, 353.6, 438.6, 622.24, 630.2, 714,
809, 1021, 1024, 1084.2.
COMMENTS: Although Raun and Gehlbach (770.3) suggested that
the knowledge of the taxonomy and distribution of map turtles in Texas
was poor, it is not the case today. There are several herpetologists who
have examined Texas specimens of *Graptemys* in museums as well as in
the wild and have clarified the species distribution and taxonomy.

Graptemys pseudogeographica
False Map Turtle (Map 51)

Emys pseudogeographica Gray 1831. *Syn. Rept.* 1831:31.
Graptemys pseudogeographica: Gray 1863. *Ann. Mag. Nat. Hist.* (3)12:
180.

REFERENCES: 59.8, 122, 162, 201, 211, 212, 228, 311, 323.1, 353.6, 353.7, 495.05, 726, 734, 765, 809, 821, 821.2, 847, 858, 910, 915, 918, 925, 932, 968, 970, 971, 972, 973, 974, 1050, 1084.2.

FOSSIL RECORD: Dallas, Denton, and Henderson counties (910).

SUBSPECIES: *ouachitensis, sabinensis* Cagle 1953, *Occ. Papers Mus. Zool. Univ. Michigan* 546:2, 10.

COMMENTS: This species is principally a turtle of the Red, Sabine, and Neches river basins of Texas.

Graptemys versa
Texas Map Turtle (Map 52)

Graptemys pseudogeographica versa Stejneger 1925. *J. Washington Acad. Sci.* 15:463.
Graytemys versa: Smith and Sanders 1952. *Texas J. Sci.* 4(2):211.

REFERENCES: 59.8, 162, 211, 212, 223, 228, 230, 353.6, 454.1, 470.3, 545.59, 613, 714, 725.2, 753.4, 809, 818, 847, 858, 865, 895, 918, 956, 967, 1021, 1047.1, 1084.2.

COMMENTS: This species is restricted to the middle Colorado River basin of Texas.

Genus *Malaclemys* Gray
Cat. Tort. Brit. Mus. 1844:28
Malaclemys terrapin
Diamondback Terrapin (Map 53)

Testudo terrapin Schoepff 1793. *Hist. Testud.* 13:64.
Malaclemys terrapin: Bangs 1896. *Proc. Boston Soc. Nat. Hist.* 27:159.

REFERENCES: 74, 210, 212, 223, 228, 353.6, 451.5, 451.51, 734, 809, 858, 871, 872, 932, 1084.2

SUBSPECIES: *littoralis* Hay 1904, *Bull. U.S. Bur. Fish.* 24:18.

COMMENTS: The Texas population of diamondback terrapins is currently undergoing a crisis because of urbanization of coastal waters, increased crustacean fishing with gear that drowns turtles, and general pollution.

Genus *Pseudemys* Gray
Cat. Shield Rept. Brit. Mus. 1855, 1:33
Pseudemys concinna
River Cooter (Map 54)

Testudo concinna Le Conte 1830. *Ann. Lyc. Nat. Hist. N.Y.* 3:106.
Pseudemys concinna: Gray 1855. *Cat. Shield Rept. Brit. Mus.* 1:34.

REFERENCES: 14, 59, 162, 195, 208, 212, 228, 230.13, 230.14, 330.91, 353.6, 353.7, 391, 438.6, 439, 450, 454.1, 490, 529.51, 622.1, 642.06, 662, 681, 683.2, 701.1, 714, 734, 765, 809, 858, 865, 871, 872, 885, 896, 912, 913, 915, 918, 919, 947, 951, 952, 956, 967, 968, 1021, 1047.15, 1050.02, 1098.

SUBSPECIES: *gorzugi, metteri* Ward 1984, *Spec. Publ. Mus. Texas Tech Univ.* 21:29–38.

COMMENTS: There has been considerable controversy over the status of the turtle genera *Chrysemys, Pseudemys,* and *Trachemys.* The 1970s and much of the 1980s literature is replete with the use of one, two, or three generic names. For the purposes of this report, I follow Ward (1050.02) and recognize three genera.

Pseudemys texana
Texas River Cooter (Map 55)

Pseudemys texana Baur 1893. *Proc. Amer. Philos. Soc.* 31:223.

REFERENCES: 162, 175, 205.11, 212, 223, 228, 353.6, 439, 622.24, 732.5, 734, 753.4, 809, 858, 865, 947, 1050.02, 1056.

COMMENTS: To date, most of the literature for *P. texana* is completely confused with that of *P. floridana.* Ward (1050.02) has pointed out that *P. floridana* does not occur in Texas and that most recent literature placed *P. texana* as a subspecies of *P. concinna.*

Genus *Terrapene* Merrem
Tent. Syst. Amphib. 1820:27
Terrapene carolina
Eastern Box Turtle (Map 56)

Testudo carolina Linnaeus 1758. *Syst. Nat.* 1:198.
Terrapene carolina: Bell 1825. *Zool. J. London* 2:309.

REFERENCES: 14, 74, 92, 122, 162, 212, 212.5, 228, 303, 353.6, 353.7, 391, 399.4, 439, 451.51, 454.1, 463, 464, 467, 469, 470, 494, 495.02, 495.04, 495.05, 502, 588.6, 609.5, 622.233, 622.24, 625.5, 632.2, 649, 660, 661, 661.1, 681.3, 699.3, 714, 726, 734, 753.4, 765, 809, 819, 821, 821.2, 858, 865, 866, 923, 928, 932, 947, 956, 967, 1003, 1042.12, 1072.3, 1098.

FOSSIL RECORD: Archer, Atascosa, Bee, Bexar, Brazos, Dallas, Denton, Duval, Harris, Henderson, Kendall, Lubbock, San Patricio, Travis, and Uvalde counties (467, 469, 470, 494, 495.02, 495.04, 495.05, 609.5, 625.5, 649, 660, 661, 661.1, 681.3, 821, 821.2).

SUBSPECIES: *triunguis* Agassiz 1857, *Contr. Nat. Hist. U.S.* 1:445.

Terrapene ornata
Western Box Turtle (Map 57)

Cistudo ornata Agassiz 1857. *Contr. Nat. Hist. U.S.* 1:445.
Terrapene ornata: Baur 1891. *Science* 17:191.
   REFERENCES: 14, 74, 92, 100.05, 122, 162, 195, 212, 228, 230.15, 250, 253, 303, 353.6, 353.7, 380, 391, 394.4, 451.5, 451.51, 454.1, 463, 490, 495.05, 521, 529.51, 545.51, 576.06, 583, 613, 622.233, 632.2, 634, 642.06, 649, 657, 661, 661.1, 662, 665, 683.2, 699.3, 714, 726, 734, 747.12, 753.4, 765, 775.1, 786.31, 809, 811, 816.3, 858, 864, 865, 872, 873, 883, 885, 907, 912, 913, 915, 918, 919, 922, 927, 947, 951, 952, 956, 964, 965, 966, 967, 977.42, 1003, 1042.12, 1050.01, 1055.41, 1072.3, 1073.1, 1085.21.
   FOSSIL RECORD: Culberson and Denton counties (394.4, 490, 495.05).
   SUBSPECIES: *ornata, luteola* Smith and Ramsey 1952, *Wassman J. Biol.* 10:45.

Genus *Trachemys* Agassiz
Contr. Nat. Hist. U.S., 1:434
Trachemys gaigeae
Big Bend Slider (Map 41)

Pseudemys gaigeae Hartweg 1938. *Occ. Papers Mus. Zool. Univ. Michigan* 397:1.
Trachemys gaigeae: Ward 1984. *Spec. Publ. Mus. Texas Tech Univ.* 21: 45, 47.
   REFERENCES: 21, 74, 162, 212, 228, 353.6, 453, 460, 461, 584, 585, 665, 725, 809, 871, 872, 885, 1055.41, 1056.
   COMMENTS: For generic clarification see "account" of *Pseudemys concinna*.

Trachemys scripta
Slider (Map 58)

Testudo scripta Schoepff 1792. *Hist. Test.* (1–2):16.
Trachemys scripta: Ward 1984. *Spec. Publ. Mus. Texas Tech Univ.* 21:46.
   REFERENCES: 14, 61, 74, 122, 162, 168, 209, 212, 228, 230.14, 250, 253, 265.3, 353.6, 353.7, 353.8, 355.3, 380, 387, 391, 454.1, 461, 464, 473.2, 480, 485.5, 490, 492, 495.05, 529.51, 576.06, 584, 588.6, 609.5, 615, 622.233, 622.24, 632.2, 642.06, 662, 687.5, 701.11, 712.1, 726, 734, 746.1, 753.4, 765, 770, 809, 816.3, 819, 821.1, 858, 865, 871, 872, 885, 896, 913, 915, 918, 922, 927, 928, 930, 932, 942, 944, 947, 951, 956, 965,

966, 967, 968, 970, 977.3, 977.51, 1042.12, 1047.15, 1050.02, 1056, 1098.
    FOSSIL RECORD: Denton, Harris, Knox, and San Patricio counties
(480, 490, 492, 495.05, 609.5, 746.1, 821.1).
    SUBSPECIES: *elegans* Wied 1838, *Reise Nord. Amer.* 1:213.

Family Testudinidae
Genus *Gopherus* Rafinesque
Atlantic J. 1832, 1:64
Gopherus berlandieri
Texas Tortoise (Map 59)

Xerobates berlandieri Agassiz 1857. *Contr. Nat. Hist. U.S.* 1:447.
Gopherus berlandieri: Stejneger 1893. *N. Amer. Fauna* 7:161.
    REFERENCES: 4, 13.13, 13.2, 13.22, 14, 14.1, 59.3, 74, 86.1, 119,
137.5, 143.5, 143.51, 145.01, 162, 170, 212, 223, 250, 353.6, 428, 430,
441, 452, 529.4, 529.41, 529.45, 529.46, 529.49, 529.51, 545.6, 582,
612.2, 673, 683.2, 701.2, 701.27, 714, 714.12, 722, 734, 770, 786.46,
786.47, 786.8, 793, 795, 809, 857, 858, 872, 941, 947, 950, 966, 967, 985,
1031, 1047.2, 1047.21, 1055.41, 1055.5, 1098.
    FOSSIL RECORD: "Texas" (143.51).
    COMMENTS: Museum records from Brewster and Matagorda coun-
ties may be erroneous, but sightings of this species in Galveston and Fort
Bend counties suggest a possible range expansion of this taxon, or pets
who have escaped their confinement. Recently Ed Farmer (personal communication) saw a tortoise crossing a highway a few miles south of Sonora,
Texas.
    I have not followed Bramble's (143.51) recognition of *Scaptochelys*
as the generic name for the Texas Tortoise. Bramble may be correct, but
all of the evidence is not available for a final decision.

Family Trionychidae
Genus *Trionyx* Geoffroy
Ann. Mus. Hist. Nat. Paris 1809, 14:1
Trionyx muticus
Smooth Softshell (Map 60)

Trionyx muticus Le Sueur 1827. *Mem. Mus. Hist. Nat. Paris* 15:263.
    REFERENCES: 122, 162, 167.04, 212, 228, 353.6, 353.8, 529.51,
588.6, 622.232, 734, 753.4, 820, 858, 885, 898, 967, 1060, 1061.1.
    SUBSPECIES: *muticus* (see above).
    COMMENTS: This taxon has a wide distribution over the eastern

two-thirds of Texas, but with very curious gaps. The Texas distribution of this species needs intensive study.

Trionyx spiniferus
Spiny Softshell (Map. 61)

Trionyx spiniferus Le Sueur 1827. *Mem. Mus. Hist. Nat. Paris* 15:258.

REFERENCES: 4, 14, 26.12, 59.65, 122, 162, 205.11, 212, 223, 228, 230.11, 233, 253, 319.5, 353.6, 353.7, 353.8, 454.1, 464, 470, 485.5, 495.05, 529.51, 574, 576, 576.06, 585, 613, 622.24, 642.06, 662, 665, 683.2, 704, 714, 726, 734, 746.1, 753.4, 765, 809, 811, 858, 871, 872, 883, 885, 898, 912, 913, 915, 918, 923, 927, 928, 930, 932, 942, 944, 947, 952, 956, 964, 966, 967, 971, 972, 1021, 1042.12, 1055.41, 1057, 1058, 1060, 1061.11, 1085.21, 1098.

FOSSIL RECORD: Brazos and Knox counties (470, 495.05, 746.1).

SUBSPECIES: *emoryi* Agassiz 1857, *Contr. Nat. Hist. U.S.* 1:407; *guadalupensis, pallidus* Webb 1962, *Univ. Kansas Publ. Mus. Nat. Hist.* 13:517, 522; *hartwegi* Conant and Goin 1948, *Occ. Papers Mus. Zool. Michigan* 501:1.

Family Chelonidae
Genus *Caretta* Rafinesque
Spec. Sci. Palermo, 1814:66
Caretta caretta
Loggerhead (Map 62)

Testudo caretta Linnaeus 1758. *Syst. Nat.* 1:197.
Caretta caretta: Stejneger 1904. *Ann. Rept. U.S. Natl. Mus.* 1904:715.

REFERENCES: 9.16, 162, 353.6, 384.34, 753.3, 885.

SUBSPECIES: *caretta* (see above).

COMMENTS: This species and all other sea turtles are extremely rare along the Texas coast. All U.S. species are considered endangered, and there are special efforts to build trawling gear that will prevent turtles from being trapped in nets.

Genus *Chelonia* Latreille
Hist. Nat. Rept. 1801, 1:22
Chelonia mydas
Green Turtle (Map 62)

Testudo mydas Linnaeus 1758. *Syst. Nat.* 1:197.
Chelonia mydas: Schweigger 1812. *Konigsberg Arch. Natur. Math.* 1:412.

REFERENCES: 9.16, 162, 353.6, 495.7, 753.3, 885, 892.
COMMENTS: see comments under *Caretta*.

Genus *Eretmochelys* Fitzinger
Syst. Rept. 1843:30
Eretmochelys imbricata
Hawksbill (Map 62)

Testudo imbricata Linnaeus 1766. *Syst. Nat.* 1:350.
Eretmochelys imbricata: Agassiz 1857. *Contr. Nat. Hist. U.S.* 1:381.
REFERENCES: 353.6, 495.7, 753.3.

Genus *Lepidochelys* Fitzinger
Syst. Rept. 1843:30
Lepidochelys kempi
Atlantic Ridley (Map 62)

Thalassochelys kempi Garman 1880. *Bull. Mus. Comp. Zool.* 6:123.
Lepidochelys kempi: Baur 1890. *Amer. Nat.* 24:487.
    REFERENCES: 0.1, 9.15, 162, 212, 216.5, 289.6, 353.6, 361.21, 384.2, 384.34, 701.21, 734, 753.3, 872, 1055.4, 1067, 1076.2, 1108.
    COMMENTS: There is a long-term project under way to reestablish a breeding population of Atlantic Ridleys along South Padre Island.

Family Dermochelyidae
Genus *Dermochelys* Blainville
Bull. Soc. Philos. Paris 1816:111
Dermochelys coriacea
Leatherback (Map 62)

Testudo coriacea Linnaeus 1766. *Syst. Nat.* 1:350.
Dermochelys coriacea: Boulenger 1889. *Cat. Chelon. Rhynch. Crocod. British Mus.* 1889:10.
    REFERENCES: 162, 353.6, 353.7, 439, 495.7, 580, 746.5, 753.3, 872, 885.
    COMMENTS: see comments under *Caretta*.

Order Squamata
Suborder Lacertilia
Family Gekkonidae
Genus *Coleonyx* Gray
Ann. Mag. Nat. Hist. 1845, 16:162.
Coleonyx brevis
Texas Banded Gecko (Map 65)

Coleonyx brevis Stejneger 1893. *N. Amer. Fauna* 7:163.
REFERENCES: 21, 26.12, 26.16, 74, 129, 162, 223, 228, 247, 257, 288, 296.11, 296.31, 312.1, 312.12, 323.21, 356.2, 387, 393.07, 521, 529.5, 560, 568, 568.02, 622.232, 642.06, 648, 662, 665, 683.2, 683.21, 689, 700, 747.11, 747.14, 786, 809, 811, 822, 824, 844, 871, 872, 878.3, 883, 885, 919, 947, 948, 957, 965, 967, 1003.2, 1055.41, 1067, 1085.21, 1091, 1098.

Coleonyx reticulatus
Reticulated Gecko (Map 76)

Coleonyx reticulatus Davis and Dixon 1958. *Proc. Biol. Soc. Washington* 71:151.
REFERENCES: 9.16, 288, 296.1, 296.11, 296.31, 312.11, 312.12, 332.1, 388.4, 473.4, 568.02, 644.13, 683.2, 683.21, 786, 816.6, 816.7, 1055.41.
COMMENTS: This species is more common in Brewster and Presidio counties than formerly believed. The Reticulated Gecko has curious gaps in its distribution; it also occurs in Southern Coahuila and northeastern Durango, Mexico.

Genus *Cyrtodactylus* Gray
Philos. Mag. London 1827, (2) 2:56
Cyrtodactylus scaber
Rough-scaled Gecko (Map 66)

Stenodactylus scaber Heyden 1827. In Ruppell, *Atl. Reise Nord Africa Rept.* 1827:15.
Cyrtodactylus scaber: Underwood 1954. *Proc. Zool. Soc. London* 1954:475.
REFERENCES: 817.1
COMMENTS: A recent introduction into Texas, this species seems to be reproducing along the commercial shipping docks of Galveston.

Genus *Hemidactylus* Oken
Isis von Oken 1817:1183
Hemidactylus turcicus
Mediterranean Gecko (Map 67)

Lacerta turcica Linnaeus 1758. *Syst. Nat.* 1:202.
Hemidactylus turcicus: Boettger 1876. *Ber. Offenbach Ber. Naturk.*
1876:57.
REFERENCES: 162, 226, 228, 230.13, 289.4, 308, 332.03, 391.4,
432.2, 454.1, 545.1, 627.1, 643.6, 683.2, 686, 746.3, 786, 786.43, 817.2,
844, 862.5, 872, 1027.25, 1028, 1042.12, 1055.41, 1080.
COMMENTS: This species is continuing to spread rapidly over the
state. The Mediterranean Gecko has spread to 41 Texas counties since its
1955 discovery in Cameron County by Conant (226).

Family Iguanidae
Genus *Anolis* Daudin
Hist. Nat. Rept. 1803, 4:50
Anolis carolinensis
Green Anole (Map 68)

Anolis carolinensis Voigt 1832. *Cuvier's Thierreich* 2:71.
REFERENCES: 14, 29, 53.1, 53.2, 74, 84, 92, 162, 198.5, 220.13,
220.3, 228, 230.13, 257, 265.3, 351, 369.2, 387, 439, 443.02, 454.1, 464,
487.5, 502, 542, 588.39, 616.2, 643.6, 643.7, 643.72, 643.8, 726, 753.4,
765, 809, 844, 858, 859, 862.5, 912, 913, 915, 928, 932, 942, 943, 947,
956, 967, 968, 1003.2, 1042.12, 1042.13, 1042.16, 1048.2.
COMMENTS: Museum records for Atascosa, Brown, Cameron, Frio,
Hidalgo, Maverick, Menard, Uvalde, and Willacy counties may represent
introductions.

Anolis sagrei
Brown Anole (Map 66)

Anolis sagrei Dumeril and Bibron 1837. *Erpetol. Gen. Hist. Rept.* 4:149.
REFERENCES: This volume.
COMMENTS: A new introduction to Texas through the interstate
plant trade.

Genus *Cophosaurus* Troschel
Arch. Naturg. 1852, 16(1):389
Cophosaurus texanus
Greater Earless Lizard (Map 69)

Cophosaurus texanus Troschel 1852. *Arch. Naturg.* 16(1):389.
REFERENCES: 3, 21, 27, 31, 33, 36, 39, 53.2, 53.31, 54.5, 74, 150, 155, 162, 200, 215, 221, 223, 228, 250, 253, 257, 290, 290.11, 323.21, 380, 387, 393.07, 423.5, 434, 454.1, 495.01, 495.02, 495.05, 521, 522, 524, 567, 604, 613, 616.2, 616.5, 634, 642.06, 648, 654, 662, 665, 683.2, 683.21, 687, 700, 719.2, 724, 747, 747.12, 747.13, 756, 758, 794, 805, 809, 811, 811.1, 844, 858, 865, 871, 872, 878.31, 883, 885, 907, 908, 909, 912, 915, 918, 919, 922, 924, 927, 929, 938, 944, 947, 950, 952, 956, 957, 964, 965, 967, 1003.2, 1030, 1045.1, 1055.41, 1085.21.
FOSSIL RECORD: Kendall County (495.01, 495.02, 495.05).
SUBSPECIES: *texanus; scitulus* Peters 1951, *Occ. Papers Mus. Zool. Univ. Michigan* 537:8.
COMMENTS: Museum records from Fayette and Gonzales counties are questionable.

Genus *Crotaphytus* Holbrook
N. Amer. Herp. 1842, 2:79
Crotaphytus collaris
Collared Lizard (Map 70)

Agama collaris Say 1823. In *Long's Exped. Rocky Mts.* 2:252.
Crotaphytus collaris Holbrook 1842. *N. Amer. Herp.* 2:79.
REFERENCES: 3, 14, 21, 29, 31, 33, 53.23, 53.24, 74, 122, 150, 155, 162, 179, 183, 188, 197, 228, 250, 253, 257, 277.8, 323.21, 363, 372, 380, 393.07, 394.4, 395.4, 398, 423.5, 443.02, 450, 451.5, 451.51, 454.1, 458.2, 491, 494, 495, 495.02, 495.04, 495.05, 509.3, 521, 587.5, 604, 613, 616.5, 622.11, 622.13, 634, 639, 642.06, 643.6, 648, 662, 665, 681.1, 681.12, 681.15, 683.2, 687, 719.2, 720.2, 726, 747, 753.4, 809, 811, 816.3, 822.02, 844, 858, 865, 872, 873.2, 873.22, 883, 885, 886, 907, 908, 911, 918, 919, 922, 927, 930, 947, 948, 951, 952, 956, 957, 964, 965, 967, 1003.2, 1014, 1017.4, 1022, 1049.2, 1055.41, 1085.21, 1091, 1098.
FOSSIL RECORD: Bexar, Culberson, Hardeman, Kendall, Llano, and Lubbock counties (394.4, 458.2, 491, 494, 495, 495.02, 495.04, 495.05, 639).
SUBSPECIES: *collaris*, Stejneger 1890, *N. Amer. Fauna* 3:103; *fuscus* Ingram and Tanner 1971, *Brigham Young Univ. Sci. Bull.* 13(2):23.
COMMENTS: Burleson County (179) and Limestone County (162)

records and a museum record for Falls County are questionable. Cameron (179), Duval (250), and Starr (129) county records of this species are of the Reticulate Collared Lizard.

Crotaphytus reticulatus
Reticulate Collared Lizard (Map 11)

Crotaphytus reticulatus Baird 1858. *Proc. Acad. Nat. Sci. Philadelphia* 10:253.

REFERENCES: 9.16, 29, 31, 74, 160, 162, 183, 223, 228, 257, 423.5, 566, 643.6, 681.11, 681.12, 681.13, 681.15, 683.2, 714, 809, 833, 844, 858, 871, 872, 997, 1067, 1089, 1098.

COMMENTS: This species is threatened because of habitat modification through the introduction of non-native grasses and other land-use practices.

Genus *Ctenosaura* Wiegmann
Isis von Oken 1828:371
Ctenosaura pectinata
Western Spiny-tailed Iguana (Map 11)

Cyclura pectinata Wiegmann 1834. *Herpetol. Mex.* 1834:42.
Ctenosaura pectinata: Gray 1845. *Cat. Liz. Brit. Mus.* 1845:191.

REFERENCES: 230.13, 862.5.

COMMENTS: This taxon is apparently well established in parks and near the zoo grounds in Brownsville, Texas.

Genus *Gambelia* Baird
U.S. and Mex. Bound. Surv., 1859, 2:7
Gambelia wislizeni
Leopard Lizard (Map 76)

Crotaphytus wislizenii Baird and Girard 1852. *Stansbury's Expl. Surv. Valley Gt. Salt Lake* 1852:340.
Gambelia wislizeni: Smith 1946. *Handbk. Liz.* 1946:159.

REFERENCES: 29, 34, 75, 150, 155, 162, 197, 257, 393.07, 398, 642.06, 662.1, 683.2, 809, 816.1, 844, 858, 872, 883, 885, 908, 919, 947, 982, 982.1, 1012, 1014, 1017.2, 1023, 1029, 1055.41, 1085.21, 1098.

SUBSPECIES: *wislizeni* (see above).

Genus *Holbrookia* Girard
Proc. Amer. Assoc. Adv. Sci. 1851, 4:201
Holbrookia lacerata
Spot-tailed Earless Lizard (Map 71)

Holbrookia lacerata Cope 1880. *Bull. U.S. Natl. Mus.* 17:15.
REFERENCES: 19, 26.1, 29, 162, 223, 228, 245, 257, 454.1, 529.51, 613, 617, 683.2, 786, 805, 809, 844, 865, 871, 872, 886, 915, 938, 1017.4.
SUBSPECIES: *lacerata; subcaudalis* Axtell 1956, *Bull. Chicago Acad. Sci.* 10:174.
COMMENTS: Museum records of this species from Dallas, Donley, Garza, McLennan, and Young counties represent the Lesser Earless Lizard.

Holbrookia maculata
Lesser Earless Lizard (Map 72)

Holbrookia maculata Girard 1851. *Proc. Amer. Assoc. Adv. Sci.* 4:201.
REFERENCES: 19, 22, 26.12, 29, 31, 34, 35, 74, 103, 155, 162, 172, 223, 228, 253, 257, 277.8, 380, 449, 451, 451.5, 451.51, 521, 529.51, 613, 642.06, 657, 662.1, 665, 683.2, 730, 792, 794, 805, 809, 816.3, 844, 858, 871, 872, 883, 885, 886, 912, 919, 951, 952, 967, 1017.2, 1022, 1023, 1045.1, 1085.21, 1098.
SUBSPECIES: *maculata; approximans* Baird 1858, *Proc. Acad. Nat. Sci. Philadelphia* 10:253; *perspicua* Axtell 1956, *Bull. Chicago Acad. Sci.* 10:166.
COMMENTS: Records for Houston (162) and Kimble (770.3) counties are erroneous.

Holbrookia propinqua
Keeled Earless Lizard (Map 73)

Holbrookia propinqua Baird and Girard 1852. *Proc. Acad. Nat. Sci. Philadelphia* 6:126.
REFERENCES: 26.13, 26.15, 27, 29, 36, 39, 74, 162, 223, 228, 233.4, 233.5, 250, 257, 267, 387, 455, 529.3, 529.31, 529.32, 529.33, 529.34, 529.48, 529.51, 630.5, 714, 786.7, 805, 809, 817, 817.2, 844, 858, 871, 872, 913, 947, 967, 1003.2, 1017.2, 1055.3, 1098.
SUBSPECIES: *propinqua:* Smith and Burger 1950, *Trans. Kansas Acad. Sci.* 53:169.
COMMENTS: A museum record for Real County is questionable.

Genus *Phrynosoma* Wiegmann
Isis von Oken 1828, 21:367
Phrynosoma cornutum
Texas Horned Lizard (Map 74)

Agama cornutum Harlan 1825. *J. Acad. Nat. Sci. Philadelphia* 4:299.
Phrynosoma cornutum: Gray 1831. *Syn. Rept.*, in *Griffith's Anim. King.*
9:45.

REFERENCES: 3, 9.16, 21, 29, 33, 53.13, 53.2, 54.2, 61, 61.31, 74,
92, 113.55, 122, 126, 150, 155, 162, 170.5, 185, 195, 197, 204, 213,
220.13, 223, 228, 257, 267, 294, 323.21, 338, 339, 340, 341, 380, 384.12,
384.3, 391, 393.07, 397, 401, 439, 443.02, 446, 449, 454.1, 464, 478,
487.5, 495.02, 495.04, 495.05, 502, 521, 529.5, 529.51, 573.55, 581, 604,
613, 616.5, 622.233, 634, 642.06, 645, 662, 662.1, 665, 681.14, 683.2,
687, 726, 730.2, 739, 740, 741, 742, 747, 753.4, 762, 765, 770, 783, 809,
811, 816.3, 844, 858, 862.5, 865, 871, 872, 873, 875, 883, 885, 908, 912,
913, 915, 916, 918, 922, 930, 938, 942, 944, 947, 951, 952, 956, 965, 966,
967, 968, 975, 977.2, 1014, 1017.2, 1017.4, 1023, 1042.12, 1055.41, 1062,
1076.1, 1082, 1083, 1085.21, 1098, 1100.

FOSSIL RECORD: Kendall and Lubbock counties (495.02, 495.04,
495.05).

COMMENTS: The Texas Horned Lizard is protected by state law from
commercial collecting. Proposed new regulations will protect an additional species in the state.

Phrynosoma douglassi
Short-horned Lizard (Map 76)

Agama douglassii Bell 1829. *Trans. Linn. Soc. London* 16:105.
Phrynosoma douglassi: Wagler 1830. *Syst. Amphib.* 1830:146.

REFERENCES: 9.16, 26.12, 29, 61.31, 162, 257, 393.07, 394.4, 458.2,
487.5, 613, 642.06, 681.14, 683.2, 783, 809, 844, 858, 872, 883, 885,
1098.

SUBSPECIES: *hernandesi* Girard 1858, *U.S. Expl. Exped., Herp.*
1858:395.

FOSSIL RECORD: Culberson County (394.4).

COMMENTS: Recent herpetological activities in the El Paso area
have included the discovery of the Short-horned Lizard in the Hueco
Mountains.

Phrynosoma modestum
Roundtail Horned Lizard (Map 75)

Phrynosoma modestum Girard 1852. *Stansbury's Expl. Surv. Valley Gt. Salt Lake* 1852:361.
REFERENCES: 21, 29, 35, 58.2, 61.31, 74, 155, 162, 197, 223, 228, 253, 355.2, 357, 380, 387, 393.07, 397, 401, 403, 423.5, 451.5, 451.51, 521, 613, 622.233, 634, 642.06, 643.6, 648, 654, 657, 662, 665, 681.14, 683.2, 683.21, 719.2, 783, 809, 811, 816.3, 844, 858, 872, 883, 885, 908, 909, 919, 977.2, 1045.1, 1055.41, 1085.21, 1098, 1100.
COMMENTS: A museum record for Zapata County is questionable.

Genus *Sceloporus* Wiegmann
Isis von Oken 1828, 21:369
Sceloporus cyanogenys
Blue Spiny Lizard (Map 64)

Sceloporus torquatus cyanogenys Cope 1885. *Proc. Amer. Philos. Soc.* 22:402.
Sceloporus cyanogenys: Smith 1938. *Univ. Kansas Sci. Bull.* 24:599.
REFERENCES: 74, 162, 228, 250, 368.1, 432.1, 505, 539, 699.1, 809, 827, 835, 844, 858, 872, 986, 1003.2, 1089, 1098.
COMMENTS: A museum record for Kinney County has been verified, but the specimen has been lost (Dalquest, personal communication).

Sceloporus graciosus
Sagebrush Lizard (Map 76)

Sceloporus graciosus Baird and Girard 1852. *Stansbury's Expl. Surv. Valley Gt. Salt Lake* 1852:346.
REFERENCES: 223.13, 291.5, 545.2, 683.2, 792, 872, 885.
SUBSPECIES: *arenicolus* Degenhardt and Jones 1972, *Herpetologica* 28(3):213.
COMMENTS: The Texas subspecies is restricted to the sand dunes of Andrews, Crane, Ward, and Winkler counties.

Sceloporus grammicus
Mesquite Lizard (Map 64)

Sceloporus grammicus Wiegmann 1828. *Isis von Oken* 21:370.
REFERENCES: 15.5, 29, 74, 162, 191, 223, 228, 643.6, 683.2, 820.1, 820.11, 820.12, 820.16, 820.2, 820.22, 835, 844, 894, 1089.

SUBSPECIES: *microlepidotus* Wiegmann 1834, *Herpetol. Mex.* 1834:51.

COMMENTS: Sites and Dixon (820.2) show that characters used to separate *S. g. disparlis* and *S. g. microlepidotus* are clinal and that the two taxa should be treated as a single form. The Kleberg County (770.3) and Refugio County (643.6) records represent accidental introductions.

Sceloporus magister
Desert Spiny Lizard (Map 76)

Sceloporus magister Hallowell 1854. *Proc. Acad. Nat. Sci. Philadelphia* 7:93.

REFERENCES: 14, 21, 29, 74, 162, 190, 223, 257, 323.21, 654, 665, 683.2, 729, 809, 811, 835, 844, 858, 871, 872, 883, 885, 1055.41, 1085.21.

SUBSPECIES: *bimaculosus* Phelan and Brattstrom 1955, *Herpetologica* 11:9.

COMMENTS: Museum records from Ector and Val Verde counties are questionable.

Sceloporus merriami
Canyon Lizard (Map 77)

Sceloporus merriami Stejneger 1904. *Proc. Biol. Soc. Washington* 17:17.

REFERENCES: 9.16, 21, 29, 74, 162, 191, 206, 206.1, 215, 223, 223.11, 323.2, 323.21, 368.1, 392, 451.51, 613, 648, 655, 658, 661.2, 665, 683.2, 683.21, 700, 714.1, 714.14, 725, 809, 811, 828, 835, 844, 858, 871, 872, 873, 878.31, 891, 919, 965, 999, 1047.05, 1055.41, 1090.

SUBSPECIES: *merriami; annulatus* Smith 1937, *Proc. Biol. Soc. Washington* 50:83; *longipunctatus* Olson 1973, *Herpetologica* 29(2):124.

COMMENTS: The life history of this taxon is well known through the works of Dunham (323.2, 323.21). A museum record for San Saba County is erroneous.

Sceloporus olivaceus
Texas Spiny Lizard (Map 78)

Sceloporus olivaceus Smith 1934. *Trans. Kansas Acad. Sci.* 37:263.

REFERENCES: 29, 33, 53.1, 53.2, 74, 84, 92, 101, 135, 150, 162, 191, 192, 206.1, 223.1, 228, 250, 257, 330.5, 330.91, 368.1, 380, 398, 399, 451.5, 451.51, 454.1, 529.2, 535, 543.02, 576.2, 604, 613, 616.5, 622.233, 662, 683.2, 707, 726, 747, 748, 753.4, 758, 765, 786.2, 809, 822, 825, 835, 844, 845, 858, 865, 871, 872, 873, 912, 913, 915, 916, 918, 919, 927, 930,

938, 942, 944, 945, 952, 956, 957, 964, 966, 967, 999, 1003.2, 1062, 1098, 1107.

COMMENTS: A record for El Paso County is erroneous. Museum records of the species from east of the Trinity River are questionable. The Brewster County record (162) is verified.

Sceloporus poinsetti
Crevice Spiny Lizard (Map 79)

Sceloporus poinsetti Baird and Girard 1852. *Proc. Acad. Nat. Sci. Philadelphia* 6:126.

REFERENCES: 17, 26.12, 29, 53.1, 53.2, 74, 135, 155, 162, 191, 215, 223, 228, 257, 368.1, 393.07, 495.02, 495.05, 521, 573, 588.39, 602.2, 613, 616.5, 642.06, 648, 655, 683.2, 683.21, 687, 700, 714, 747.14, 748, 763, 809, 811, 827, 835, 844, 858, 865, 871, 872, 883, 885, 909, 919, 947, 957, 964, 967, 986, 1003.2, 1045.1, 1055.41, 1085.21, 1098.

FOSSIL RECORD: Culberson and Kendall counties (495.02, 495.05, 602.2).

SUBSPECIES: *poinsetti* (see above).

Sceloporus undulatus
Eastern Fence Lizard (Map 80)

Stellio undulatus Latreille 1802. *Hist. Nat. Rept.* 2:40.
Sceloporus undulatus: Wiegmann 1828. *Isis von Oken* 21:369.

REFERENCES: 14, 21, 26.12, 29, 53.1, 53.2, 54.41, 61, 74, 122, 135, 155, 162, 175, 191, 192, 195, 204.4, 215, 220.14, 223, 223.12, 228, 257, 277.8, 290, 323.21, 359.1, 368.1, 380, 393.07, 394.4, 398, 439, 454.1, 458.2, 474.1, 495.02, 495.04, 495.05, 521, 529, 529.2, 538, 543.01, 573.32, 573.33, 602.2, 613, 616.11, 616.13, 616.5, 622.233, 634, 642.06, 643.6, 643.8, 648, 657, 662, 665, 683.2, 687, 700, 712, 726, 753.4, 765, 809, 811, 816.3, 831, 844, 858, 865, 871, 872, 875, 878.31, 883, 885, 907, 908, 909, 912, 913, 915, 918, 919, 922, 944, 956, 957, 964, 965, 966, 967, 968, 1003.2, 1014, 1017.4, 1021, 1022, 1023, 1042.12, 1055.41, 1085.21, 1098.

FOSSIL RECORDS: Culberson, Kendall, and Lubbock counties (394.4, 495.02, 495.04, 495.05, 602.2).

SUBSPECIES: *consobrinus* Baird and Girard 1854. In *Marcy's Expl. Red River* 3:237; *garmani* Boulenger 1882, *Proc. Zool. Soc. London* 1882:762; *hyacinthinus* Green 1818, *J. Acad. Nat. Sci. Philadelphia* 1:349.

COMMENTS: Conant (230.12) records isolated populations of *Sceloporus u. garmani* from extreme eastern New Mexico. Therefore it is not surprising to find a population of *S. u. garmani* in the northwest Texas counties of Cochran and Yoakum (see Map 80).

Sceloporus variabilis
Rosebelly Lizard (Map 81)

Sceloporus variabilis Wiegmann 1834. *Herpetol. Mex.* 1834:51.
REFERENCES: 74, 135, 162, 191, 223, 223.14, 228, 250, 257, 439.2, 446, 495.02, 495.05, 529.5, 587.5, 616.11, 616.12, 616.13, 616.2, 622.232, 770, 809, 820.21, 826, 830, 844, 858, 871, 872, 887, 957, 966, 967, 1003.2.
FOSSIL RECORD: Kendall County (495.02, 495.05).
SUBSPECIES: *marmoratus* Hallowell 1852, *Proc. Acad. Nat. Sci. Philadelphia* 6:178.
COMMENTS: Published records for Dallas (835, 844) and El Paso (826, 835) counties are erroneous, as is a museum record for Lee County.

Genus *Urosaurus* Hallowell
Proc. Acad. Nat. Sci. Philadelphia 1854, 7:92
Urosaurus ornatus
Tree Lizard (Map 82)

Uta ornata Baird and Girard 1852. *Proc. Acad. Nat. Sci. Philadelphia* 6:128.
Urosaurus ornatus: Etheridge 1964. *Copeia* 1964(4):626.
REFERENCES: 14, 21, 26.12, 29, 36, 53.14, 74, 129, 155, 162, 215, 223, 228, 257, 323.21, 323.22, 393.07, 443.02, 451.5, 451.51, 454.1, 521, 529.51, 602.2, 613, 614.12, 614.15, 616.5, 642.06, 658, 661.2, 662, 665, 669, 670, 683.2, 687, 700, 753.4, 809, 811, 844, 858, 871, 872, 878.31, 883, 885, 886, 919, 930, 956, 965, 967, 1003.2, 1045.1, 1047.05, 1055.41, 1085.21, 1086.
FOSSIL RECORDS: Culberson County (602.2).
SUBSPECIES: *ornatus; schmidti* Mittleman 1940, *Herpetologica* 2(2):33.
COMMENTS: The natural history of this species is documented by Dunham (323.21, 323.22) and Martin (614.12, 614.14).

Genus *Uta* Baird and Girard
In *Stansbury's Expl. Surv. Valley Gt. Salt Lake* 1852:345
Uta stansburiana
Side-blotched Lizard (Map 83)

Uta stansburiana Baird and Girard 1852. In *Stansbury's Expl. Surv. Valley Gt. Salt Lake* 1852:345.

REFERENCES: 21, 29, 54, 54.4, 155, 162, 197, 206, 257, 266, 267, 277.8, 279, 290, 290.11, 323.21, 358, 359, 359.01, 359.02, 359.03, 359.2, 380, 384.1, 384.11, 384.12, 384.13, 393.07, 398, 432.2, 445, 510, 521, 571, 613, 631.1, 642.06, 648, 654, 662.1, 665, 683.2, 700, 746, 753.4, 792, 793, 804, 809, 811, 816.3, 844, 858, 872, 883, 885, 908, 919, 947, 965, 1014, 1016, 1017, 1017.1, 1017.2, 1020, 1023, 1024.1, 1034.2, 1055.41, 1085.21, 1085.23, 1098.

SUBSPECIES: *stejnegeri* Schmidt 1921, *Amer. Mus. Novitates* 15:1.

COMMENTS: Museum records from Coke, Kimble, and Palo Pinto counties are questionable.

Family Scincidae
Genus *Eumeces* Wiegmann
Herpetol. Mex. 1834:36
Eumeces anthracinus
Coal Skink (Map 66)

Plestiodon anthracinus Baird 1849. *J. Acad. Nat. Sci. Philadelphia* (2)1:294.
Eumeces anthracinus: Cope 1875. *Bull. U.S. Natl. Mus.* 1:45.

REFERENCES: 165, 177, 228, 257, 362, 753.4, 809, 816.51, 844, 848, 858, 876, 990, 1019, 1062.

SUBSPECIES: *pluvialis* Cope 1880, *Bull. U.S. Natl. Mus.* 17:19.

COMMENTS: A literature record (816.51) for Dallas County and a museum record for Brazos County are questionable.

Eumeces fasciatus
Five-lined Skink (Map 84)

Lacerta fasciata Linnaeus 1758. *Syst. Nat.* 1:209.
Eumeces fasciatus: Cope 1875. *Bull. U.S. Natl. Mus.* 1:45.

REFERENCES: 29, 53.2, 122, 162, 165, 175, 228, 257, 361, 362, 431, 439, 464, 502, 503, 534, 714, 726, 753.4, 809, 844, 858, 865, 912, 924, 927, 928, 932, 933, 939, 947, 952, 968, 990, 1042.12, 1098.

COMMENTS: Museum records from Bexar, Brown, and Mason counties are questionable.

Eumeces laticeps
Broadhead Skink (Map 85)

Scincus laticeps Schneider 1901. *Hist. Amphib.* 2:189.
Eumeces laticeps: Peters 1864. *Monatsber. Akad. Wiss. Berlin* 1864:49.

REFERENCES: 74, 162, 228, 361, 362, 443.02, 529.51, 622.233, 726, 753.4, 809, 844, 858, 865, 990.

COMMENTS: A Bexar County literature record (990) is erroneous, and a museum record for Llano County is questionable.

Eumeces multivirgatus
Many-lined Skink (Map 86)

Plestiodon multivirgatum Hallowell 1857. *Proc. Acad. Nat. Sci. Philadelphia* 9:215.
Eumeces multivirgatus: Cope 1875. *Bull. U.S. Natl. Mus.* 1:45.

REFERENCES: 21, 26.12, 74, 162, 167, 223, 228, 245, 257, 312.13, 355.4, 362, 393.07, 394.4, 458.2, 479, 602.2, 606, 637, 642.02, 642.06, 642.07, 683.2, 687, 725, 809, 842, 844, 858, 872, 885, 989, 990, 998, 1098.

FOSSIL RECORD: Culberson County (394.4, 458.2, 602.2).

SUBSPECIES: *epipleurotus* Cope 1880, *Bull. U.S. Natl. Mus.* 17:40.

COMMENTS: Both Mecham (642.02) and Dixon (312.13) suggest that their specimen records are intergrades between *E. m. gaigeae* (= *epipleurotus*) and *E. m. multivirgatus*. It is also possible that the southern plains population may represent a distinct subspecies (642.07).

Eumeces obsoletus
Great Plains Skink (Map 87)

Plestiodon obsoletum Baird and Girard 1852. *Proc. Acad. Nat. Sci. Philadelphia* 6:129.
Eumeces obsoletus Cope 1875. *Bull. U.S. Natl. Mus.* 1:45.

REFERENCES: 3, 21, 29, 31, 36, 53.2, 74, 155, 162, 180, 223, 228, 250, 253, 257, 323.21, 362, 380, 384.12, 393.07, 394.4, 445.2, 448, 449, 451.5, 451.51, 454.1, 458.2, 495, 495.02, 495.05, 613, 622.233, 624, 634, 642.06, 648, 662, 662.1, 665, 683.2, 687, 700, 714, 719.2, 775.6, 809, 811, 816.3, 844, 858, 871, 872, 883, 885, 909, 915, 918, 919, 922, 951, 956, 964, 967, 990, 1014, 1017.2, 1045.1, 1055.41, 1085.21, 1098.

FOSSIL RECORDS: Culberson, Kendall, and Llano counties (394.4, 458.2, 495, 495.02, 495.05).

COMMENTS: The eastern limit of this species in Texas appears to be restricted by the edge of the "rough" calcareous soils that border an ancient reef.

Eumeces septentrionalis
Prairie Skink (Map 88)

Plestiodon septentrionalis Baird 1858. *Proc. Acad. Nat. Sci. Philadelphia*
10:256.
Eumeces septentrionalis: Cope 1875. *Bull. U.S. Natl. Mus.* 1:44.

REFERENCES: 124, 149, 162, 164, 165, 223, 228, 245, 295, 362,
380, 622.232, 630, 726, 765, 794, 809, 844, 865, 867, 873, 904, 923, 943,
990, 1098.

SUBSPECIES: *obtusirostris* Boucourt 1879, *Miss. Sci. Mex.* 6:423.

COMMENTS: A Brewster County record (867, 990) and a museum
record for San Saba County are questionable.

Eumeces tetragrammus
Four-lined Skink (Map 89)

Plestiodon tetragrammus Baird 1858. *Proc. Acad. Nat. Sci. Philadelphia*
10:256.
Eumeces tetragrammus: Cope 1875. *Bull. U.S. Natl. Mus.* 1:45.

REFERENCES: 9, 17, 21, 27, 29, 31, 74, 129, 162, 215, 223, 228, 245,
257, 292, 362, 380, 443.02, 454.1, 495.02, 495.05, 521, 529.5, 529.51,
546, 588.36, 613, 648, 656, 662, 665, 683.2, 794, 809, 811, 844, 858, 865,
871, 872, 913, 916, 918, 919, 930, 947, 956, 957, 964, 965, 966, 967, 990,
1003.2, 1055.41, 1067, 1103.

FOSSIL RECORDS: Kendall County (495.02, 495.05).

SUBSPECIES: *brevilineatus* Cope 1880, *Bull. U.S. Natl. Mus.* 17:18;
tetragrammus (see above).

COMMENTS: Lieb's work (588.36) is the most comprehensive taxonomic treatment of the Four-lined Skink and its allies. Museum records
for Henderson and Limestone counties (588.36) are questionable.

Genus *Scincella* Mittleman
Herpetologica 1950, 6(2):19
Scincella lateralis
Ground Skink (Map 90)

Scincus lateralis Say 1823. In *Long's Exped. Rocky Mts.* 2:324.
Scincella lateralis: Mittleman 1950. *Herpetologica* 6(2):19.

REFERENCES: 3, 14, 29, 33, 53.2, 74, 92, 122, 150.5, 150.51, 162,
175, 220.14, 220.15, 220.2, 228, 250, 257, 284, 369, 372.7, 391, 431,
454.1, 463, 464, 465, 502, 503, 529.2, 588, 616.1, 616.2, 634, 655, 656,
662, 683.2, 701.12, 714, 726, 753.4, 765, 809, 844, 858, 865, 875, 907,
911, 912, 914, 915, 918, 924, 927, 928, 930, 932, 942, 944, 947, 952, 956,
957, 964, 965, 966, 967, 968, 1003.2, 1022, 1067, 1098.

Family Teiidae
Genus *Cnemidophorus* Wagler
Syst. Amphib. 1830:154

SPECIAL COMMENT: Information on Texas Whiptail Lizards has exploded over the past 15 years. A total of 205 papers have appeared on whiptails during the past 133 years. Of the 205 papers 78 (38 percent) have appeared in the last 15 years. Currently, there are five bisexual and six unisexual species in Texas. The uniqueness of parthenogenesis and its evolutionary implications have led to the explosive growth in the amount of literature.

Cnemidophorus dixoni
Gray-checkered Whiptail (Map 91)

Cnemidophorus dixoni Scudday 1973. *J. Herp.* 7(4):364.
REFERENCES: 816.11, 1042.1.
COMMENTS: This species is restricted to river benches along the Rio Grande in Presidio County. Parthenoform species.

Cnemidophorus exsanguis
Chihuahuan Spotted Whiptail (Map 91)

Cnemidophorus sacki exsanguis Lowe 1956. *Bull. Chicago Acad. Sci.* 10:138.
Cnemidophorus exsanguis: Duellman and Zweifel 1962. *Bull. Amer. Mus. Nat. Hist.* 123:184.
REFERENCES: 27.5, 212.6, 322, 393.07, 394.4, 642.06, 657, 683.2, 719.2, 747.12, 802.41, 802.42, 816.11, 816.2, 871, 1042.1, 1085.21, 1097.11, 1105.
FOSSIL RECORD: Culberson County (394.4).
COMMENTS: A Pecos County record (27.5) and museum records for Terrell and Reeves counties are questionable. Parthenoform species.

Cnemidophorus gularis
Texas Spotted Whiptail (Map 92)

Cnemidophorus gularis Baird and Girard 1852. *Proc. Acad. Nat. Sci. Philadelphia* 6:128.
REFERENCES: 3, 21, 27.5, 29, 33, 36, 39, 53.2, 54.3, 54.31, 60.2, 61, 74, 92, 139.5, 150, 155, 162, 173, 181, 184, 195, 212.6, 223, 228, 250, 252.1, 253, 257, 322, 380, 392, 393.07, 434, 448, 449, 451, 454.1, 490, 495.05, 521, 566, 567, 604, 607, 609, 613, 622.2, 622.233, 634, 642.06,

645, 651, 652, 653, 655, 657, 658, 662, 665, 683.2, 687, 701.29, 726, 732.4, 753.4, 756, 758, 765, 809, 844, 858, 871, 872, 883, 885, 907, 909, 912, 913, 915, 916, 918, 919, 922, 930, 932, 938, 944, 947, 951, 952, 956, 957, 967, 993, 997, 1003.2, 1017.4, 1027.2, 1042.1, 1042.12, 1042.17, 1042.18, 1045.1, 1072.13, 1096, 1105.

FOSSIL RECORD: Denton County (490, 495.05).

SUBSPECIES: *gularis* (see above).

COMMENTS: Museum records from Anderson, Cass, Harrison, Henderson, and Morris counties are questionable.

Cnemidophorus inornatus
Little Striped Whiptail (Map 93)

Cnemidophorus inornatus Baird 1858. *Proc. Acad. Nat. Sci. Philadelphia* 10:255.

REFERENCES: 21, 23, 26.12, 27.5, 173, 212.6, 267.5, 290, 290.11, 322, 393.07, 609, 642.06, 648, 654, 655, 658, 659, 661.4, 661.5, 662, 683.2, 683.21, 792, 802.2, 802.4, 802.41, 802.42, 809, 811, 816.11, 816.12, 816.2, 858, 865, 872, 878.3, 878.31, 883, 885, 1002, 1042.1, 1055.41, 1096.1, 1098.

SUBSPECIES: *heptogrammus* Axtell 1961, *Copeia* 1961(6):156.

COMMENTS: A museum record for Gillespie County is erroneous, and a record for Mitchell County is questionable.

Cnemidophorus laredoensis
Laredo Striped Whiptail (Map 64)

Cnemidophorus laredoensis McKinney, Kay, and Anderson 1973. *Herpetologica* 29(4):361.

REFERENCES: 60.2, 319.6, 622.231, 630.16, 632, 753.4, 1042.1, 1049.9, 1097.2.

COMMENTS: Recent collections have extended the distribution of this species southeast along the Rio Grande from Webb County to Starr County. Parthenoform species.

Cnemidophorus marmoratus
Marbled Whiptail (Map 96)

Cnemidophorus marmoratus Baird and Girard 1852. *Proc. Acad. Nat. Sci. Philadelphia* 6:128.

REFERENCES: 14, 21, 26.12, 27.5, 36, 54.1, 162, 173, 184, 212.6, 223, 267.5, 277.8, 290, 290.11, 323.21, 359.2, 384.12, 387.5, 393.07, 398,

423.5, 473.41, 473.42, 473.43, 622.232, 629, 642.06, 648, 651, 652, 653, 654, 658, 659, 661.4, 661.5, 662.1, 665, 665.5, 683.2, 718.4, 718.41, 718.5, 719.2, 730.2, 802.2, 802.4, 802.41, 802.42, 809, 816.12, 816.2, 871, 872, 878.3, 878.31, 883, 885, 987, 1012, 1014, 1017.2, 1023, 1042.1, 1055.41, 1085.41, 1085.21, 1097.11, 1098, 1104.

SUBSPECIES: New taxa are currently being described by Hendricks and Dixon (in preparation).

COMMENTS: Isolated records from Borden, Fisher, Garza, and Webb counties are verified specimens of *C. marmoratus*. Justification for the use of the name *marmoratus* rather than *tigris* is presented by Hendricks and Dixon (in preparation).

Cnemidophorus neomexicanus
New Mexico Whiptail (Map 91)

Cnemidophorus neomexicanus Lowe and Zweifel 1952. *Bull. Chicago Acad. Sci.* 9:230.
REFERENCES: 26, 26.12, 29, 36, 39, 74, 103, 155, 162, 184, 223, 257, 322, 521, 609, 613, 616, 650, 652, 653, 665, 683.2, 683.21, 700, 809, 811, 844, 871, 919, 947, 1042.1, 1085.21, 1096.11, 1097.1, 1097.11, 1100.

COMMENTS: Museum records from Culberson and Presidio counties are questionable. Parthenoform species.

Cnemidophorus septemvittatus
Plateau Spotted Whiptail (Map 91)

Cnemidophorus septemvittatus Cope 1892. *Trans. Amer. Philos. Soc.* 1892:42.
REFERENCES: 27.5, 212.6, 290, 290.11, 322, 323.21, 393.07, 659, 661.4, 661.5, 683.3, 718.41, 718.5, 732.4, 816.11, 816.2, 871, 872, 878.3, 1042.1, 1047.05, 1055.41.

COMMENTS: Because of an initial misunderstanding about type localities and their associated taxa by Burger (173), the correct name for this taxon should be *septemvittatus* rather than *scalaris*.

Cnemidophorus sexlineatus
Six-lined Racerunner (Map 94)

Lacerta sexlineata 1766. *Syst. Nat.* 1:364.
Cnemidophorus sexlineatus: Dumeril and Bibron 1839. *Erpetol. Gen.* 5:131.
REFERENCES: 3, 14, 29, 53.2, 60.2, 74, 122, 155, 162, 175, 184, 195,

220.14, 220.15, 220.2, 228, 257, 277.8, 322, 348, 365, 380, 443.02, 451.5, 451.51, 454.1, 464, 485, 495, 495.05, 529.51, 604, 608, 613, 622.19, 622.233, 683.2, 718.41, 726, 732.4, 747, 753.4, 765, 809, 816.3, 844, 858, 865, 872, 883, 885, 908, 912, 915, 928, 947, 951, 952, 956, 966, 967, 968, 975, 977, 1003.2, 1014, 1022, 1042.1, 1042.12, 1098.

FOSSIL RECORD: Llano County (495, 495.05).

SUBSPECIES: *sexlineatus; viridis* Lowe 1966, *J. Arizona Acad. Sci.* 4(1):44.

COMMENTS: The taxonomic boundary between subspecies in Texas is not well defined.

Cnemidophorus tesselatus
Colorado Checkered Whiptail (Map 95)

Ameiva tesselata Say 1823. *In Long's Exped. Rocky Mts.* 2:50.
Cnemidophorus tesselatus: Baird 1859. *Pacif. R.R. Surv.* 10(4):18.

REFERENCES: 21, 26.12, 27.5, 29, 36, 39, 74, 155, 162, 184, 212.6, 215, 223, 253, 257, 267.5, 290, 380, 393.07, 394.4, 398, 521, 545.53, 613, 622.14, 634, 642.06, 648, 651, 652, 653, 655, 658, 662, 665, 683.2, 683.21, 700, 718.4, 718.41, 718.5, 719.2, 747.14, 792, 802.2, 802.21, 802.22, 802.4, 802.41, 802.42, 809, 812, 816.11, 816.12, 816.2, 816.3, 844, 858, 860, 865, 871, 872, 883, 885, 909, 919, 922, 947, 965, 977, 1012, 1022, 1042.1, 1045.1, 1055.41, 1085.21, 1106.

FOSSIL RECORD: Culberson County (394.4).

COMMENTS: Univerified museum records of this species for Kent and Webb counties probably represent *C. marmoratus*. Parthenoform species.

Cnemidophorus uniparens
Desert Grassland Whiptail (Map 91)

Cnemidophorus uniparens Wright and Lowe 1965. *J. Arizona Acad. Sci.* 3(3):167.

REFERENCES: 683.3, 885, 1042.1, 1085.21, 1097, 1097.11.

COMMENTS: The Texas distribution of this species is restricted to the immediate environs of El Paso. Parthenoform species.

Family Anguinidae
Genus *Gerrhonotus* Wiegmann
Isis von Oken 1828, 21:380
Gerrhonotus liocephalus
Texas Alligator Lizard (Map 97)

Gerrhonotus liocephalus Wiegmann 1828. *Isis von Oken* 21:381.

REFERENCES: 21, 29, 31, 71, 74, 150, 162, 176, 223, 228, 257, 290.2, 292, 373, 433, 443.02, 454.1, 624, 644.15, 665, 683.2, 700, 701.4, 747, 753.4, 809, 811, 816.52, 844, 858, 871, 872, 884, 918, 919, 930, 947, 948, 956, 964, 967, 1007, 1032.7, 1055.41, 1066, 1067, 1098.

SUBSPECIES: *infernalis* Baird 1858, *Proc. Acad. Nat. Sci. Philadelphia* 10:255.

COMMENTS: The isolated records for Fayette (701.4) and Dallas (816.52) counties are verified, but the Dallas record may be an introduction.

Genus *Ophisaurus* Daudin
Bull. Soc. Philos. Paris 1803, 3:188
Ophisaurus attenuatus
Slender Glass Lizard (Map 98)

Ophisaurus ventralis attenuatus Baird 1880. In Cope, *Bull. U.S. Natl. Mus.* 17:18.
Ophisaurus attenuatus: Boulenger 1885. *Cat. Liz. Brit. Mus.* 2:282.

REFERENCES: 29, 61, 74, 122, 162, 228, 245, 257, 331, 391, 439, 450, 454.1, 463, 485.5, 490, 495.06, 495.07, 529.5, 626, 726, 753.4, 809, 844, 865, 904, 912, 913, 915, 930, 947, 956, 965, 968, 1042.12, 1050.12, 1098.

FOSSIL RECORD: Denton County (490).

SUBSPECIES: *attenuatus* (see above).

COMMENTS: A museum record for Kerr County is questionable.

Suborder Serpentes
Family Leptotyphlopidae
Genus *Leptotyphlops* Fitzinger
Syst. Rept. 1843:24
Leptotyphlops dulcis
Texas Blind Snake (Map 99)

Rena dulcis Baird and Girard 1853. *Cat. N. Amer. Rept.* 1:142.
Leptotyphlops dulcis: Stejneger 1891. *Proc. U.S. Natl. Mus.* 14:501.

REFERENCES: 21, 33, 38, 55, 74, 92, 122, 131, 148.01, 151, 155,

162, 185, 220, 220.11, 223, 228, 252, 257, 277.8, 281, 290.12, 290.2, 332.02, 372.2, 380, 389, 393.03, 395.2, 395.21, 415, 443.3, 443.31, 451.5, 451.51, 454.1, 511.2, 521, 529.51, 529.53, 555, 573.5, 588.39, 616.2, 642.06, 662, 665, 683.2, 699.01, 726, 765, 768, 784, 809, 810, 811, 816.3, 858, 865, 869, 871, 883, 885, 887, 907, 915, 918, 930, 947, 956, 967, 995, 1021, 1045.11, 1046, 1055, 1055.1, 1055.2, 1055.41, 1085.21, 1094, 1095, 1098.

SUBSPECIES: *dulcis; dissecta* Cope 1896, *Amer. Nat.* 30:753.

COMMENTS: A museum record for Montgomery County is questionable.

Leptotyphlops humilis
Western Blind Snake (Map 100)

Rena humilis Baird and Girard 1853. *Cat. N. Amer. Rept.* 1:143.
Leptotyphlops humilis: Ruthven 1907. *Bull. Amer. Nat. Hist.* 23:573.

REFERENCES: 162, 223, 415, 443.3, 443.32, 554, 555, 648, 662, 665, 683.2, 699.01, 768, 809, 810, 811, 858, 865, 869, 871, 883, 885, 985, 1055.41, 1085.21, 1094, 1095.

SUBSPECIES *segregus* Klauber 1939, *Trans. San Diego Soc. Nat. Hist.* 9:67.

COMMENTS: This species is more widely distributed in western Texas than formerly believed.

Family Colubridae
Genus *Arizona* Kennicott
in Baird, *U.S. and Mex. Bound. Surv.* 1859, 212:18
Arizona elegans
Glossy Snake (Map 101)

Arizona elegans Kennicott 1859. In Baird, *U.S. and Mex. Bound. Surv.* 212:18.

REFERENCES: 21, 26.12, 45.3, 74, 108, 132, 148.01, 151, 155, 162, 186, 223, 228, 257, 281, 307, 308.5, 309, 310, 312.3, 313, 354, 359.2, 359.3, 372.4, 380, 394.4, 415, 451.5, 451.51, 458.2, 490, 491, 495.05, 495.7, 508, 529.51, 545.57, 561, 602.2, 613, 631.2, 642.06, 665, 683.2, 714, 753.4, 759, 765, 768, 802.21, 809, 810, 811, 816.3, 816.7, 858, 865, 869, 871, 883, 885, 967, 976, 985.3, 1017.2, 1021, 1023, 1045.11, 1055.41, 1070, 1075, 1085.21, 1094, 1095.

FOSSIL RECORD: Culberson, Denton, Hardeman, Kendall, and Llano counties (394.4, 490, 495, 495.05, 602.2).

SUBSPECIES: *elegans; arenicola* Dixon 1960, *Southwest. Nat.* 5(4):226; *philipi* Klauber 1946, *Trans. San Diego Soc. Nat. Hist.* 10:333.

COMMENTS: The distributional hiatus on the Edwards Plateau (770.3) has recently been eliminated by the collection of several specimens of *A. e. arenicola* X *A. e. elegans* across the eastern end of the plateau (Llano Uplift).

Genus *Carphophis* Gervais
D'Orbigny's Dict. Univ. Hist. Nat. 1843, 3:191
Carphophis amoenus
Worm Snake (Map 66)

Coluber amoenus Say 1825. *J. Acad. Nat. Sci. Philadelphia* (1) 4:237.
Carphophis amoenus: Gervais 1843. *D'Orbigny's Dict. Univ. Hist. Nat.* 3:191.
REFERENCES: 162, 228, 415, 630.2, 768, 810, 858, 1094, 1095.
SUBSPECIES: *vermis* Kennicott 1859, *Proc. Acad. Nat. Sci. Philadelphia* 11:99.
COMMENTS: A museum record for Bosque County is erroneous.

Genus *Cemophora* Cope
Proc. Acad. Nat. Sci. Philadelphia 1860, 12:244
Cemophora coccinea
Scarlet Snake (Map 102)

Coluber coccineus Blumenbach 1788. Voigt's *Mag. Neu. Phys. Naturg.* 5(1):11.
Cemophora coccinea: Cope 1860. *Proc. Acad. Nat. Sci. Philadelphia* 12:244.
REFERENCES: 11, 228, 495.7, 573.7, 588.01, 622.232, 768, 770.1, 816.55, 1078, 1079, 1094, 1095.
SUBSPECIES: *copei* Jan 1863, *Arch. Zool. Anat. Fish.* 2:231; *lineri* Williams, Brown, and Williams 1966, *Texas J. Sci.* 18(1):85.
COMMENTS: A distribution gap of approximately 185 km exists between the eastern- and westernmost localities of the Texas subspecies.

Genus *Coluber* Linnaeus
Syst. Nat. 1758, 1:216
Coluber constrictor
Racer (Map 103)

Coluber constrictor Linnaeus 1758. *Syst. Nat.* 1:216.
REFERENCES: 12, 13, 38, 74, 76, 92, 122, 131, 148.01, 151, 162, 223, 228, 256, 257, 269, 270, 355, 367, 372.6, 380, 391, 408.5, 432.23,

439, 451.5, 451.51, 464, 482.2, 495.05, 495.7, 498.2, 529.2, 529.51, 529.53, 587.5, 588.39, 613, 622.233, 622.24, 642.08, 656, 683.2, 696, 714, 717, 726, 753.4, 765, 768, 770, 809, 810, 818, 821, 821.2, 858, 865, 869, 871, 883, 885, 904, 910.1, 912, 915, 918, 922, 928, 930, 932, 938, 939, 942, 947, 951, 952, 956, 964, 965, 967, 1042.12, 1081.11, 1081.16, 1082, 1089, 1094, 1095, 1098.

FOSSIL RECORD: Dallas, Denton, and Kendall counties (494.05, 821, 821.2).

SUBSPECIES: *anthicus* Cope 1862, *Proc. Acad. Nat. Sci. Philadelphia* 14:338; *etheridgei* Wilson 1970, *Texas J. Sci.* 22:75; *flaviventris* Say 1823, in *Long's Exped. Rocky Mts.* 1:185; *mormon* Baird and Girard 1852, in *Stansbury's Exped. Gt. Salt Lake* 1852:351; *oaxaca* Jan 1863, *Elenco Sist. Degli Ofidi* 1863:63; *priapus* Dunn and Wood 1939, *Notulae Nat.* 5:4.

COMMENTS: There is a recent trend to recognize the western subspecies (*mormon*) as a species. Because of suggested intergradation of *C. c. flaviventris* and *mormon* in Texas, I retain the latter taxon as a subspecies.

Genus *Coniophanes* Hallowell
In Cope, *Proc. Acad. Nat. Sci. Philadelphia* 1860, 12:248
Coniophanes imperialis
Black-striped Snake (Map 104)

Taeniophis imperialis Baird 1859. *U.S. Mex. Bound. Surv.* 2(2):23.
Coniophanes imperialis: Cope 1861. *Proc. Acad. Nat. Sci. Philadelphia* 13:74.

REFERENCES: 9.16, 28, 33, 74, 134, 151, 157, 158, 162, 223, 226, 228, 252, 257, 286, 389, 415, 529.5, 632.1, 768, 809, 810, 819, 858, 869, 888, 1065, 1089, 1094, 1095.

SUBSPECIES: *imperialis* (see above).

COMMENTS: This species seems to be surviving in the Rio Grande Valley despite habitat alteration and intensive application of agricultural chemicals.

Genus *Diadophis* Baird and Girard
Cat. N. Amer. Rept. 1853, 1:112
Diadophis punctatus
Ringneck Snake (Map 105)

Coluber punctatus Linnaeus 1766. *Syst. Nat.* 1:376.
Diadophis punctatus: Baird and Girard 1853. *Cat. N. Amer. Rept.* 1:112.

REFERENCES: 26.12, 29, 38, 74, 107, 113, 122, 148.01, 151, 155, 162, 205.1, 223, 228, 252, 257, 269, 270, 277.8, 290.2, 332.03, 380, 391, 393, 393.03, 393.06, 415, 439, 451.51, 454.1, 482.2, 483, 495.05, 495.7, 521, 544, 602.2, 614, 615, 622.233, 636, 642.06, 656, 662, 665, 683.2, 714, 753.4, 768, 793, 809, 810, 811, 816.3, 858, 865, 869, 871, 883, 885, 912, 915, 919, 944, 956, 967, 968, 1055.1, 1055.41, 1085.21, 1094, 1095.

FOSSIL RECORD: Culberson and Kendall counties (482.2, 495.05, 602.2).

SUBSPECIES: *arnyi* Kennicott 1858, *Proc. Acad. Nat. Sci. Philadelphia* 10:99; *regalis* Baird and Girard 1853, *Cat. N. Amer. Rept.* 1:115; *stictogenys* Cope 1860, *Proc. Acad. Nat. Sci. Philadelphia* 12:250.

COMMENTS: The zone of intergradation between *D. p. regalis* and *D. p. arnyi* is unclear in Texas.

Genus *Drymarchon* Fitzinger
Syst. Rept. 1843:26
Drymarchon corais
Indigo Snake (Map 106)

Coluber corais Boie 1827. *Isis von Oken* 20:537.
Drymarchon corais: Amaral 1929. *Mem. Inst. Butantan* 4:84.

REFERENCES: 9.16, 29, 33, 38, 59.3, 74, 86.1, 132, 151, 162, 199, 223, 228, 236, 238, 250, 257, 281, 389, 415, 458, 495.7, 503, 529.5, 587.5, 616.2, 630.1, 683.2, 714, 753.4, 768, 809, 810, 836, 858, 869, 871, 945, 947, 1010, 1094.

FOSSIL RECORD: (genus only) Denton County (458, 495.05).

SUBSPECIES: *erebennus* Cope 1860, *Proc. Acad. Nat. Sci. Philadelphia* 12:342.

COMMENTS: Despite continued protection under state law, this species remains uncommon throughout its Texas distribution.

Genus *Drymobius* Fitzinger
Syst. Rept. 1843:26
Drymobius margaritiferus
Speckled Racer (Map 104)

Herpetodryas margaritiferus Schlegel 1837. *Essai Physion. Serp.* 2:184.
Drymobius margaritiferus: Cope 1860. *Proc. Acad. Nat. Sci. Philadelphia* 12:561.

REFERENCES: 29, 74, 132, 162, 228, 415, 612.3, 768, 809, 810, 838, 858, 867.5, 869, 888, 1081.4, 1081.5.

SUBSPECIES: *margaritiferus* (see above).

COMMENTS: The Speckled Racer is occasionally seen in the Audubon Preserve near Brownsville. The museum records for Hidalgo and Kleberg counties are questionable.

Genus *Elaphe* Fitzinger
In Wagler, *Descr. Icon. Amphib.* 1833 (3) pl. 27 (text)
Elaphe bairdi
Baird's Rat Snake (Map 107)

Coluber bairdi Yarrow 1880. *Bull. U.S. Natl. Mus.* 17:41.
Elaphe bairdi: Stejneger 1917. *Checklist N.A. Amphib. Rept.* 1917:82.

REFERENCES: 132, 148.5, 162, 223, 228, 230.12, 252, 257, 296, 317, 394, 415, 588.35, 655, 662, 665, 695, 714, 714.13, 720.22, 768, 809, 810, 811, 858, 869, 871, 925, 1055.41, 1089, 1094, 1095, 1098.

COMMENTS: This taxon has been elevated to specific status by Olson (714.13), and more recent genic data support this decision (Lawson and Lieb, personal communication). A record from Cameron County (947, 1095) is erroneous.

Elaphe guttata
Corn Snake (Map 108)

Coluber guttatus Linnaeus 1766. *Syst. Nat.* 1:385.
Elaphe guttata: Dumeril, Bibron, and Dumeril 1854. *Erpetol. Gen.* 7:273.

REFERENCES: 26.12, 29, 33, 38, 45.2, 45.3, 61, 74, 132, 151, 155, 162, 228, 250, 255, 257, 269, 270, 281, 295, 316, 317, 380, 394.4, 410, 415, 451.5, 451.51, 454.1, 458.2, 477, 482.2, 483, 485.5, 495.05, 495.7, 521, 529.5, 529.51, 529.53, 588.39, 613, 616.2, 622.233, 622.24, 634, 642.06, 643.71, 665, 683.2, 687, 720.21, 726, 753.4, 765, 768, 771.3, 809, 810, 816.3, 819, 858, 865, 869, 883, 885, 922, 923, 927, 938, 947, 951, 952, 956, 957, 964, 966, 967, 1042.14, 1055.41, 1085, 1085.21, 1094, 1095, 1098.

FOSSIL RECORD: Culberson and Kendall counties (394.4, 458.2, 482.2, 495.05).

SUBSPECIES: R. A. Thomas (personal communication and unpublished) has not settled the issue of subspecies within this taxon. If current practices are accepted, *emoryi* Baird and Girard 1853, *Cat. N. Amer. Rept.* 1:157, is one of the subspecies in Texas.

Elaphe obsoleta
Rat Snake (Map 109)

Coluber obsoletus Say 1823. In *Long's Exped. Rocky Mts.* 1:140.
Elaphe obsoleta: Garman 1883. *Mem. Mus. Comp. Zool.* 8(3):54.
REFERENCES: 9.16, 33, 38, 45.3, 74, 76, 86.1, 92, 121, 122, 123, 132, 148.01, 148.5, 151, 155, 162, 195, 205.11, 223, 228, 250, 252, 257, 269, 270, 281, 293.6, 296, 316, 317, 330.91, 372.6, 377.3, 380, 389, 391, 394, 415, 439, 450, 451.5, 451.51, 454.1, 464, 474, 477, 485.5, 495.7, 502, 529.51, 529.53, 542, 558, 588.35, 588.39, 616.2, 622.24, 624, 632.2, 642.08, 655, 683.4, 699.1, 703, 714.13, 715, 720.2, 720.22, 726, 753.4, 765, 768, 770, 775.1, 785.2, 809, 810, 853, 865, 871, 910.2, 912, 913, 915, 923, 925, 926, 928, 930, 931, 932, 933, 935, 938, 944, 947, 952, 956, 964, 965, 966, 967, 968, 984, 1042.12, 1042.15, 1045.3, 1065, 1067, 1077, 1094, 1095.
SUBSPECIES: *lindheimeri* Baird and Girard 1853, *Cat. N. Amer. Rept.* 1:74.
COMMENTS: Culberson and Reeves county records (687, 155) probably represent *E. guttata* or *E. bairdi*. The Cameron County record (947, 1095) is validated.

Elaphe subocularis
Trans-Pecos Rat Snake (Map 110)

Coluber subocularis Brown 1901. *Proc. Acad. Nat. Sci. Philadelphia* 53:492.
Elaphe subocularis: Stejneger and Barbour 1917. *Checklist N.A. Amphib. Rept.* 1:84.
REFERENCES: 9.16, 9.19, 21, 26.12, 45.2, 45.3, 74, 151, 155, 162, 204.3, 291, 296, 317, 319, 374, 415, 495.7, 518, 520, 521, 529.53, 573.6, 602.2, 613, 616.2, 642.06, 644.14, 662, 665, 683.2, 683.21, 699.1, 720.22, 768, 775.1, 804, 809, 810, 811, 822.01, 858, 869, 871, 883, 885, 1032.2, 1045.3, 1055.41, 1085.21, 1085.22, 1089, 1094, 1095.
FOSSIL RECORD: Culberson County (602.2).
COMMENTS: Lamoureaux (573.6) has described a distinctive color phase of this species.

Genus *Farancia* Gray
Zool. Misc. 1842:78
Farancia abacura
Mud Snake (Map 111)

Coluber abacurus Holbrook 1836. *N. Amer. Herpetol.* 1:119.
Farancia abacura: Baird and Girard 1853. *Cat. N. Amer. Rept.* 1:123.

REFERENCES: 10, 14, 162, 171, 175, 228, 282, 415, 439, 464, 474, 495.7, 502, 503, 511.5, 537, 622.232, 630.2, 726, 753.4, 768, 809, 810, 832, 858, 865, 913, 928, 931.

SUBSPECIES: *reinwardti* Schlegel 1837, *Essai Physion. Serp.* 1:173.

COMMENTS: An isolated Dallas County record has been verified by W. W. Lamar (personal communication).

Genus *Ficimia* Gray
Cat. Snakes Brit. Mus. 1849:80
Ficimia streckeri
Mexican Hooknose Snake (Map 104)

Ficimia streckeri Taylor 1931. *Copeia* 1931(1):5.

REFERENCES: 16, 26.11, 74, 162, 228, 321, 415, 454.31, 454.32, 529.5, 588.39, 643.6, 697, 714.11, 768, 809, 810, 858, 869, 871, 987, 999, 1040.5, 1042.12, 1045.11, 1085.21, 1089, 1094, 1095.

COMMENTS: The most recent taxonomic work for this taxon is Hardy (454.31).

Genus *Gyalopion* Cope
Proc. Acad. Nat. Sci. Philadelphia 1860, 12:243
Gyalopion canum
Western Hooknose Snake (Map 112)

Gyalopium canum Cope 1860. *Proc. Acad. Nat. Sci. Philadelphia* 12:243.

REFERENCES: 74, 132, 148.01, 151, 162, 218, 228, 271, 290.2, 357, 454.3, 454.33, 495.7, 531, 622.232, 627, 642.06, 662, 665, 683.2, 683.21, 768, 809, 810, 811, 842, 858, 869, 883, 885, 1042.12, 1055.41, 1094, 1095.

COMMENTS: The Wise County record (1042.12) is questionable.

Genus *Heterodon* Latreille
Hist. Nat. Rept. 1802, 4:32
Heterodon nasicus
Western Hognose Snake (Map 113)

Heterodon nasicus Baird and Girard 1852. In *Stansbury's Expl. Surv. Valley Gt. Salt Lake* 1852:352.

REFERENCES: 26.12, 29, 33, 34, 35, 38, 45.3, 132, 139.02, 151, 162, 223, 228, 230.15, 252, 253, 257, 324, 335, 359.2, 380, 389, 398, 415, 434, 451.5, 451.51, 480, 482.2, 483, 490, 491, 493, 495.05, 495.7, 521, 529.53, 544, 573.32, 573.33, 573.34, 588.39, 613, 622.232, 622.233, 631.2, 642.06, 665, 683.2, 726, 732.6, 768, 793, 794, 809, 810, 816.3, 858, 865, 869, 871, 876, 883, 885, 909, 922, 951, 1045.11, 1067, 1085.21, 1094, 1095.

FOSSIL RECORD: Denton, Hardeman, Kendall, and Knox counties (482.2, 490, 491, 493, 495.05).

SUBSPECIES: *nasicus; gloydi* Edgren 1952, *Nat. Hist. Misc.* 112:3; *kennerlyi* Kennicott 1860, *Proc. Acad. Nat. Sci. Philadelphia* 12:336.

COMMENTS: There are no records of this taxon from the center of the Edwards Plateau. Its distribution is similar to that of the Glossy Snake in Texas.

Heterodon platyrhinos
Eastern Hognose Snake (Map 114)

Heterodon platyrhinos Latreille 1802. *Hist. Nat. Rept.* 4:32.

REFERENCES: 26.14, 29, 74, 113.6, 122, 148.01, 151, 162, 228, 250, 253, 265.3, 269, 270, 281, 330.91, 336, 337, 380, 391, 393.03, 415, 439, 451.51, 454.1, 463, 464, 482.2, 483, 495, 495.05, 495.7, 529.5, 529.53, 540, 542, 573.32, 573.33, 588.39, 613, 622.233, 630.4, 726, 732.6, 753.4, 766, 768, 809, 810, 821.1, 858, 879, 883, 910.2, 912, 913, 915, 927, 932, 933, 935, 942, 947, 952, 956, 965, 966, 967, 968, 1042.12, 1045.2, 1075, 1094, 1095, 1098.

FOSSIL RECORD: Harris and Kendall counties (482.2, 495, 495.05, 821.1).

Genus *Hypsiglena* Cope
Proc. Acad. Nat. Sci. Philadelphia 1860, 12:246
Hypsiglena torquata
Night Snake (Map 115)

Hypsiglena torquata Cope 1887. *Bull. U.S. Natl. Mus.* 32:78.

REFERENCES: 21, 26.12, 56.4, 74, 132, 148.01, 151, 162, 220.4, 223, 228, 250, 255, 257, 281, 296.3, 312, 328, 332.02, 380, 394, 394.4, 415, 458.2, 495.7, 521, 522, 529.51, 529.52, 622.23, 622.232, 624, 642.06, 648, 662, 665, 683.2, 714, 768, 775.1, 802.21, 809, 810, 816.3, 858, 865, 869, 883, 885, 910.1, 939, 944, 947, 980, 1023, 1055.41, 1067, 1085.21, 1094, 1095.

FOSSIL RECORD: Culberson County (394.4, 458.2).

SUBSPECIES: *jani* Duges 1866, *Mém. Acad. Sci. Lett. Montpellier* 6:32.

COMMENTS: Isolated records from Anderson, Brazoria, Henderson, and Smith counties are verified field-collected specimens of the Night Snake.

Genus *Lampropeltis* Fitzinger
Syst. Rept. 1843:25
Lampropeltis alterna
Gray-banded Kingsnake (Map 116)

Ophibolus alternus Brown 1902. *Proc. Acad. Nat. Sci. Philadelphia* 53:612.
Lampropeltis alterna: Stejneger and Barbour 1917. *Checklist N.A. Amphib. Rept.* 197:87.
REFERENCES: 9.16, 18, 21, 26.12, 45.3, 74, 104, 105, 113.5, 153, 155, 162, 290.2, 292, 332.02, 375, 391.6, 393.02, 394, 395, 415, 495.7, 521, 642.06, 643, 644.1, 644.11, 662, 665, 683.2, 699.2, 700, 768, 775.1, 786, 809, 810, 815, 838, 858, 869, 871, 984.1, 1032.21, 1032.23, 1032.33, 1032.4, 1045.3, 1055.41, 1059, 1085.21, 1085.3, 1094, 1095.
COMMENTS: There is considerable breeding data for this species (645.11, 984.1, 1032.23). The most recent taxonomic work is Garstka (391.6).

Lampropeltis calligaster
Prairie Kingsnake (Map 117)

Coluber calligaster Harlan 1827. *J. Acad. Nat. Sci. Philadelphia* 5:359.
Lampropeltis calligaster: Cope 1860. *Proc. Acad. Nat. Sci. Philadelphia* 12:255.
REFERENCES: 45.3, 104, 105, 113.5, 113.52, 122, 151, 162, 205.11, 220.15, 228, 252, 257, 269, 270, 271, 330.91, 380, 391, 415, 434, 439, 451.5, 451.51, 454.1, 482.2, 482.3, 495, 495.05, 495.7, 529.5, 622.233, 714, 721, 726, 753.4, 768, 780, 810, 858, 865, 883, 912, 915, 965, 985.5, 1021, 1042.12, 1073.1, 1075, 1094, 1095.
FOSSIL RECORD: Kendall and Llano counties (482.2, 495, 495.05, 721).
COMMENTS: The Jeff Davis County record (105, 257) is in error.

Lampropeltis getulus
Common Kingsnake (Map 118)

Coluber getulus Linnaeus 1766. *Syst. Nat.* 12:382.
Lampropeltis getulus: Cope 1860. *Proc. Acad. Nat. Sci. Philadelphia* 12:255.
REFERENCES: 29, 38, 45.3, 74, 113.5, 113.51, 122, 132, 151, 155, 162, 205.11, 205.15, 220.15, 228, 250, 253, 257, 269, 270, 281, 372.3, 372.6, 380, 391, 393.03, 394.4, 415, 434, 439, 451.5, 451.51, 454.1, 458.2, 482.2, 483, 485.5, 491, 495.04, 495.05, 495.7, 521, 529.5, 529.51,

529.53, 612.4, 613, 616.2, 622.233, 622.24, 624, 631.2, 642.06, 662, 665, 683.2, 714, 726, 746.4, 753.4, 768, 770, 809, 810, 816.3, 858, 869, 883, 885, 912, 915, 918, 929, 939, 947, 951, 952, 956, 964, 965, 967, 968, 1042.12, 1055.41, 1067, 1073.1, 1075, 1080.1, 1085.21, 1094, 1095, 1098.

FOSSIL RECORD: Culberson, Hardeman, Kendall, and Lubbock counties (394.4, 458.2, 482.2, 491, 495.04, 495.05).

SUBSPECIES: *holbrooki* Stejneger 1902, *Proc. U.S. Natl. Mus.* 25: 152; *splendida* Baird and Girard 1853, *Cat. N. Amer. Rept.* 1:83.

COMMENTS: Blaney (113.51) is the most recent taxonomic account of this species.

Lampropeltis triangulum
Milk Snake (Map 119)

Coluber triangulum Lacepede 1788. *Hist. Nat. Quad. Serpens.* 2:86.
Lampropeltis triangulum: Stejneger and Barbour 1917. *Checklist N.A. Amphib. Rept.* 1917:90.
REFERENCES: 9.16, 26.12, 27, 38, 104, 105, 113.5, 132, 151, 223, 228, 235, 252, 257, 269, 270, 290.2, 377, 387, 391, 415, 439, 450, 451.5, 451.51, 454.1, 482.2, 490, 491, 495, 495.05, 495.7, 529.5, 529.53, 544, 573.25, 576.04, 612.4, 630.15, 632.3, 662, 683.2, 698, 726, 753.4, 768, 809, 810, 839, 858, 869, 883, 885, 888, 912, 913, 915, 947, 956, 967, 968, 983, 1021, 1032.23, 1045.11, 1055.1, 1055.41, 1067, 1077.1, 1094, 1095, 1098.

FOSSIL RECORD: Denton, Hardeman, Kendall, and Llano counties (482.2, 490, 491, 495, 495.05).

SUBSPECIES: *amaura* Cope 1860, *Proc. Acad. Nat. Sci. Philadelphia* 12:258; *annulata* Kennicott 1860, *Proc. Acad. Nat. Sci. Philadelphia* 12:329; *celaenops* Stejneger 1903, *Proc. U.S. Natl. Mus.* 25:153; *gentilis* Baird and Girard 1853, *Cat. N. Amer. Rept.* 1:90.

COMMENTS: Williams (1077.1) is the most recent taxonomic work for the species.

Genus *Leptodeira* Fitzinger
Syst. Rept. 1843:27
Leptodeira septentrionalis
Cat-eyed Snake (Map 104)

Dipsas septentrionalis Kennicott 1859. In Baird, *U.S. and Mex. Bound. Surv.* 2:16.
Leptodeira septentrionalis: Stejneger 1891. *Proc. U.S. Natl. Mus.* 14:505.
REFERENCES: 9.16, 32, 74, 134, 151, 162, 223, 228, 252, 257,

320, 328, 387, 389, 415, 632.1, 768, 809, 810, 869, 871, 888, 992, 1094, 1095, 1098.

COMMENTS: An isolated museum record for Kleberg County is questionable.

Genus *Masticophis* Baird and Girard
Cat. N. Amer. Rept. 1853, 1:98
Masticophis flagellum
Coachwhip (Map 120)

Coluber flagellum Shaw 1802. *Gen. Zool.* 3:475.
Masticophis flagellum: Baird and Girard 1853. *Cat. N. Amer. Rept.* 1:98.
REFERENCES: 14, 21, 26.12, 29, 33, 38, 45.3, 57, 76, 92, 122, 123, 131, 148.01, 155, 162, 195, 220.15, 228, 233, 248, 253, 257, 269, 270, 277.8, 281, 296.3, 323.21, 331, 332.02, 359.2, 380, 393.03, 415, 434, 439, 450, 451.5, 451.51, 454.1, 464, 477, 483, 485.5, 495.7, 521, 529.2, 529.51, 529.52, 529.53, 573.23, 588.3, 613, 622.233, 622.24, 631.2, 642.06, 648, 657, 662, 665, 683.2, 700, 714, 717, 726, 747.12, 753.4, 765, 768, 770, 802.21, 809, 810, 816.3, 819, 858, 865, 869, 883, 885, 909, 913, 915, 918, 919, 922, 927, 928, 930, 939, 944, 945, 947, 951, 956, 964, 967, 1012, 1017.2, 1023, 1042.12, 1055.41, 1067, 1073.1, 1081.1, 1081.12, 1081.13, 1085.21, 1094, 1098, 1099, 1100.
SUBSPECIES: *flagellum; testaceus* Say 1823, in *Long's Exped. Rocky Mts.* 2:48.
COMMENTS: Wilson (1081.1) is the most recent taxonomic treatment of this species.

Masticophis taeniatus
Striped Whipsnake (Map 121)

Leptophis taeniata Hallowell 1852. *Proc. Acad. Nat. Sci. Philadelphia* 6:181
Masticophis taeniatus: Baird and Girard 1853. *Cat. N. Amer. Rept.* 1:98.
REFERENCES: 21, 26.12, 29, 33, 38, 45.3, 101, 123, 148.01, 151, 155, 162, 215, 223, 228, 252, 257, 281, 323.21, 389, 415, 420, 454.1, 477, 521, 529.5, 529.52, 529.53, 587.5, 588.3, 613, 622.232, 642.06, 648, 662, 665, 683.2, 687, 700, 716, 717, 725, 768, 769, 802.21, 809, 810, 811, 819, 858, 869, 871, 883, 885, 909, 918, 947, 956, 964, 967, 985.5, 1055.41, 1081.12, 1085.21, 1091, 1094, 1095, 1098.
SUBSPECIES: *taeniatus; girardi* Stejneger and Barbour 1917, *Checklist N.A. Amphib. Rept.* 1917:80; *ruthveni* Ortenburger 1923, *Occ. Papers Mus. Zool. Univ. Michigan* 139:3; *schotti* Baird and Girard 1853, *Cat. N. Amer. Rept.* 1:160.

COMMENTS: A museum record from Throckmorton County is questionable. The taxonomy of this species is currently under study by J. Camper (personal communication).

Genus *Nerodia* Baird and Girard
Cat. N. Amer. Rept. 1853, 1:38
Nerodia cyclopion
Green Water Snake (Map 122)

Tropidonotus cyclopion Dumeril, Bibron, and Dumeril 1854. *Erpetol. Gen.* 7:576.
Nerodia cyclopion: Rossman and Eberle 1977. *Herpetoligica* 33(1):42.
    REFERENCES: 14, 162, 222, 228, 423, 439, 529.53, 643.6, 753.4, 768, 809, 810, 858, 929, 1064, 1094, 1095.
    SUBSPECIES: *cyclopion* (see above).
    COMMENTS: The Harrison County record (770.3) is verified through recent records of specimens by W. W. Lamar (personal communication).

Nerodia erythrogaster
Plainbelly Water Snake (Map 123)

Coluber erythrogaster Forster 1771. In Bossu, *Trav. through Pt. Amer. Louisiana* 1771:364.
Nerodia erythrogaster: Baird and Girard 1853. *Cat. N. Amer. Rept.* 1:40.
    REFERENCES: 21, 29, 33, 38, 45.3, 57, 74, 76, 91, 92, 122, 148.01, 151, 155, 162, 195, 205.11, 222, 223, 225, 228, 230.1, 230.14, 230.15, 252, 253, 257, 269, 270, 281, 298, 372.3, 372.6, 380, 384.26, 391, 394.4, 395.3, 415, 432, 439, 450, 451.5. 451.51, 454.1, 482.2, 483, 485.5, 490, 491, 495.05, 495.7, 506, 509.2, 511.5, 529.53, 565, 613, 614.6, 622.233, 632.2, 642.06, 655, 662, 665, 683.2, 700, 714, 720.27, 726, 753.4, 765, 768, 809, 810, 811, 816.12, 816.3, 819, 858, 865, 869, 878.5, 883, 885, 907, 910.2, 912, 913, 915, 919, 922, 927, 928, 930, 932, 947, 951, 952, 956, 957, 964, 966, 967, 968, 977.5, 1018, 1042.12, 1047, 1055.41, 1094, 1095, 1098.
    FOSSIL RECORD: Hardeman, Kendall, and Lubbock counties (482.2, 490, 491, 495.05).
    SUBSPECIES: *flavigaster* Conant 1949, *Copeia* 1949(1):2; *transversa* Hallowell 1852, *Proc. Acad. Nat. Sci. Philadelphia* 6:177.
    COMMENTS: A museum record for Starr County is questionable. See Conant (230.13) for a summary of the distribution in south Texas.

Nerodia fasciata
Southern Water Snake (Map 124)

Coluber fasciatus Linnaeus 1766. *Syst. Nat.* 1:378.
Nerodia fasciata: Baird and Girard 1853. *Cat. N. Amer. Rept.* 1:39.
REFERENCES: 14, 29, 33, 38, 74, 86.1, 106, 122, 131, 151, 155, 162, 168, 214, 222, 223, 228, 230, 230.13, 252, 257, 269, 270, 322.2, 372.3, 372.6, 415, 439, 454.1, 464, 495.7, 511.5, 529.53, 542, 687.5, 726, 728, 753.4, 765, 768, 794, 809, 810, 858, 859, 862.5, 865, 878.5, 883, 910.2, 913, 915, 928, 933, 947, 952, 956, 968, 1042.12, 1067, 1094, 1095, 1098.
SUBSPECIES: *clarki* Baird and Girard 1853, *Cat. N. Amer. Rept.* 1:48; *confluens* Blanchard 1923, *Occ. Papers Mus. Zool. Univ. Michigan* 140:1; *pictiventris* Cope 1895, *Amer. Nat.* 29:677.
COMMENTS: Conant (230.13) discusses the history of the introduction of *Nerodia f. pictiventris* into the Brownsville area.

Nerodia harteri
Harter's Water Snake (Map 125)

Natrix harteri Trapido 1941. *Amer. Midl. Nat.* 25:673.
Nerodia harteri: Rossman and Eberle 1977. *Herpetologica* 33(1):42.
REFERENCES: 45.3, 74, 162, 205.12, 223, 224, 228, 321, 333.1, 388.2, 415, 613, 617, 623, 630, 768, 809, 810, 820.3, 822.03, 858, 873, 1018, 1021, 1025, 1048.5, 1085.1, 1094, 1095.
SUBSPECIES: *harteri; paucimaculata* Tinkle and Conant 1961, *Southwest. Nat.* 6:34.
COMMENTS: This species is currently under review for endangered species status.

Nerodia rhombifera
Diamondback Water Snake (Map 126)

Tropidonotus rhombifera Hallowell 1852. *Proc. Acad. Nat. Sci. Philadelphia* 6:177.
Nerodia rhombifera: Rossman and Eberle 1977. *Herpetologica* 33(1):42.
REFERENCES: 10, 45.3, 57, 74, 122, 139, 148.01, 151, 155, 162, 168, 195, 205.11, 222, 228, 230.1, 230.13, 230.14, 250, 252, 255, 257, 269, 270, 281, 322.2, 372.3, 380, 415, 432, 439, 454.1, 464, 483, 502, 509.22, 511.5, 529.5, 529.51, 529.53, 542, 565, 588.39, 622.12, 622.2, 622.233, 643.6, 656, 683.2, 726, 753.4, 765, 768, 770, 809, 810, 858, 862.5, 865, 869, 878.5, 910.2, 912, 913, 915, 918, 919, 928, 930, 932, 942, 944, 947, 951, 952, 956, 957, 964, 966, 967, 968, 1018, 1021, 1035, 1050.15, 1094, 1095.

SUBSPECIES: *rhombifera* (see above).

COMMENTS: Conant (230.1) is the latest taxonomic reviser of this taxon.

Nerodia sipedon
Northern Water Snake (Map 127)

Coluber sipedon Linnaeus 1758. *Syst. Nat.* 1:219.

Nerodia sipedon: Baird and Girard 1853. *Cat. N. Amer. Rept.* 1:38.

REFERENCES: 451.51.

SUBSPECIES: *pleuralis* Cope 1892, *Proc. U.S. Natl. Mus.* 14:672.

COMMENTS: Two specimens that were found five miles north of Sherman, Grayson County, are housed in the Carnegie Museum. These represent the first verification of the species in Texas.

Genus *Opheodrys* Fitzinger
Syst. Rept. 1843:26
Opheodrys aestivus
Rough Green Snake (Map 128)

Coluber aestivus Linnaeus 1766. *Syst. Nat.* 1:387.

Opheodrys aestivus: Cope 1860. *Proc. Acad. Nat. Sci. Philadelphia* 12:560.

REFERENCES: 29, 38, 74, 76, 92, 122, 132, 148.01, 162, 205.11, 223, 228, 238, 250, 257, 269, 270, 272, 281, 372.3, 372.6, 380, 391, 399, 415, 438.1, 439, 450, 451, 454.1, 485.5, 486, 487.5, 489, 490, 495, 495.05, 503, 529.2, 529.5, 529.51, 529.53, 588.22, 622.233, 622.24, 634, 642.08, 662, 683.2, 726, 753.4, 765, 768, 794, 807, 809, 810, 869, 885, 904, 912, 913, 915, 918, 922, 927, 928, 930, 932, 933, 947, 952, 956, 964, 965, 967, 968, 1042.12, 1085.2, 1094, 1095, 1098.

FOSSIL RECORDS: Denton, Foard, and Llano counties (489, 490, 495, 495.05).

SUBSPECIES: *aestivus; majalis* Baird and Girard 1853, *Cat. N. Amer. Rept.* 1:107.

COMMENTS: Grobman (438.1) is the latest taxonomic reviser of the taxon. Raun and Gehlbach (770.3) comment on erroneous locality data for this species in west and northwest Texas.

Opheodrys vernalis
Smooth Green Snake (Map 127)

Coluber vernalis Harlan 1828. *J. Acad. Nat. Sci. Philadelphia* 5:361.

Opheodrys vernalis: Schmidt and Necker 1936. *Herpetologica* 1(2):64.

REFERENCES: 29, 86.1, 228, 257, 281, 285, 287, 391, 415, 435, 437, 495.7, 602.2, 625.4, 642.06, 768, 858, 885, 1085.2, 1094, 1095, 1098.

FOSSIL RECORD: Culberson County (602.2).

SUBSPECIES: *blanchardi* Grobman 1941, *Misc. Publ. Mus. Zool. Univ. Michigan* 50:38.

COMMENTS: Worthington (1085.2) has reviewed the doubtful locality records of this species in Texas. I regard the Armstrong, Bosque, and Ellis county records as erroneous.

Genus *Pituophis* Holbrook
N. Amer. Herp. 1842, (2) 4:7
Pituophis melanoleucus
Bullsnake (Map 129)

Coluber melanoleucus Daudin 1803. *Hist. Nat. Rept.* 6:409.
Pituophis melanoleucus: Holbrook 1842. *N. Amer. Herp.* (2) 4:7.

REFERENCES: 9.16, 14, 21, 26.12, 29, 34, 38, 43.5, 74, 122, 132, 155, 162, 186, 195, 205.11, 218, 223, 227, 228, 233, 250, 252, 253, 257, 269, 270, 277.8, 281, 293.6, 305, 380, 385, 415, 451.5, 451.51, 454.1, 482.2, 483, 485.5, 487.5, 495.05, 495.7, 521, 529.5, 529.51, 529.53, 558, 562, 588.39, 613, 614.2, 622.15, 622.233, 631.2, 639, 642.06, 662, 665, 668, 683.2, 687, 692, 700, 747.12, 753.4, 765, 768, 770, 802.21, 809, 810, 811, 816.3, 819, 858, 862, 869, 883, 885, 904, 907, 912, 915, 918, 945, 947, 951, 952, 956, 967, 969, 1003.4, 1023, 1055.41, 1074, 1075, 1085.21, 1094, 1095, 1098, 1100.

FOSSIL RECORD: Bexar and Kendall counties (482.2, 495.05, 639).

SUBSPECIES: *affinis* Hallowell 1852, *Proc. Acad. Nat. Sci. Philadelphia* 6:181; *ruthveni* Stull 1929, *Occ. Papers Mus. Zool. Univ. Michigan* 205:1; *sayi* Schlegel 1837, *Essai Physion. Serp.* 2:157.

COMMENTS: S. S. Sweet (personal communication) suggests that there are three distinct species of *Pituophis*. I retain the Texas taxa of *Pituophis* as subspecies until Sweet's work is published.

Genus *Regina* Baird and Girard
Cat. N. Amer. Rept. 1853, 1:45
Regina grahami
Graham's Crayfish Snake (Map 130)

Regina grahami Baird and Girard 1853. *Cat. N. Amer. Rept.* 1:47.

REFERENCES: 33, 38, 151, 162, 222, 223, 228, 255, 257, 269, 270, 276, 281, 372.3, 372.6, 415, 439, 451.5, 451.51, 542, 545.61, 565, 573.1, 588.4, 613, 622.233, 643.6, 753.4, 761, 768, 788, 809, 810, 858, 865, 910.2, 912, 915, 928, 929, 947, 965, 967, 968, 1021, 1042.12, 1094, 1095, 1098.

COMMENTS: The isolated geographic records from Bexar, Dimmit, Frio, Garza, Haskell, Hemphill, Runnels, Sterling, and Taylor counties represent verified specimens of Graham's Crayfish Snake.

Regina rigida
Glossy Crayfish Snake (Map 129)

Coluber rigidus Say 1825. *J. Acad. Nat. Sci. Philadelphia* (1) 4:239.
Regina rigida: Rossman 1963. *Occ. Papers Mus. Zool. Louisiana St. Univ.* 29:20.
REFERENCES: 14, 161, 162, 228, 277, 439, 504, 529.5, 599, 726, 753.4, 768, 788, 809, 865, 873, 929, 947, 1094, 1095.
SUBSPECIES: *sinicola* Huheey 1959, *Copeia* 1959 (4):305.
COMMENTS: The majority of the isolated museum records for *R. rigida* have been verified as belonging to that species.

Genus *Rhinocheilus* Baird and Girard
Cat. N. Amer. Rept. 1853, 1:120
Rhinocheilus lecontei
Longnose Snake (Map 131)

Rhinocheilus lecontei Baird and Girard 1853. *Cat. N. Amer. Rept.* 1:120.
REFERENCES: 26.12, 29, 38, 74, 132, 151, 155, 162, 218, 228, 235, 250, 255, 257, 271, 281, 297, 332.01, 359.2, 451.5, 451.51, 454.1, 458.2, 482.2, 495.04, 495.05, 521, 529.5, 529.52, 529.53, 557, 575, 613, 616.2, 628, 631.2, 634, 642.06, 643.5, 662, 665, 683.2, 700, 753.4, 768, 809, 810, 811, 816.3, 858, 869, 883, 885, 912, 915, 918, 947, 951, 952, 956, 965, 967, 1017.2, 1023, 1055.41, 1070, 1085.21, 1094, 1095, 1098.
FOSSIL RECORD: Culberson, Kendall, and Lubbock counties (458.2, 482.2, 495.04, 495.05).
SUBSPECIES: *tessellatus* Garman 1883, *Mem. Mus. Comp. Zool.* 8:74.
COMMENTS: Medica (643.5, 643.51) is the most recent reviser of this taxon.

Genus *Salvadora* Baird and Girard
Cat. N. Amer. Rept. 1853, 1:104
Salvadora deserticola
Big Bend Patchnose Snake (Map 132)

Salvadora hexalepis deserticola Schmidt 1940. *Field Mus. Nat. Hist., Zool. Ser.* 24:146.

Salvadora deserticola: Bogert and Degenhardt 1961. *Amer. Mus. Novitates* 2064:13.

REFERENCES: 21, 74, 115, 116, 162, 296.3, 323.21, 415, 521, 529.53, 615, 642.06, 665, 683.2, 725, 768, 802.21, 808, 809, 810, 811, 858, 869, 871, 883, 885, 1055.41, 1085.21, 1094, 1095, 1100.

COMMENTS: This taxon and the Mountain Patchnose Snake are currently under study by C. M. Bogert (personal communication).

Salvadora grahamiae
Mountain Patchnose Snake (Map 133)

Salvadora grahamiae Baird and Girard 1853. *Cat. N. Amer. Rept.* 1:104.

REFERENCES: 6, 21, 26.12, 45.3, 74, 76, 92, 114, 115, 131, 148.01, 151, 155, 162, 172.5, 205.11, 223, 224, 228, 257, 281, 323.21, 415, 454.1, 462, 521, 529.51, 529.52, 529.53, 588.22, 588.3, 602.2, 615, 622.22, 642.06, 662, 683.12, 687, 759, 765, 768, 770, 808, 809, 810, 811, 816.53, 834, 858, 869, 871, 880, 883, 885, 907, 908, 913, 915, 930, 947, 956, 964, 966, 967, 1055.41, 1085.21, 1094, 1095.

FOSSIL RECORD: Culberson County (602.2).

SUBSPECIES: *grahamiae; lineata* Schmidt 1940, *Field Mus. Nat. Hist., Zool. Ser.* 24:148.

Genus *Sonora* Baird and Girard
Cat. N. Amer. Rept 1853, 1:117
Sonora semiannulata
Ground Snake (Map 134)

Sonora semiannulata Baird and Girard 1853. *Cat. N. Amer. Rept.* 1:117.

REFERENCES: 21, 26.12, 29, 74, 132, 148.01, 151, 155, 162, 186, 220, 223, 228, 236, 245, 250, 252, 253, 257, 269, 270, 277.8, 380, 384.4, 389, 393.03, 393.05, 395.2, 415, 434, 454.1, 482.4, 483, 511.2, 521, 529.51, 529.53, 530, 573.3, 576.03, 615, 622.16, 622.233, 624, 642.06, 648, 662, 665, 682.2, 688, 695, 725, 753.4, 768, 790, 802.11, 809, 810, 811, 816.3, 816.7, 858, 865, 869, 871, 883, 885, 905, 906, 909, 922, 936, 951, 952, 957, 965, 967, 1045.11, 1055.1, 1055.41, 1085.21, 1094, 1095, 1098.

SUBSPECIES: *taylori* Boulenger 1894, *Cat. Snakes Brit. Mus.* 2:265.

COMMENTS: Frost and Van Devender (384.4) are the latest revisers of this species. *Sonora s. taylori* is primarily restricted to the Tamaulipan biotic province and prairies to the northeast (Austin, Bastrop, Brazos, Freestone, Harris, Robertson, and Wilson counties).

Genus *Storeria* Baird and Girard
Cat. N. Amer. Rept. 1853, 1:135
Storeria dekayi
Brown Snake (Map 135)

Tropidonotus dekayi Holbrook 1842. *N. Amer. Herp.* (2) 4:53.
Storeria dekayi: Baird and Girard 1853. *Cat. N. Amer. Rept.* 1:135.
REFERENCES: 7, 29, 38, 45.3, 74, 122, 131, 148.01, 162, 178.2, 223, 228, 257, 269, 270, 275, 281, 372.3, 372.6, 380, 391, 415, 439, 450, 451.5, 451.51, 454.1, 463, 464, 483, 485.5, 489, 495.05, 495.7, 509.2, 509.5, 529.5, 529.53, 588.39, 603, 622.24, 630, 642.08, 726, 753.4, 765, 768, 793.5, 794, 809, 852, 853, 855, 858, 865, 869, 871, 927, 930, 947, 956, 957, 967, 968, 1021, 1027, 1042.3, 1094, 1095, 1098.
SUBSPECIES: *limnetes* Anderson 1961, *Amer. Midl. Nat.* 66:246; *texana* Trapido 1944, *Amer. Midl. Nat.* 31:63.
FOSSIL RECORD: Foard County (489, 495.05).
COMMENTS: Isolated museum records from Crosby and Lubbock counties may represent accidental introductions.

Storeria occipitomaculata
Redbelly Snake (Map 127)

Coluber occipito-maculatus Storer 1839. *Rept. Mass.* 1839:230.
Storeria occipitomaculata: Cope 1900. *Ann. Rept. U.S. Natl. Mus.* 1900: 1003.
REFERENCES: 295, 603, 614, 753.4, 768, 788.2, 858, 885, 963, 1027, 1094, 1095.
SUBSPECIES: *obscura* Trapido 1944, *Amer. Midl. Nat.* 31:33.
COMMENTS: Species has not been found west of the Trinity River.

Genus *Tantilla* Baird and Girard
Cat. N. Amer. Rept. 1853, 1:131
Tantilla atriceps
Mexican Blackhead Snake (Map 64)

Homalocranium atriceps Gunther 1895. *Biol. Centr. Amer., Rept. Batr.* 1895:146.
Tantilla atriceps: do Amaral 1929. *Mem. Inst. Butantan* 4:219.
REFERENCES: 223.2, 809, 840 (perhaps 529.51, 643.6).
COMMENTS: Prior to Cole and Hardy's review (223.2) of *T. atriceps* and *T. hobartsmithi*, most literature references for *T. atriceps* were combined with those for *T. hobartsmithi*. Appropriate references are listed with the latter species; those pertaining to *T. atriceps* are listed above.

Tantilla gracilis
Flathead Snake (Map 136)

Tantilla gracilis Baird and Girard 1853. *Cat. N. Amer. Rept.* 1:132.

REFERENCES: 29, 38, 43, 92, 112, 151, 162, 190, 220.11, 220.12, 223.2, 228, 250, 252, 257, 269, 270, 281, 295, 389, 395.2, 415, 451.51, 454.1, 483, 511.2, 529.51, 529.53, 548, 587.5, 613, 622.233, 683.2, 725, 726, 753.4, 765, 768, 802.1, 809, 810, 858, 865, 874, 907, 912, 915, 918, 920, 927, 928, 929, 936, 944, 947, 952, 956, 957, 964, 967, 968, 985, 991, 1021, 1055.1, 1094, 1095, 1098.

COMMENTS: Isolated museum records of this species from Brewster, Hale, Kent, Lamb, and Randall counties are questionable.

Tantilla hobartsmithi
Southwestern Blackhead Snake (Map 137)

Tantilla hobartsmithi Taylor 1937. *Trans. Kansas Acad. Sci.* 39:340.

REFERENCES: 21, 74, 112, 162, 223.2, 228, 290.2, 292, 332.02, 495.7, 521, 529.51, 622.233, 642.06, 643.6, 662, 665, 683.2, 683.21, 700, 768, 809, 811, 840, 858, 883, 885, 981, 1055.41, 1085.21, 1094, 1095.

COMMENTS: See Cole and Hardy (223.2) for the taxonomy of this species.

Tantilla nigriceps
Plains Blackhead Snake (Map 138)

Tantilla nigriceps Kennicott 1860. *Proc. Acad. Nat. Sci. Philadelphia* 12:328.

REFERENCES: 74, 112, 134, 151, 155, 162, 166, 190, 220.12, 223, 223.2, 228, 237, 250, 252, 257, 281, 380, 389, 415, 451.5, 451.51, 488, 511.2, 529.51, 544, 613, 631.2, 642.06, 683.2, 714, 753.4, 768, 809, 810, 816.3, 833, 840, 858, 869, 871, 883, 885, 909, 967, 1045.11, 1045.21, 1094, 1095.

SUBSPECIES: *nigriceps; fumiceps* Cope 1860, *Proc. Acad. Nat. Sci. Philadelphia* 12:371.

COMMENTS: The McLennan County record is based on a specimen housed in the Field Museum of Natural History. This specimen could not be located for verification.

Tantilla rubra
Big Bend Blackhead Snake (Map 132)

Tantilla rubra Cope 1876. *J. Acad. Nat. Sci. Philadelphia* (2) 8:144.

REFERENCES: 290.2, 292, 332,2, 382, 482.5, 615, 665, 683.2, 736.1, 768, 869, 885, 1055.41.

SUBSPECIES: *cucullata* Minton 1956, *Field Zool.* 34:449; *diabola* Fouquette and Potter 1961, *Copeia* 1961(2):144.

COMMENTS: Degenhardt, Brown, and Esterla (290.2) have commented on the taxonomic status of the Texas populations of *T. rubra*.

Genus *Thamnophis* Fitzinger
Syst. Rept. 1843:26
Thamnophis cyrtopsis
Blackneck Garter Snake (Map 139)

Eutaenia cyrtopsis Kennicott 1860. *Proc. Acad. Nat. Sci. Philadelphia* 12:133.
Thamnophis cyrtopsis: Cope 1892. *Proc. U.S. Natl. Mus.* 14:656.

REFERENCES: 21, 29, 45.3, 74, 151, 155, 162, 223, 228, 245, 257, 371, 378, 394, 394.4, 415, 451.5, 451.51, 454.1, 517, 521, 529.53, 577, 613, 616.2, 642.06, 647, 648, 662, 665, 683.2, 687, 700, 768, 775.1, 791, 809, 810, 811, 841, 852, 858, 869, 883, 885, 904.7, 912, 915, 918, 919, 957, 967, 985.5, 1055.41, 1061, 1061.12, 1085.21, 1094, 1095, 1098.

SUBSPECIES: *cyrtopsis; ocellata* Cope 1880, *Bull. U.S. Natl. Mus.* 17:22.

COMMENTS: Museum record for Cameron County is incorrect. The McLennan County record (770.3) is probable.

Thamnophis marcianus
Checkered Garter Snake (Map 140)

Eutaenia marciana Baird and Girard 1853. *Cat. N. Amer. Rept.* 1:36.
Thamnophis marcianus: Ruthven 1908, *Bull. U.S. Natl. Mus.* 61:849.

REFERENCES: 21, 29, 33, 38, 39, 45.3, 57, 74, 76, 92, 131, 148.01, 151, 155, 162, 223, 228, 250, 252, 253, 257, 281, 378, 380, 389, 394.4, 398, 415, 450, 451.5, 451.51, 454.1, 483, 485.5, 491, 493, 495.05, 529.51, 577, 613, 622.233, 624, 631.2, 642.06, 643.71, 665, 672, 683.2, 700, 726, 765, 768, 770, 788.11, 790, 791, 809, 810, 811, 816.3, 819, 858, 865, 869, 883, 885, 912, 913, 915, 918, 919, 922, 930, 931, 945, 947, 951, 952, 956, 966, 967, 1018, 1045.11, 1055.41, 1067, 1085.21, 1094, 1095, 1098.

FOSSIL RECORD: Hardeman and Knox Counties (491, 493, 495.05), but these records may represent *T. radix*.

SUBSPECIES: *marcianus* (see above).

Thamnophis proximus
Western Ribbon Snake (Map 141)

Coluber proximus Say 1823. In *Long's Exped. Rocky Mts.* 1:339.
Thamnophis proximus: Strecker 1909. *Baylor Univ. Bull.* 12:8.
REFERENCES: 29, 33, 38, 45.3, 74, 76, 92, 122, 139.01, 148.01, 151, 155, 162, 197, 220.14, 220.15, 220.2, 228, 230.14, 252, 253, 257, 269, 270, 281, 330.91, 372.3, 372.6, 378, 380, 391, 391.8, 393, 410, 431, 439, 454.1, 464, 482.2, 485.5, 490, 491, 495, 495.04, 495.05, 506, 529.53, 542, 565, 588.39, 613, 622.233, 642.06, 653.2, 687.5, 700, 721, 726, 753.4, 765, 768, 770, 786, 786.3, 787, 788.1, 791, 809, 810, 816.12, 858, 865, 869, 883, 885, 907, 912, 913, 915, 918, 922, 927, 928, 930, 932, 938, 944, 947, 951, 952, 956, 957, 964, 966, 967, 968, 1042.12, 1063.1, 1094, 1095, 1098.
FOSSIL RECORD: Denton, Foard, Hardeman, Kendall, Llano, and Lubbock counties (482.2, 490, 491, 495, 495.04, 495.05, 721).
SUBSPECIES: *proximus, diabolicus, orarius,* and *rubrilineatus* Rossman 1963, *Bull. Florida St. Mus.* 7:132–35.
COMMENTS: Subspecies boundaries are difficult to ascertain for this species.

Thamnophis radix
Plains Garter Snake (Map 142)

Eutaenia radix Baird and Girard 1853. *Cat. N. Amer. Rept.* 1:34.
Thamnophis radix: Jordan 1899. *Man, Vert. Animals, U.S.* 1899:193.
REFERENCES: 228, 380, 768, 809, 883, 885, 1021, 1098.
SUBSPECIES: *haydeni* Kennicott 1860, *Expl. Surv. R.R. Miss. Pacific* 12:198.
COMMENTS: This species remains one of the rarest garter snakes in Texas.

Thamnophis sirtalis
Common Garter Snake (Map 143)

Coluber sirtalis Linnaeus 1758. *Syst. Nat.* 1:222.
Thamnophis sirtalis: Garman 1892. *Bull. Essex Inst.* 24:104.
REFERENCES: 26.12, 38, 74, 92, 151, 154, 155, 162, 175, 228, 230.14, 230.15, 257, 269, 270, 368.2, 370, 378, 380, 391, 439, 449, 454.1, 482.2, 489, 495.05, 495.7, 529.53, 588.22, 588.3, 613, 622.232, 634, 642.08, 662, 683.2, 725, 725.4, 753.4, 768, 791, 809, 839, 854, 858, 869, 883, 885, 904, 912, 913, 915, 918, 928, 956, 1042.12, 1045.11, 1061, 1067, 1094, 1095, 1098.
FOSSIL RECORD: Foard and Kendall counties (482.2, 489, 495.05).

SUBSPECIES: *sirtalis; annectens* Brown 1950, *Checklist Rept. Amphib. Texas* 1950:203; *dorsalis?* Baird and Girard 1853, *Cat. N. Amer. Rept.* 1:32; *parietalis?* Say 1823, in *Long's Exped. Rocky Mts.* 1:186.

COMMENTS: There is considerable confusion over the taxonomic boundaries of the above subspecies in Texas. The status of the taxa *dorsalis* and *parietalis* in Texas is unknown.

Genus *Trimorphodon* Cope
Proc. Acad. Nat. Sci. Philadelphia 1861, 13:297.
Trimorphodon biscutatus
Lyre Snake (Map 132)

Dipsas biscutata Dumeril, Bibron, and Dumeril 1854. *Erpetol. Gen.* 7:1153.

Trimorphodon biscutatus: Cope 1861. *Proc. Acad. Nat. Sci. Philadelphia* 13:297.

REFERENCES: 9.16, 26.12, 54.7, 74, 162, 260, 290.2, 292, 293, 332.2, 393.04, 415, 495.7, 521, 556, 602.2, 665, 683.2, 699.4, 768, 809, 810, 837, 858, 869, 885, 994, 1055.41, 1085.21, 1094, 1095.

FOSSIL RECORD: Culberson County (602.2).

SUBSPECIES: *vilkinsoni* Cope 1886, *Proc. Amer. Philos. Soc.* 23:285.

COMMENTS: Although Gehlbach (393.04) placed *T. vilkinsoni* as a subspecies of *T. biscutatus,* there is recent evidence that suggests that the former may be a distinct species.

Genus *Tropidoclonion* Cope
Proc. Acad. Nat. Sci. Philadelphia 1860, 12:76
Tropidoclonion lineatum
Lined Snake (Map 144)

Microps lineatum Hallowell 1856. *Proc. Acad. Nat. Sci. Philadelphia* 8:241

Tropidoclonion lineatum: Cope 1860. *Proc. Acad. Nat. Sci. Philadelphia* 12:76.

REFERENCES: 29, 59.6, 122, 151, 162, 228, 230.15, 252, 253, 257, 257.5, 269, 270, 281, 327, 330.91, 384.25, 415, 454, 454.1, 474, 480, 483, 493, 495.05, 529.5, 643.6, 683.2, 714, 753.4, 754, 755, 760, 768, 809, 810, 816.3, 820.3, 858, 878, 885, 912, 915, 929, 940, 942, 947, 952, 956, 1021, 1042.12, 1050.13, 1082.2, 1094, 1095, 1098.

FOSSIL RECORD: Knox County (493, 495.05).

SUBSPECIES: *annectens, texanum* Ramsey 1953, *Herpetologica* 9(1): 12–14; *mertensi* Smith 1965, *J. Ohio. Herp. Soc.* 5(1):3.

Genus *Virginia* Baird and Girard
Cat. N. Amer. Rept. 1853, 1:127
Virginia striatula
Rough Earth Snake (Map 145)

Coluber striatulus Linnaeus 1766. *Syst. Nat.* 1:375.
Virginia striatula: Garman 1883. *Mem. Mus. Comp. Zool.* 8:97.
REFERENCES: 74, 92, 109, 110, 122, 131, 132, 148.01, 151, 162, 219, 220.14, 220.15, 220.2, 228, 252, 255, 257, 269, 270, 281, 389, 391, 395.2, 415, 439, 454.1, 464, 490, 495.05, 495.7, 511.2, 529.51, 529.53, 588.39, 642.08, 663, 726, 753.4, 765, 768, 794, 807, 809, 810, 819, 858, 865, 912, 913, 915, 928, 932, 933, 938, 939, 947, 956, 967, 968, 985.5, 1003.41, 1045, 1055.1, 1094, 1095, 1098.
FOSSIL RECORD: Denton County (490, 495.05).
COMMENTS: Isolated museum records from El Paso, King, and Lubbock counties may represent introductions via potted plant shipments.

Virginia valeriae
Smooth Earth Snake (Map 146)

Virginia valeriae Baird and Girard 1853. *Cat. N. Amer. Rept.* 1:127.
REFERENCES: 74, 109, 110, 132, 148.01, 151, 162, 228, 252, 255, 257, 415, 454.1, 622.233, 768, 807, 809, 810, 858, 918, 933, 956, 967, 1094, 1095.
SUBSPECIES: *elegans* Kennicott 1859, *Proc. Acad. Nat. Sci. Philadelphia* 11:99.
COMMENTS: Distributional records of this species continue to defy my ability to recognize a geographic pattern.

Family Elapidae
Genus *Micrurus* Wagler
in Spix, *Serp. Brasil* 1824:48.
Micrurus fulvius
Coral Snake (Map 147)

Coluber fulvius Linnaeus 1766. *Syst. Nat.* 1:381.
Micrurus fulvius: Stejneger and Barbour 1917. *Check List N. Amer. Amphib. Rept.* 1917:106.
REFERENCES: 14, 29, 33, 38, 61, 74, 92, 134, 148.01, 151, 155, 162, 204.31, 220, 223, 228, 234, 250, 257, 261.1, 262, 264, 265, 269, 270, 275, 281, 282.2, 314, 319.1, 353, 377, 393.03, 393.05, 413, 415, 439, 451.5, 451.51, 454.1, 463, 474, 482.2, 485.5, 487.5, 495.05, 495.7, 529.51, 588.45, 665, 666, 683.2, 726, 753.11, 753.4, 765, 768, 789, 789.1, 790,

790.5, 794, 807, 809, 810, 858, 869, 871, 889, 912, 913, 915, 918, 928, 930, 939, 947, 952, 956, 957, 964, 966, 967, 1032, 1032.22, 1067, 1068, 1069, 1087, 1094, 1095, 1098.

FOSSIL RECORDS: Kendall County (482.2, 494.05).

SUBSPECIES: *tenere* Baird and Girard 1853, *Cat. N. Amer. Rept.* 1:22.

COMMENTS: Raun and Gehlbach (770.3) suggest that Brown's (155) Reeves County record is erroneous, but recent records of the species from Pecos County indicate its possible occurrence in Reeves County. The El Paso County record of *Micruroides euryxanthus* (162) is erroneous, but is cited in recent literature (789.1).

Family Viperidae
Genus *Agkistrodon* Beauvois
Trans. Amer. Philos. Soc. 1799, 4:381
Agkistrodon contortrix
Copperhead (Map 148)

Boa contortrix Linnaeus 1766. *Syst. Nat.* 1:373.
Agkistrodon contortrix: Baird 1854. *Serp. New York* 1854:13.

REFERENCES: 21, 29, 33, 38, 45.3, 74, 122, 134, 148.01, 151, 155, 162, 165, 215, 223, 228, 230.15, 237, 262, 264, 265, 269, 270, 281, 282.2, 283, 300.1, 301, 314, 315, 319.1, 332, 353, 366, 372.3, 372.6, 374, 392, 415, 418.1, 419, 421, 422, 431, 439, 449, 454.1, 464, 477, 482.2, 482.3, 483, 491, 495.05, 495.7, 517, 527, 529.2, 596, 622.233, 625.2, 644.12, 655, 656, 662, 665, 666, 683.2, 714, 725, 726, 753.4, 765, 768, 777, 778, 790.5, 809, 810, 811, 811.2, 811.32, 858, 865, 869, 871, 875.5, 878.5, 889, 904.65, 912, 913, 915, 918, 927, 928, 930, 932, 933, 944, 946, 947, 952, 960, 964, 966, 967, 968, 1042.12, 1055.41, 1067, 1068, 1069, 1073.1, 1094, 1095.

FOSSIL RECORD: Hardeman and Kendall counties (482.2, 491, 495.05).

SUBSPECIES: *contortrix; mokeson* Daudin 1803, *Hist. Nat. Rept.* 5:358; *laticinctus* Gloyd and Conant 1934, *Occ. Papers Mus. Zool. Univ. Michigan* 283:2; *pictigaster* Gloyd and Conant 1943, *Bull. Chicago Acad. Sci.* 7:156.

COMMENTS: The subspecific boundary between the Trans-Pecos and broad-banded copperheads is not well defined. A museum record for Lubbock County with attendant field data states "on load of wood from Kerrville."

Agkistrodon piscivorus
Cottonmouth (Map 149)

Crotalus piscivorus Lacepede 1789. *Hist. Nat. Serp.* 2:130.
Agkistrodon piscivorus: Stejneger 1895. *Ann. Rep. U.S. Natl. Mus.*
1893:406.
REFERENCES: 29, 38, 45.3, 48, 74, 122, 134, 148, 148.01, 151, 162,
175, 178, 195, 223, 228, 230.13, 234, 252, 257, 262, 264, 265, 269, 270,
281, 282.2, 301, 314, 315, 372.3, 372.6, 389, 391, 415, 418.1, 422, 439,
450, 454.1, 482.2, 485.5, 490, 495.05, 495.7, 502, 529.7, 578, 666, 687.5,
726, 753.4, 757, 765, 768, 790.5, 809, 810, 811, 865, 869, 878.5, 889, 912,
913, 915, 918, 931, 932, 947, 956, 960, 966, 967, 968, 1035, 1042.12,
1068, 1069, 1094, 1095.
FOSSIL RECORD: Denton and Kendall counties (482.2, 490, 495.05).
COMMENTS: Records from Cameron and Fisher counties are erroneous. Museum records from Maverick, Sterling, and Val Verde counties are
verified, but questionable.

Genus *Crotalus* Linnaeus
Syst. Nat., 1758, 1:214
Crotalus atrox
Western Diamondback Rattlesnake (Map 150)

Crotalus atrox Baird and Girard 1853. *Cat. N. Amer. Rept.* 1:5.
REFERENCES: 1, 4.2, 14, 21, 29, 33, 38, 45.3, 59.4, 59.65, 60, 61,
74, 75, 77, 92, 134, 145, 148.01, 151, 155, 162, 205.11, 228, 233, 234,
250, 252, 253, 255, 257, 261, 261.1, 262, 263, 264, 265, 265.3, 269, 270,
281, 300.1, 301, 314, 315, 315.1, 330.9, 332.02, 359.2, 377.1, 380, 384,
389, 394, 394.4, 398, 400, 408.2, 414, 415, 416, 418, 450, 451.5, 451.51,
454.1, 459, 474, 483, 485.5, 495, 495.04, 495.05, 495.3, 495.31, 495.7,
502, 511.4, 517, 521, 545.3, 545.8, 549, 550, 551, 552, 553, 559, 564, 578,
602.2, 613, 613.2, 624, 631, 631.2, 634, 639, 642.06, 643.71, 648, 662,
665, 666, 683.2, 687, 719.1, 722.1, 722.2, 722.3, 726, 753.4, 765, 768,
770, 772, 773, 774, 775.1, 776, 777, 779, 780, 790.5, 801, 802.21, 809,
810, 811, 816.3, 819, 822, 858, 869, 871, 881, 883, 885, 887, 889, 912,
913, 915, 918, 919, 927, 930, 936, 944, 945, 947, 951, 952, 956, 960, 964,
966, 967, 1015, 1017.2, 1045.11, 1055.41, 1068, 1069, 1072, 1073, 1075,
1076.1, 1085.21, 1094, 1095, 1098.
FOSSIL RECORD: Bexar, Culberson, Llano, and Lubbock counties
(394.4, 495, 495.04, 495.05, 602.2, 639).
COMMENTS: A do Amaral record (315) for Jefferson County is
erroneous.

Crotalus horridus
Timber Rattlesnake (Map 151)

Crotalus horridus Linnaeus 1758. *Syst. Nat.* 1:214.

REFERENCES: 29, 59.65, 74, 86.1, 122, 131, 151, 162, 223.5, 228, 230.15, 257, 262, 264, 265, 269, 270, 282.2, 301, 315.1, 389, 402, 414, 415, 439, 495.7, 498.21, 529.5, 550, 564, 666, 726, 745, 768, 790.5, 809, 810, 858, 865, 889, 912, 913, 915, 928, 932, 947, 960, 967, 1068, 1069, 1094, 1095, 1098.

SUBSPECIES: *horridus; atricaudatus* Latreille 1802, in Sonnini and Latreille, *Hist. Nat. Rept.* 3:209.

COMMENTS: Despite the efforts of Pisani et al. (1972, *Trans. Kansas Acad. Sci.* 75(3):255–63) to eliminate subspecies in *C. horridus*, there is a consistent effort to continue recognition of the southern form, *atricaudatus*. Records from Eastland and Taylor counties (1068, 1069) are erroneous, and isolated museum records from Bexar and Brown counties are questionable.

Crotalus lepidus
Rock Rattlesnake (Map 152)

Caudisona lepida Kennicott 1861. *Proc. Acad. Nat. Sci. Philadelphia* 13:206.
Crotalus lepidus: Cope 1883. *Proc. Acad. Nat. Sci. Philadelphia* 35:13.

REFERENCES: 9.16, 9.23, 21, 26.12, 29, 45.3, 56.4, 74, 134, 151, 162, 215, 226, 228, 257, 261.1, 262, 264, 265, 292, 306, 314, 315.1, 323.21, 356, 377.1, 389, 412, 414, 415, 458.4, 495.7, 521, 545, 563, 564, 613, 616.2, 642.06, 648, 655, 662, 665, 666, 683.2, 700, 714, 753.13, 768, 780, 790.5, 809, 810, 811, 813, 816.7, 858, 869, 871, 883, 885, 889, 911, 947, 1045.11, 1045.3, 1046.5, 1046.51, 1055.41, 1067, 1068, 1069, 1085.21, 1094, 1095.

SUBSPECIES: *lepidus; klauberi* Gloyd 1936, *Occ. Papers Mus. Zool. Univ. Michigan* 337:4.

COMMENTS: Color change and background matching in this species has been demonstrated by Vincent (1046.5, 1046.51).

Crotalus molossus
Blacktail Rattlesnake (Map 153)

Crotalus molossus Baird and Girard 1853. *Cat. N. Amer. Rept.* 1:10.

REFERENCES: 14, 21, 29, 45.2, 45.3, 56.4, 74, 148.01, 162, 169, 204.2, 223, 228, 257, 261.1, 262, 264, 265, 281, 290.2, 301, 314, 315.1, 323.21, 332.02, 353, 377.1, 414, 415, 448, 451, 454.1, 495.7, 521, 550,

564, 602.2, 642.06, 648, 655, 662, 665, 666, 683.2, 687, 700, 746.2, 747.12, 768, 775.1, 790.5, 809, 810, 811, 822.08, 858, 869, 883, 885, 889, 947, 964, 1045.11, 1055.41, 1068, 1069, 1085.21, 1094, 1095, 1098.

FOSSIL RECORD: Culberson County (602.2).

SUBSPECIES: *molossus* (see above).

COMMENTS: An isolated museum record for Coke County is questionable.

Crotalus scutulatus
Mojave Rattlesnake (Map 132)

Caudisona scutulata Kennicott 1861. *Proc. Acad. Nat. Sci. Philadelphia* 13:207.

Crotalus scutulatus: Klauber 1930. *Trans. San Diego Soc. Nat. Hist.* 6:117.

REFERENCES: 45.3, 74, 156, 162, 228, 301, 408.2, 414, 415, 495.7, 511.4, 521, 549, 550, 564, 573.21, 622.232, 642.06, 665, 683.2, 683.21, 753.35, 768, 790.5, 809, 858, 864, 883, 885, 1055.41, 1068, 1069, 1085.21, 1094, 1095.

SUBSPECIES: *scutulatus* (see above).

Crotalus viridis
Western Rattlesnake (Map 154)

Crotalinus viridis Rafinesque 1818. *Amer. Monthly Mag.* 4:41.

Crotalus viridis: Klauber 1936. *Trans. San Diego Soc. Nat. Hist.* 8:240.

REFERENCES: 26.12, 29, 38, 39, 45.3, 74, 151, 155, 162, 223, 228, 230.15, 246, 253, 257, 261.1, 262, 264, 265, 301, 315.1, 315.11, 359.2, 377.1, 380, 414, 415, 450, 495.7, 521, 545.56, 550, 564, 573.22, 613, 622.233, 631.2, 642.06, 665, 666, 683.2, 768, 790.5, 792, 809, 810, 811.3, 816.3, 858, 868, 881, 883, 885, 889, 918, 922, 947, 951, 952, 965, 967, 1055.41, 1067, 1068, 1069, 1085.21, 1095, 1098.

SUBSPECIES: *viridis* (see above).

COMMENTS: Museum records for Bexar, Burnet, and Tarrant counties are incorrect. The systematics and evolution of this species are currently under study by H. Quinn (personal communication).

Genus *Sistrurus* Garman
Mem. Mus. Comp. Zool. 1883, 8:110
Sistrurus catenatus
Massasauga (Map 155)

Crotalinus catenatus Rafinesque 1818. *Amer. Monthly Mag.* 4:41.
Sistrurus catenatus: Garman 1883. *Mem. Mus. Comp. Zool.* 8:176.
REFERENCES: 26.12, 29, 32, 45.3, 151, 162, 228, 230.15, 253, 257, 261.1, 262, 264, 265, 282.2, 301, 314, 319.1, 391, 414, 415, 417, 434, 458.4, 495.7, 550, 564, 572, 573.24, 614, 622.232, 629.2, 631.2, 643.6, 666, 683.2, 726, 753.4, 759, 768, 790.5, 809, 810, 811.31, 858, 883, 885, 889, 897, 913, 922, 947, 965, 1050.14, 1068, 1069, 1094, 1095, 1098.
SUBSPECIES: *edwardsi* Baird and Girard 1853, *Cat. N. Amer. Rept.* 1:15; *tergeminus* Say 1823, in *Long's Exped. Rocky Mts.* 1:499.
COMMENTS: The Massasauga has a spotty distribution in Texas, and very little is known of its habitat requirements. It appears to be locally abundant near Fort Worth, but extremely rare in south Texas.

Sistrurus miliarius
Pigmy Rattlesnake (Map 156)

Crotalus miliarius Garman 1883. *Mem. Mus. Comp. Zool.* 8:177.
Sistrurus miliarius: Garman 1883, *Mem. Mus. Comp. Zool.* 8:177.
REFERENCES: 14, 33, 38, 134, 151, 228, 257, 262, 264, 265, 269, 270, 282.2, 301, 314, 319.1, 372.5, 391, 411, 414, 415, 439, 451.51, 458.4, 464, 495.7, 550, 564, 666, 714, 718.3, 753.4, 768, 790.5, 794, 809, 810, 858, 889, 913, 915, 927, 928, 932, 947, 960, 968, 977.4, 1068, 1069, 1094, 1095.
SUBSPECIES: *streckeri* Gloyd 1935, *Occ. Papers Mus. Zool. Univ. Michigan* 322.4.
COMMENTS: Museum records for Mitchell and Somervell counties are erroneous, and a McLennan County record is questionable.

Species of Uncertain Position

Salamanders. The record of *Plethodon cinereus* (O. Sanders Coll. No. 556) from Fern Lake, near Nacogdoches, Nacogdoches County, Texas, taken May 5, 1940, presents a mystery. The species has never been taken since its original discovery, and herpetologists have searched the area over a period of years. We must assume that the species is extirpated from the state or that the original record may have been a cataloging error.

5
Maps

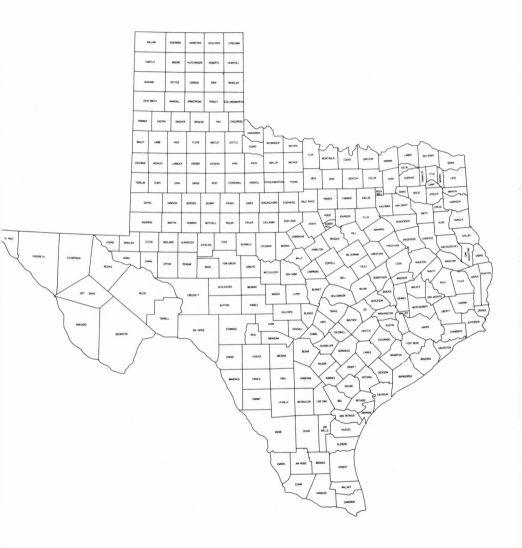

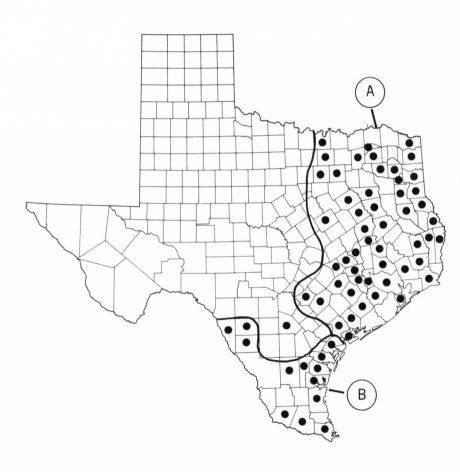

MAP 1. *Siren intermedia nettingi* (A), Western Lesser Siren. *Siren intermedia texana* (B), Rio Grande Lesser Siren.

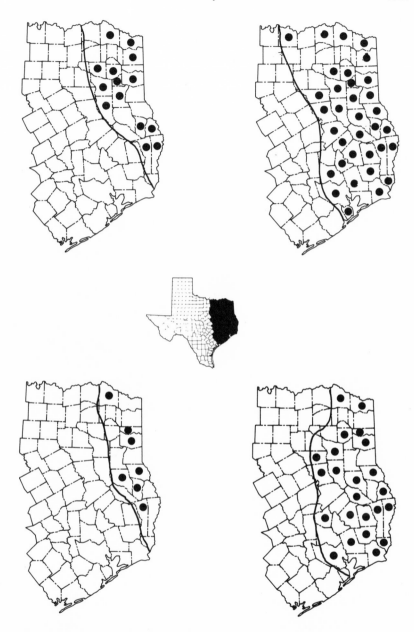

MAP 2. (*Clockwise from upper left*). *Ambystoma maculatum*, Spotted Salamander. *Ambystoma opacum*, Marbled Salamander. *Amphiuma tridactylum*,
Three-toed Amphiuma. *Ambystoma talpoideum*, Mole Salamander.

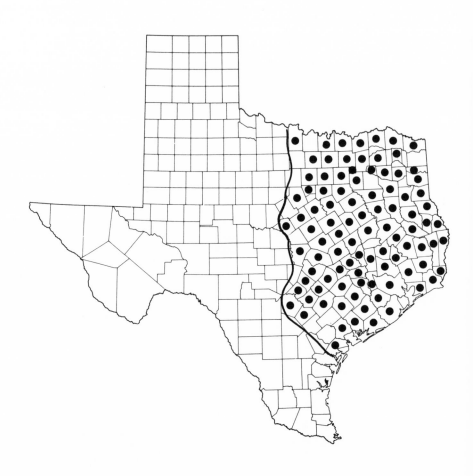

MAP 3. *Ambystoma texanum*, Smallmouth Salamander.

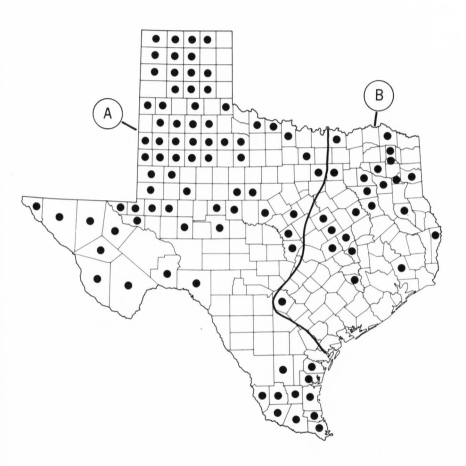

MAP 4. *Ambystoma tigrinum mavortium* (A), Barred Tiger Salamander. *Ambystoma tigrinum tigrinum* (B), Eastern Tiger Salamander.

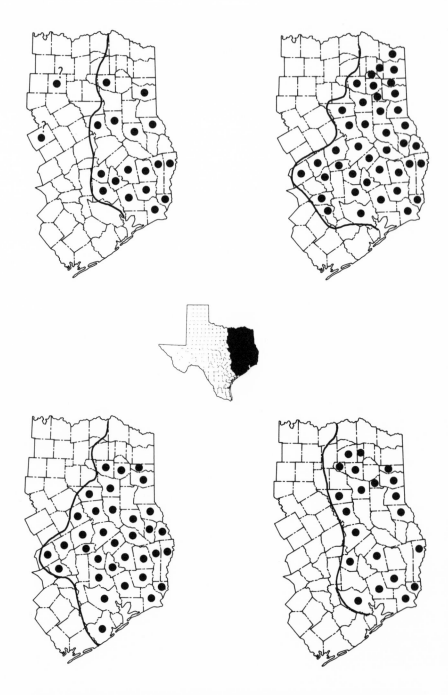

MAP 5. (*Clockwise from upper left*). *Desmognathus auriculatus*, Southern Dusky Salamander. *Eurycea quadridigitata*, Dwarf Salamander. *Macroclemys temmincki*, Alligator Snapping Turtle. *Hyla crucifer crucifer*, Northern Spring Peeper.

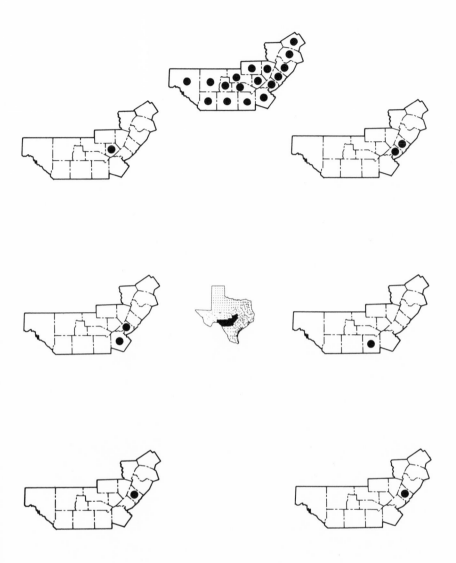

MAP 6. (*Top*) *Eurycea neotones*, Texas Salamander. (*Clockwise from upper left*) *Eurycea latitans*, Cascade Caverns Salamander. *Eurycea nana*, San Marcos Salamander. *Eurycea troglodytes*, Valdina Farms Salamander. *Typhlomolge robusta*, Blanco Blind Salamander. *Typhlomolge rathbuni*, Texas Blind Salamander. *Eurycea tridentifera*, Comal Blind Salamander.

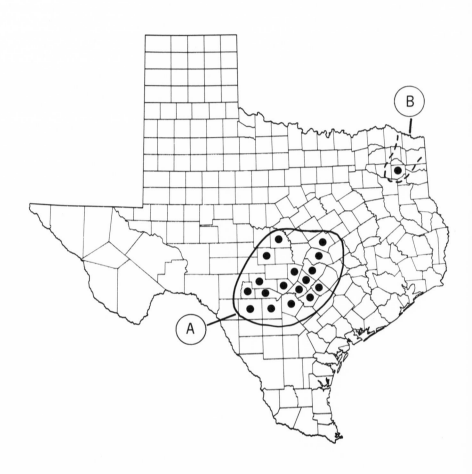

MAP 7. *Plethodon glutinosus albagula* (A), White Throat Slimy Salamander.
Plethodon glutinosus glutinosus (B), Slimy Salamander.

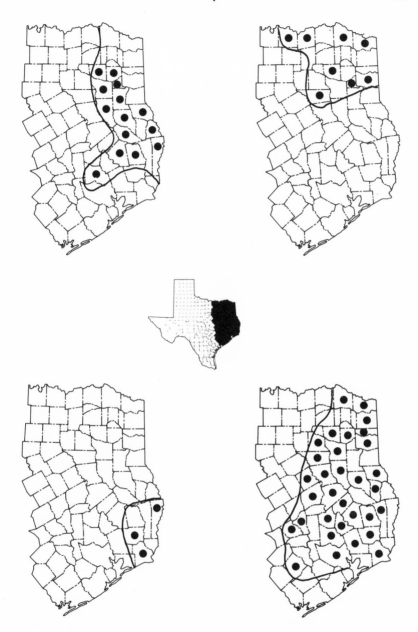

MAP 8. *(Clockwise from upper left) Necturus beyeri*, Gulf Coast Water Dog.
Bufo americanus charlesmithi, Dwarf American Toad. *Rana palustris*, Pickerel
Frog. *Rana grylio*, Pig Frog.

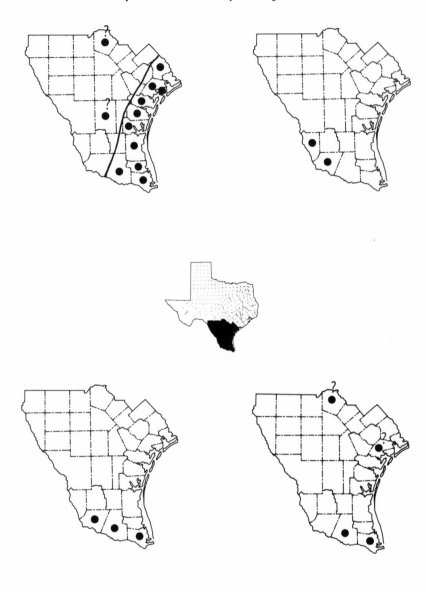

MAP 9. (*Clockwise from upper left*) *Notophthalmus meridionalis*, Black-spotted Newt. *Rhinophrynus dorsalis*, Mexican Burrowing Toad. *Smilisca baudinii*, Mexican Treefrog. *Leptodactylus fragilis*, White-lipped Frog.

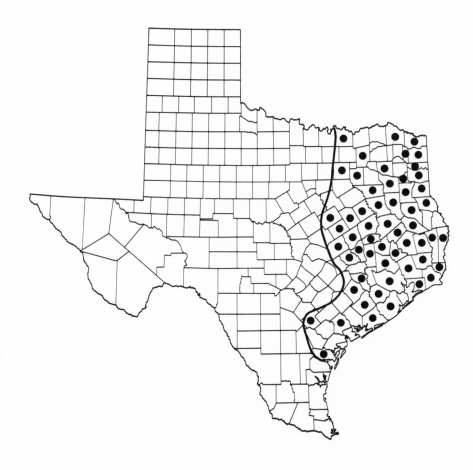

MAP 10. *Notophthalmus viridescens louisianensis,* Central Newt.

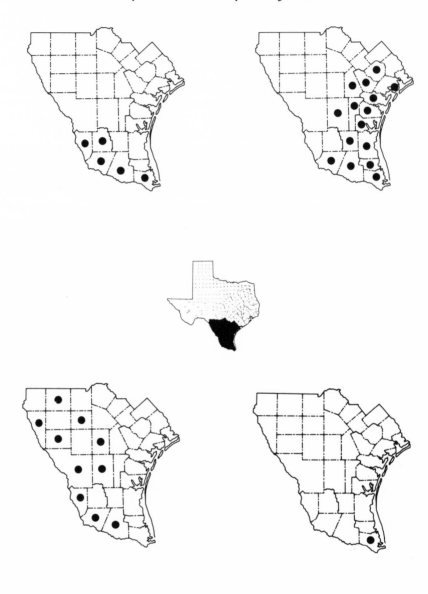

MAP 11. (*Clockwise from upper left*) *Bufo marinus*, Giant Toad. *Hypopachus variolosus*, Sheep Frog. *Ctenosaura pectinata*, Western Spiny-tailed Iguana. *Crotaphytus reticulatus*, Reticulate Collared Lizard.

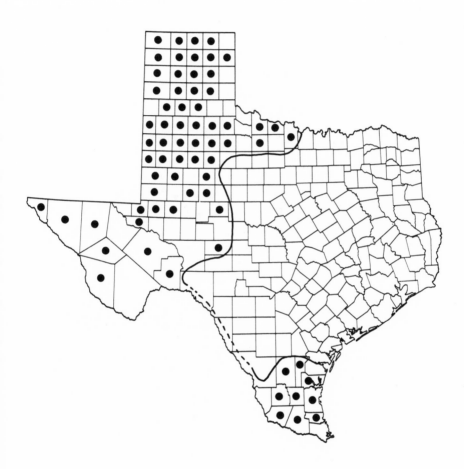

MAP 12. *Scaphiopus bombifrons*, Plains Spadefoot.

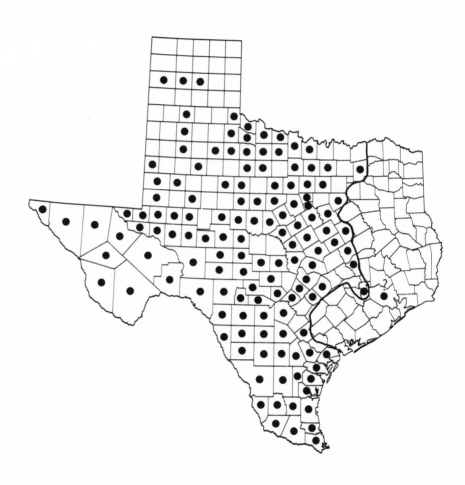

MAP 13. *Scaphiopus couchi*, Couch's Spadefoot.

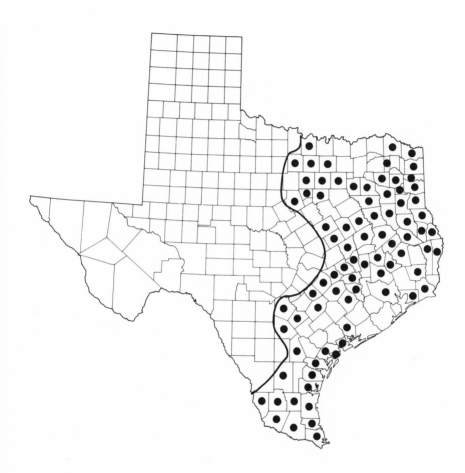

MAP 14. *Scaphiopus holbrooki hurteri,* Hurter's Spadefoot.

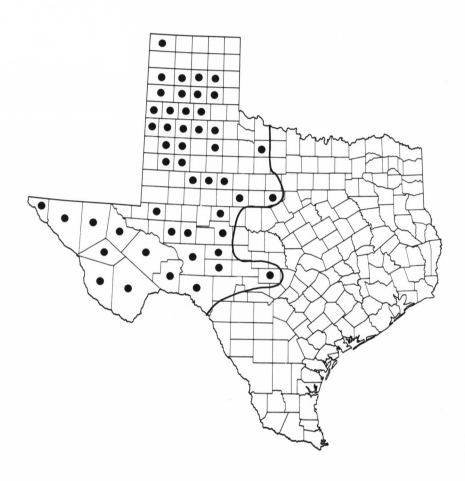

MAP 15. *Scaphiopus multiplicatus*, New Mexico Spadefoot.

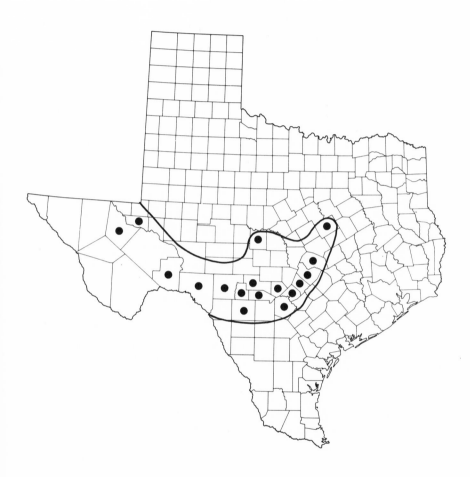

Map 16. *Hylactophryne augusti latrans*, Eastern Barking Frog.

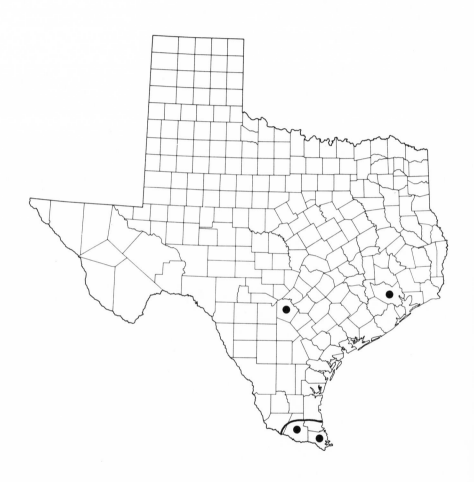

MAP 17. *Syrrhophus cystignathoides campi,* Rio Grande Chirping Frog.

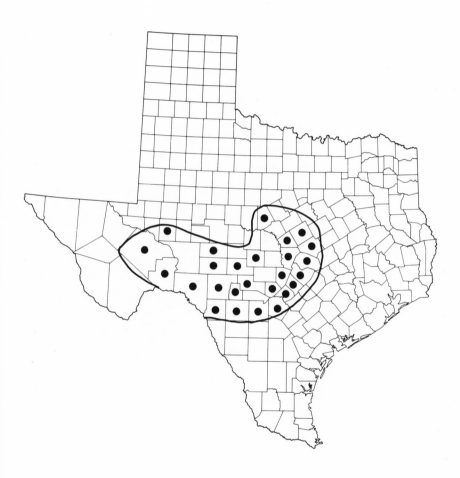

MAP 18. *Syrrhophus marnocki*, Cliff Chirping Frog.

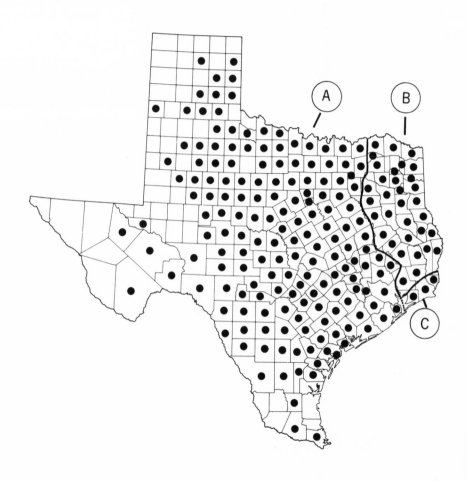

MAP 19. *Acris crepitans blanchardi* (A), Blanchard's Cricket Frog. *Acris crepitans crepitans* (B), Northern Cricket Frog. *Acris crepitans paludicola* (C), Coastal Cricket Frog.

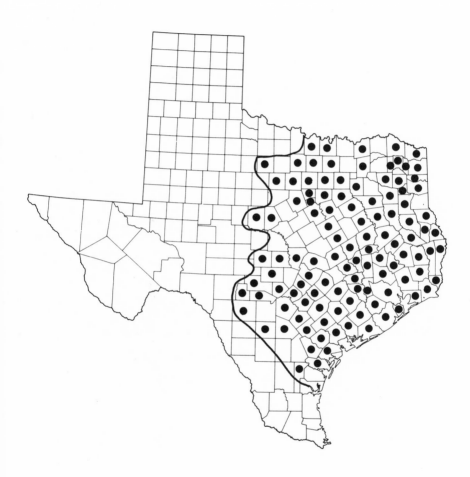

MAP 20. *Hyla chrysoscelis/versicolor*, Cope's Gray Treefrog/Gray Treefrog.

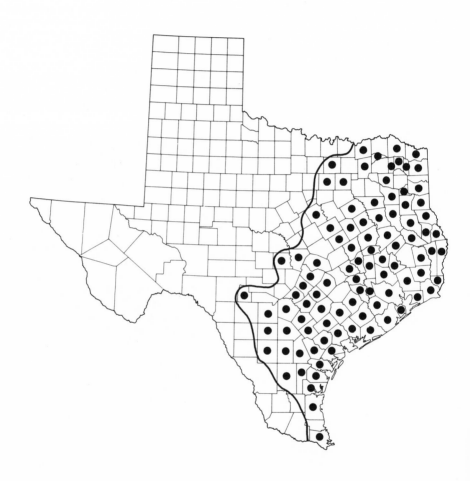

MAP 21. *Hyla cinerea*, Green Treefrog.

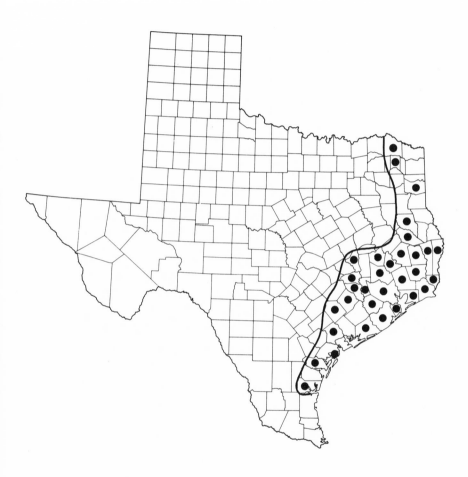

MAP 22. *Hyla squirella*, Squirrel Treefrog.

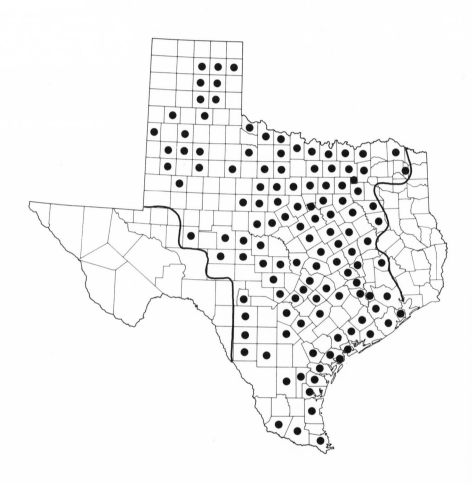

MAP 23. *Pseudacris clarki*, Spotted Chorus Frog.

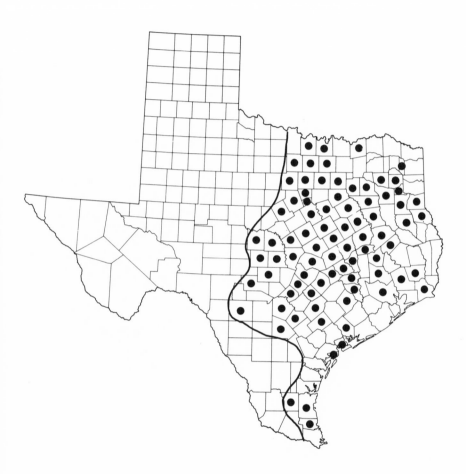

MAP 24. *Pseudacris streckeri,* Strecker's Chorus Frog.

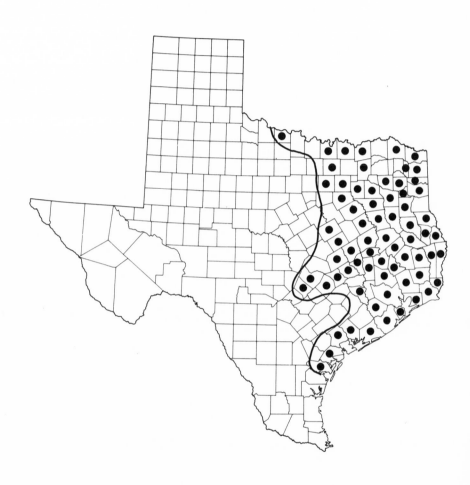

MAP 25. *Pseudacris triseriata feriarum*, Upland Chorus Frog.

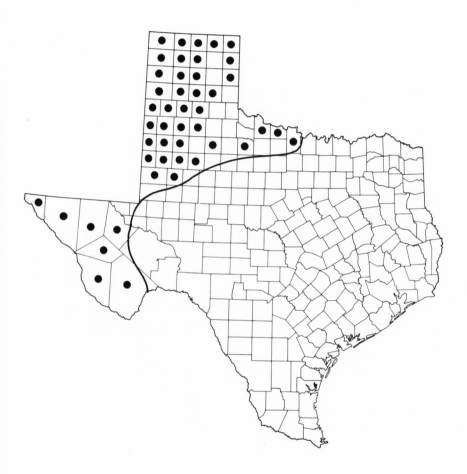

MAP 26. *Bufo cognatus*, Great Plains Toad.

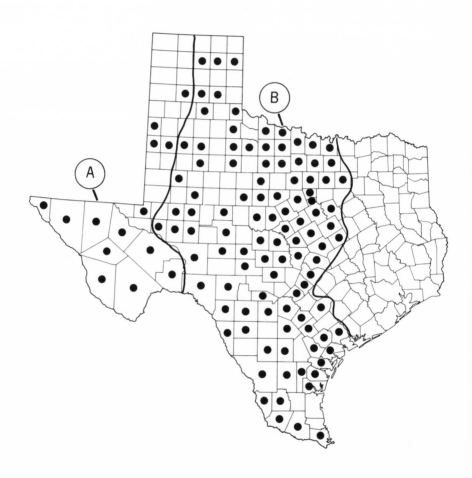

MAP 27. *Bufo debilis insidior* (A), Western Green Toad. *Bufo debilis debilis* (B), Eastern Green Toad.

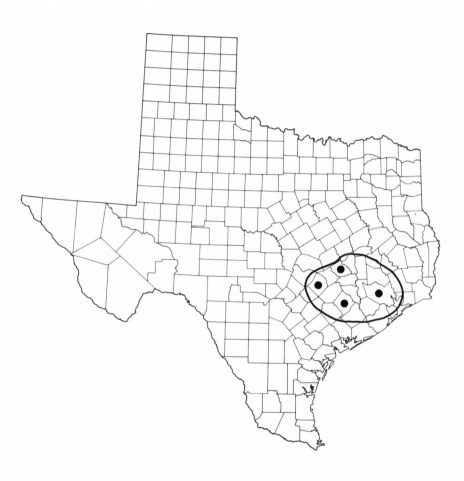

MAP 28. *Bufo houstonensis,* Houston Toad.

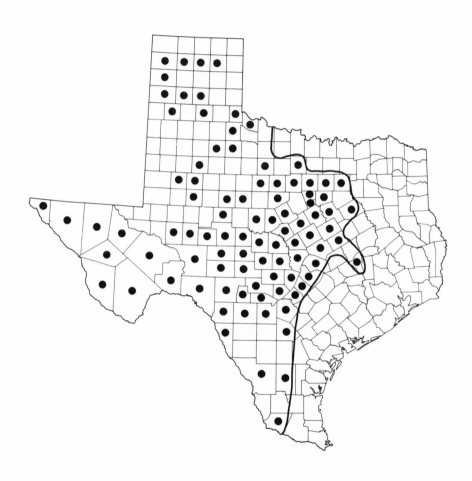

MAP 29. *Bufo punctatus*, Red-spotted Toad.

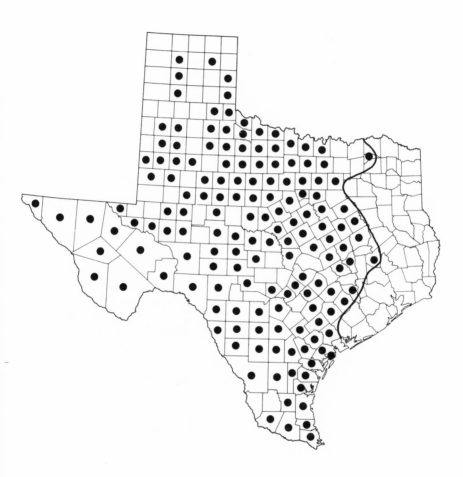

Map 30. *Bufo speciosus*, Texas Toad.

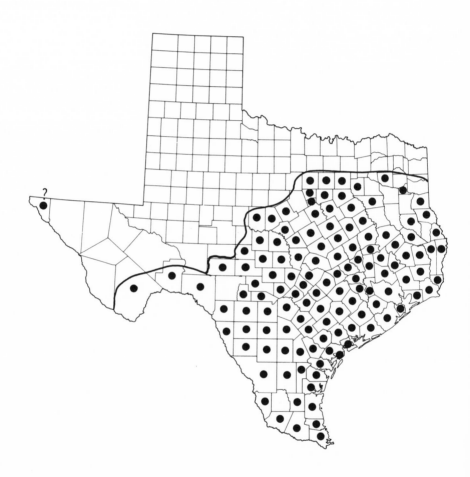

MAP 31. *Bufo valliceps valliceps*, Gulf Coast Toad.

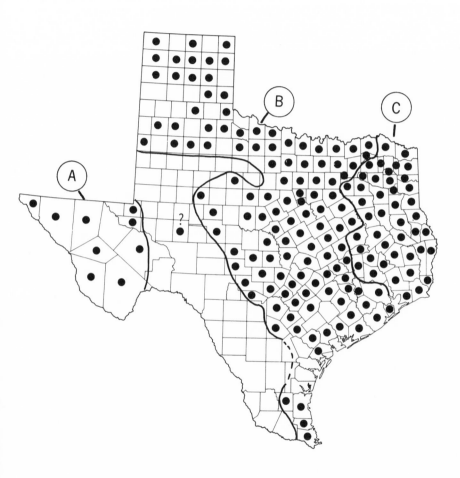

MAP 32. *Bufo woodhousei australis* (A), Southwestern Woodhouse's Toad. *Bufo woodhousei woodhousei* (B), Woodhouse's Toad. *Bufo woodhousei velatus* (C), East Texas Toad.

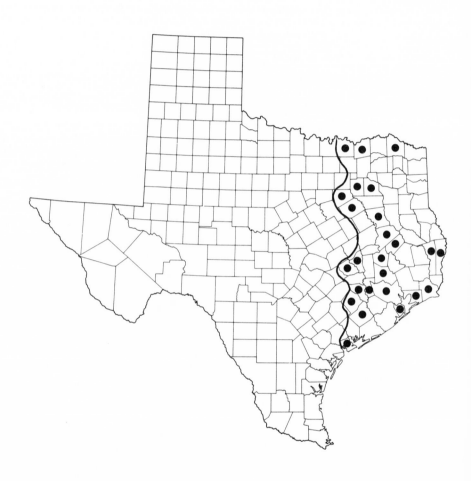

MAP 33. *Rana areolata areolata*, Southern Crawfish Frog.

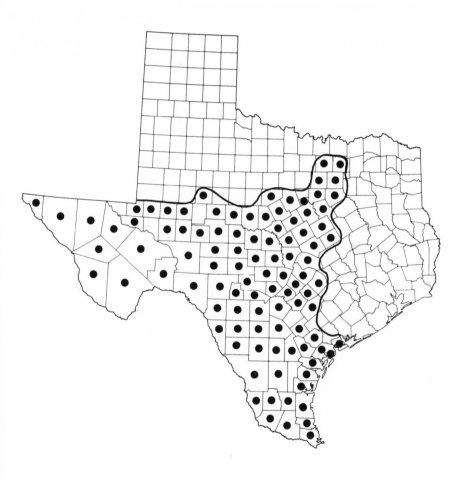

MAP 34. *Rana berlandieri*, Rio Grande Leopard Frog.

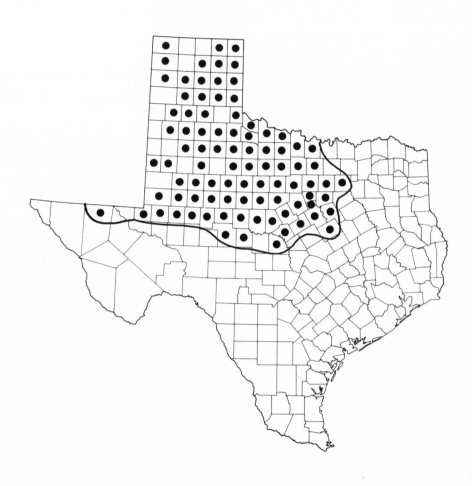

Map 35. *Rana blairi*, Plains Leopard Frog.

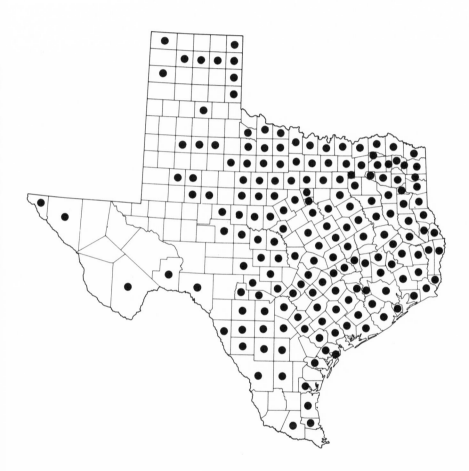

MAP 36. *Rana catesbeiana*, Bullfrog.

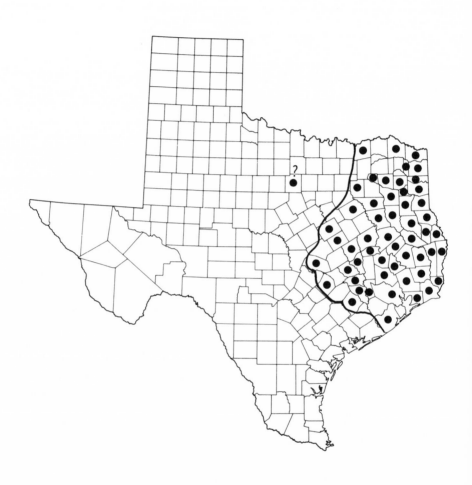

MAP 37. *Rana clamitans clamitans*, Bronze Frog.

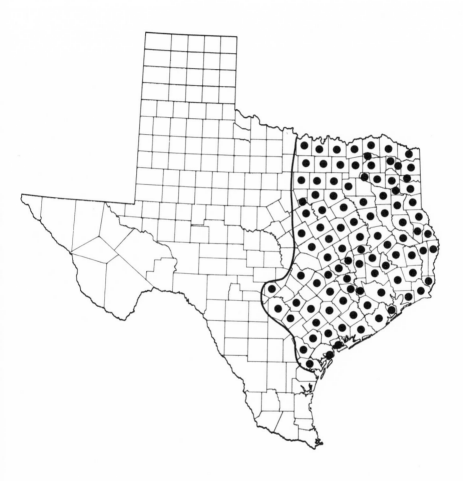

MAP 38. *Rana sphenocephala*, Southern Leopard Frog.

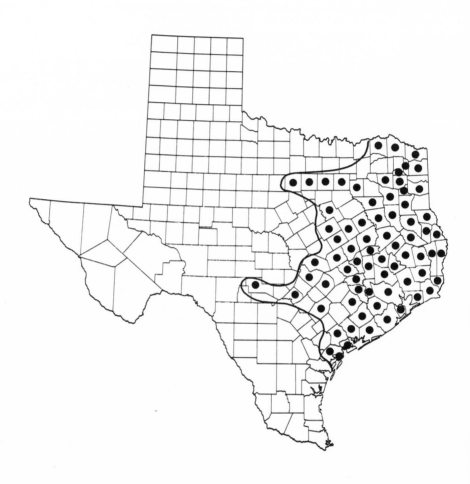

MAP 39. *Gastrophryne carolinensis*, Eastern Narrowmouth Toad.

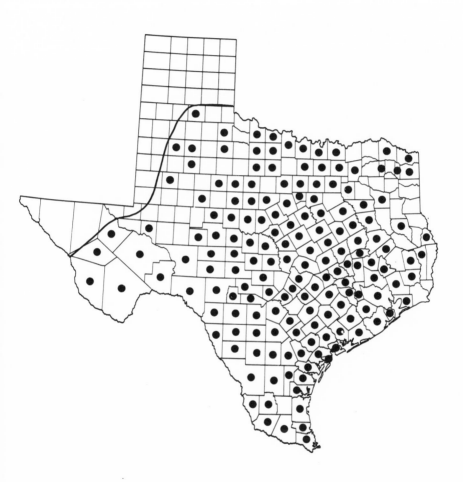

MAP 40. *Gastrophryne olivacea*, Great Plains Narrowmouth Toad.

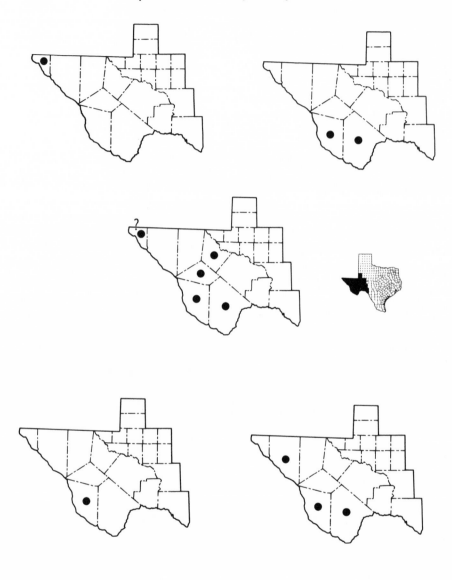

Map 41. (*Clockwise from upper left*) *Rana pipiens*, Northern Leopard Frog.
Syrrhophus guttilatus, Spotted Chirping Frog. *Trachemys gaigeae*, Big Bend
Slider. *Kinosternon hirtipes murrayi*, Big Bend Mud Turtle. (*Center*) *Hyla
arenicolor*, Canyon Treefrog.

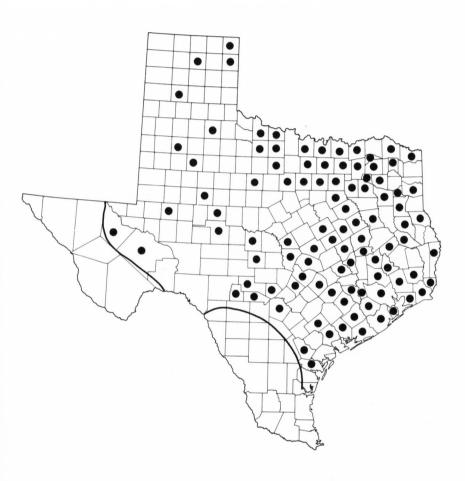

MAP 42. *Chelydra serpentina serpentina,* Common Snapping Turtle.

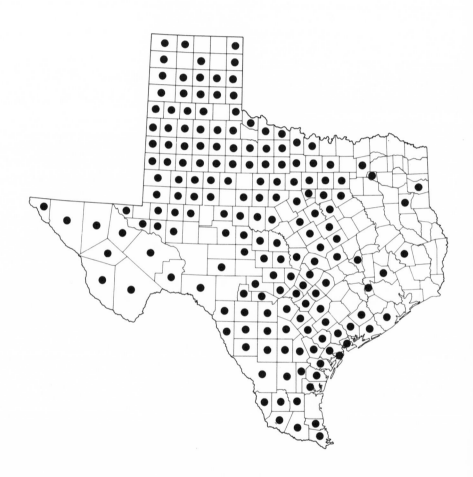

MAP 43. *Kinosternon flavescens flavescens*, Yellow Mud Turtle.

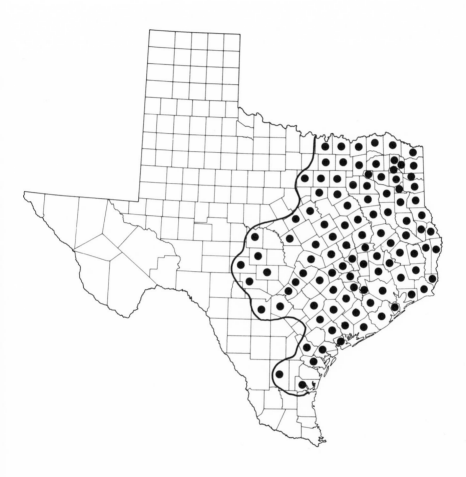

MAP 44. *Kinosternon subrubrum hippocrepis*, Mississippi Mud Turtle.

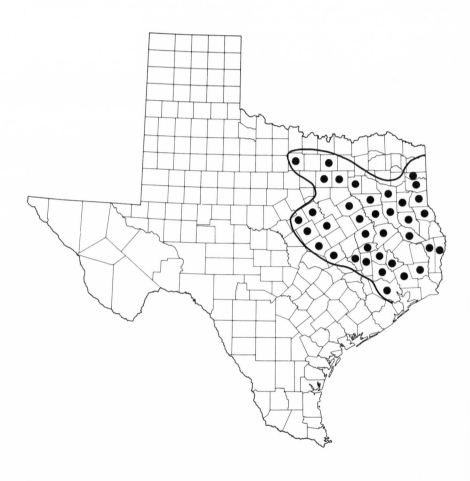

MAP 45. *Sternotherus carinatus*, Razorback Musk Turtle.

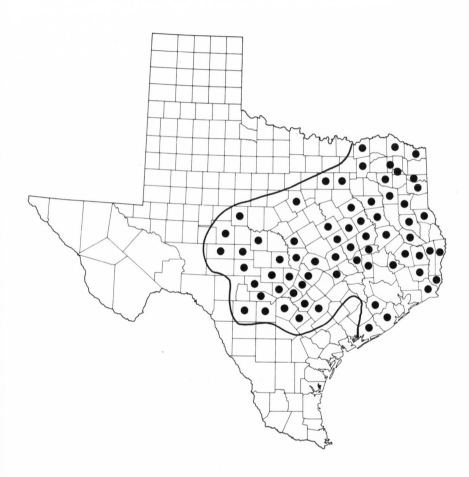

MAP 46. *Sternotherus odoratus*, Stinkpot.

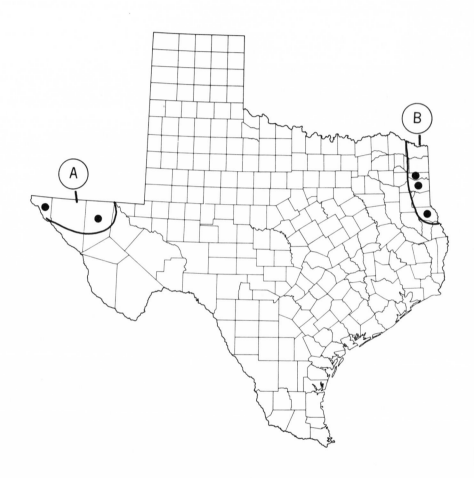

MAP 47. *Chrysemys picta belli* (A), Western Painted Turtle. *Chrysemys picta dorsalis* (B), Southern Painted Turtle.

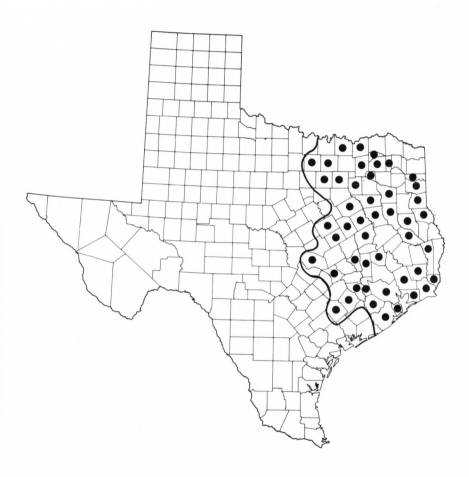

MAP 48. *Deirochelys reticularia miaria*, Western Chicken Turtle.

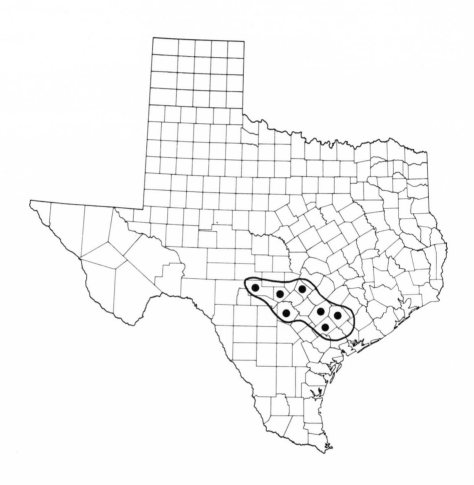

Map 49. *Graptemys caglei*, Cagle's Map Turtle.

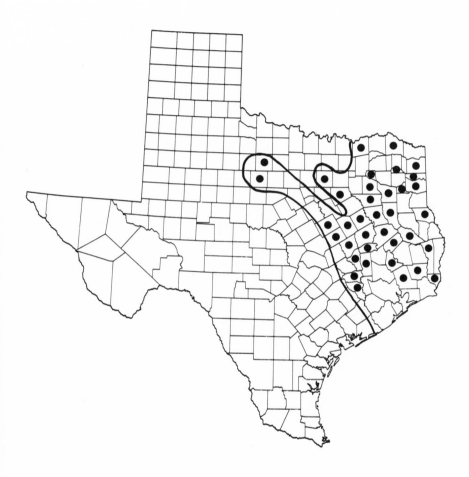

MAP 50. *Graptemys kohni*, Mississippi Map Turtle.

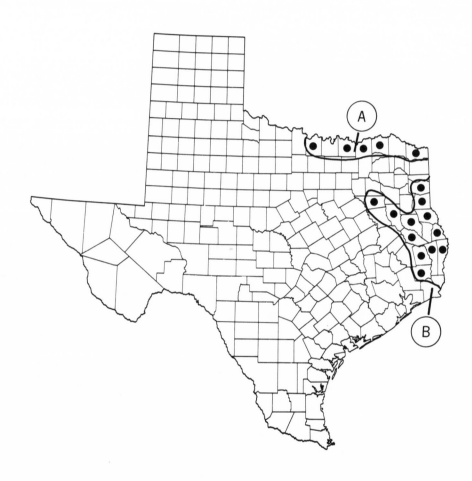

MAP 51. *Graptemys pseudogeographica ouachitensis* (A), Ouachita Map Turtle.
Graptemys pseudogeographica sabinensis (B), Sabine Map Turtle.

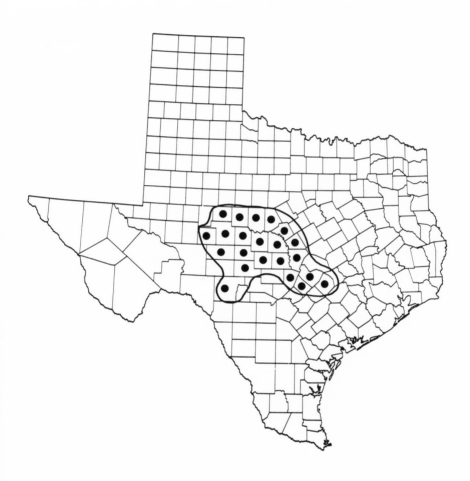

MAP 52. *Graptemys versa*, Texas Map Turtle.

Map 53. *Malaclemys terrapin littoralis*, Texas Diamondback Terrapin.

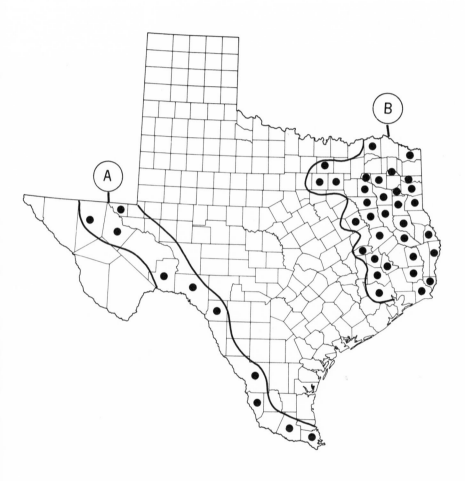

MAP 54. *Pseudemys concinna gorzugi* (A), Zug's River Cooter. *Pseudemys concinna metteri* (B), Metter's River Cooter.

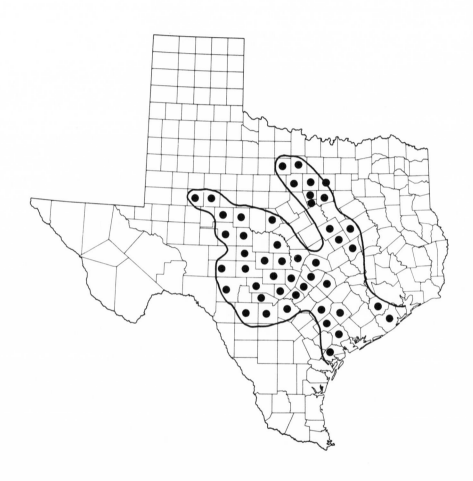

MAP 55. *Pseudemys texana*, Texas River Cooter.

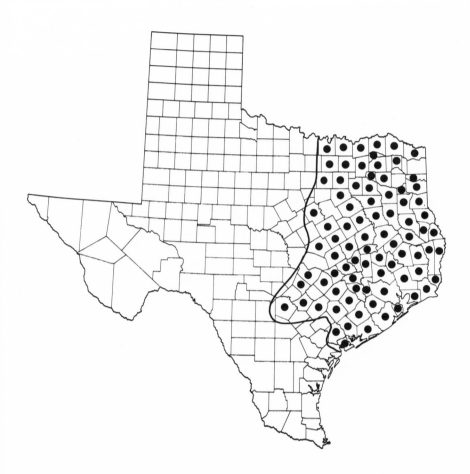

MAP 56. *Terrapene carolina triunguis*, Three-toed Box Turtle.

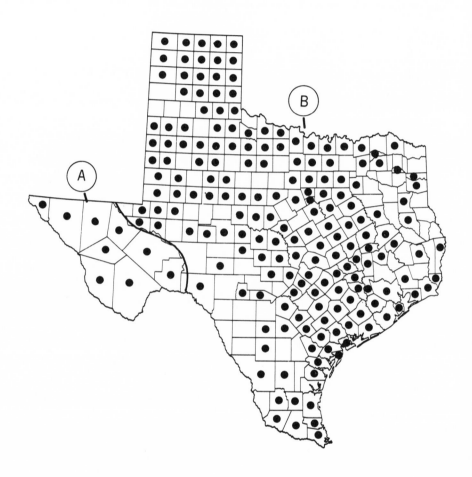

MAP 57. *Terrapene ornata luteola* (A), Desert Box Turtle. *Terrapene ornata ornata* (B), Ornate Box Turtle.

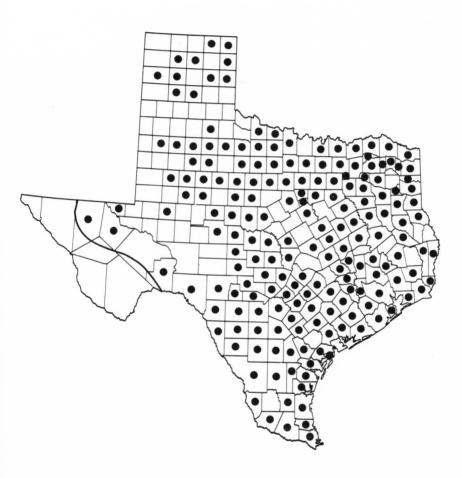

MAP 58. *Trachemys scripta elegans*, Red-eared Slider.

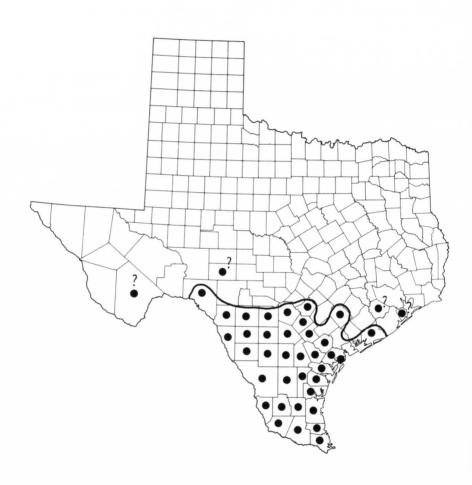

MAP 59. *Gopherus berlandieri*, Texas Tortoise.

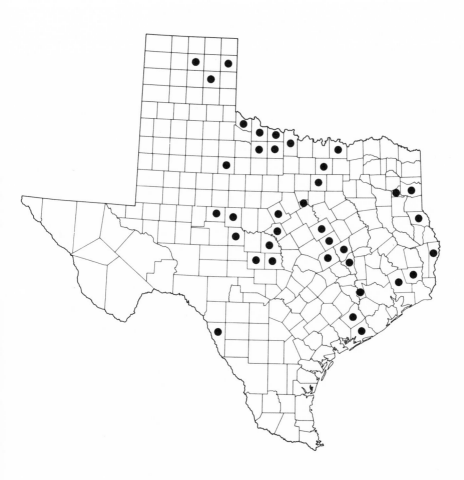

MAP 60. *Trionyx muticus muticus*, Smooth Softshell.

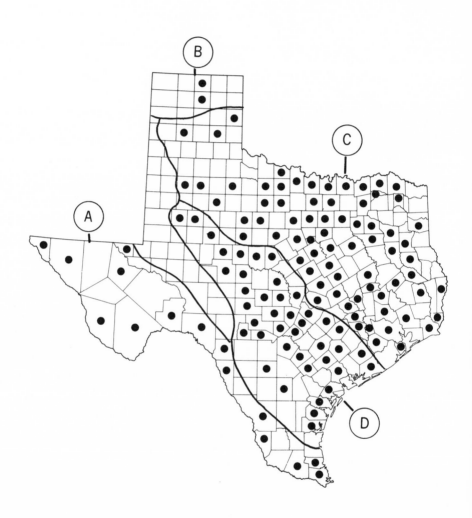

MAP 61. *Trionyx spiniferus emoryi* (A), Texas Spiny Softshell. *Trionyx spiniferus hartwegi* (B), Western Spiny Softshell. *Trionyx spiniferus pallidus* (C), Pallid Spiny Softshell. *Trionyx spiniferus guadalupensis* (D), Guadalupe Spiny Softshell.

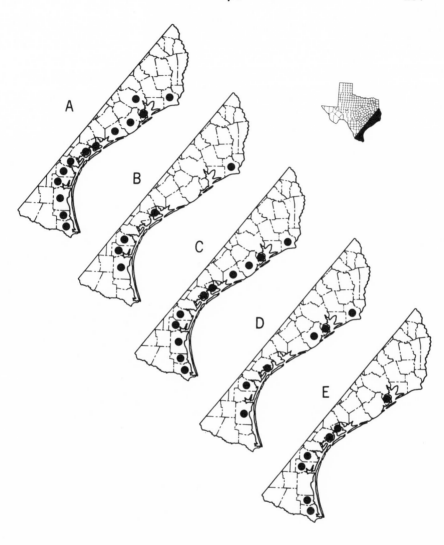

MAP 62. *Caretta caretta* (A), Loggerhead. *Chelonia mydas mydas* (B), Atlantic
Green Turtle. *Lepidochelys kempi* (C), Atlantic Ridley. *Dermochelys coriacea*
(D), Leatherback. *Eretmochelys imbricata imbricata* (E), Atlantic Hawksbill.

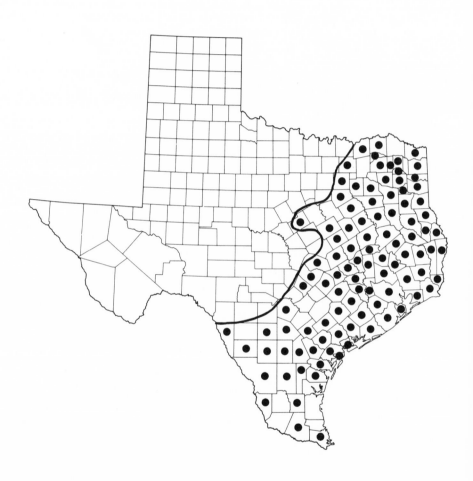

MAP 63. *Alligator mississippiensis*, American Alligator.

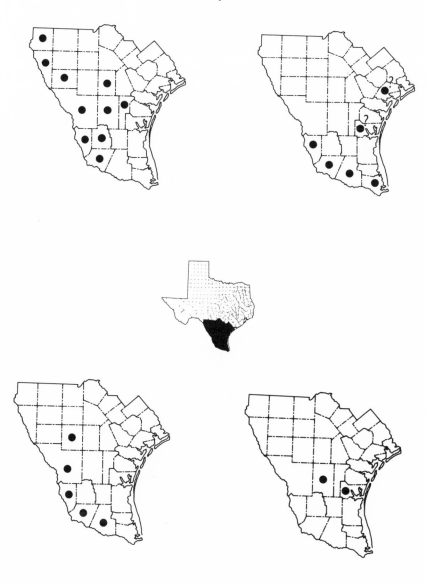

MAP 64. (*Clockwise from upper left*) *Sceloporus cyanogenys*, Blue Spiny Lizard. *Sceloporus grammicus microlepidotus*, Mesquite Lizard. *Tantilla atriceps*, Mexican Blackhead Snake. *Cnemidophorus laredoensis*, Laredo Striped Whiptail.

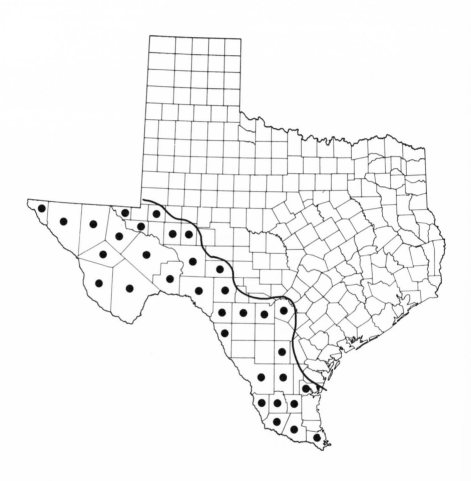

MAP 65. *Coleonyx brevis*, Texas Banded Gecko.

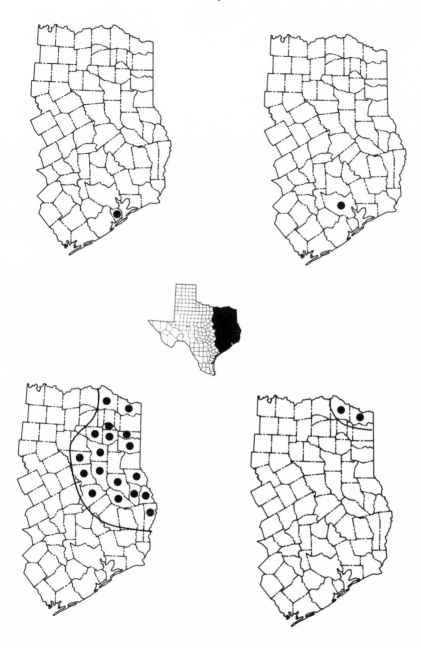

MAP 66. (*Clockwise from upper left*) *Cyrtodactylus scaber,* Rough-scaled Gecko. *Anolis sagrei,* Brown Anole. *Carphophis amoenus vermis,* Western Worm Snake. *Eumeces anthracinus pluvialis,* Southern Coal Skink.

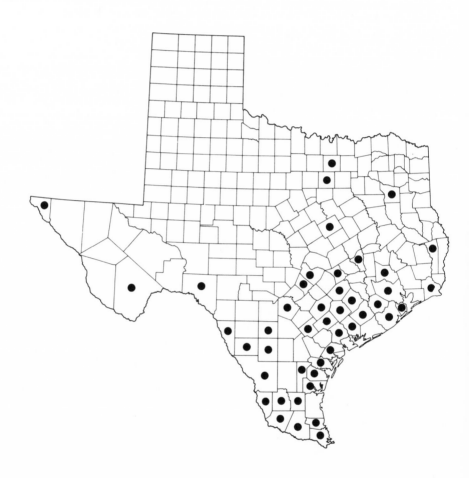

MAP 67. *Hemidactylus turcicus*, Mediterranean Gecko.

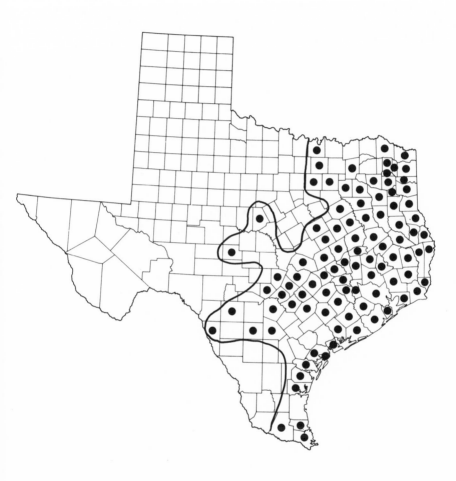

MAP 68. *Anolis carolinensis*, Green Anole.

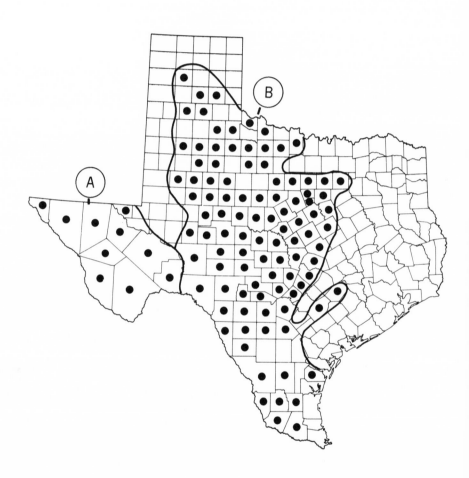

MAP 69. *Cophosaurus texanus scitulus* (A), Southwestern Earless Lizard. *Cophosaurus texanus texanus* (B), Texas Earless Lizard.

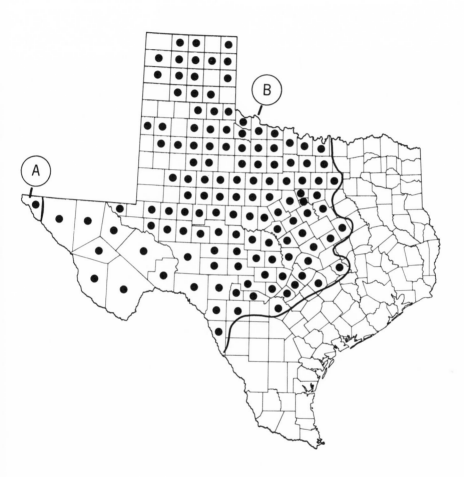

MAP 70. *Crotaphytus collaris fuscus* (A), Chihuahuan Collared Lizard. *Crotaphytus collaris collaris* (B), Eastern Collared Lizard.

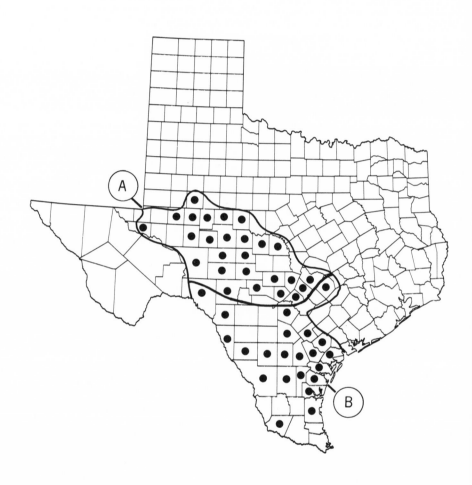

MAP 71. *Holbrookia lacerata lacerata* (A), Plateau Earless Lizard. *Holbrookia lacerata subcaudalis* (B), Southern Earless Lizard.

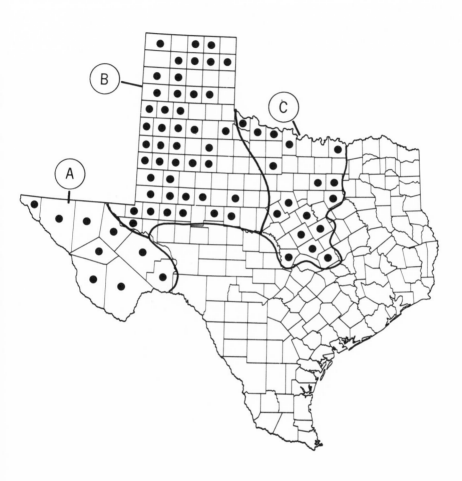

MAP 72. *Holbrookia maculata approximans* (A), Speckled Earless Lizard.
Holbrookia maculata maculata (B), Northern Earless Lizard. *Holbrookia maculata perspicua* (C), Eastern Earless Lizard.

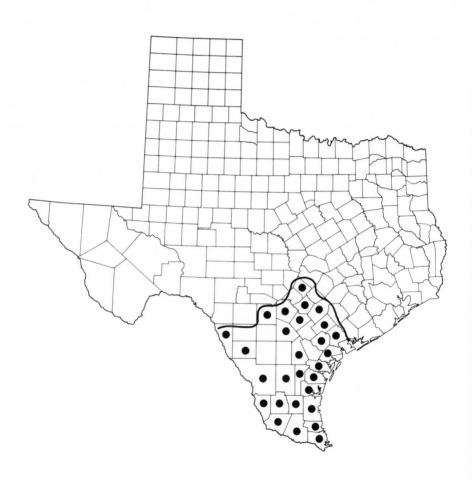

MAP 73. *Holbrookia propinqua propinqua*, Keeled Earless Lizard.

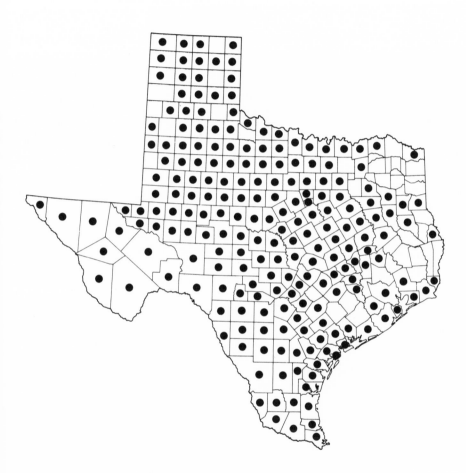

MAP 74. *Phrynosoma cornutum*, Texas Horned Lizard.

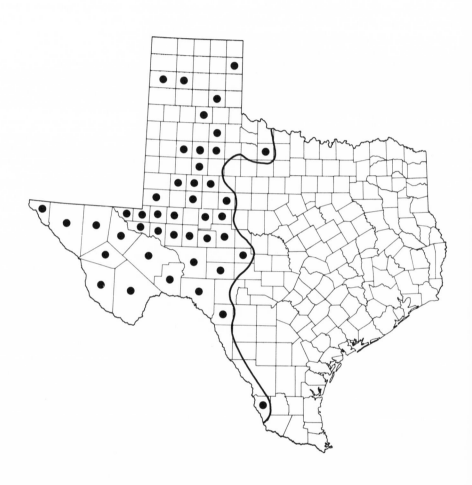

MAP 75. *Phrynosoma modestum*, Roundtail Horned Lizard.

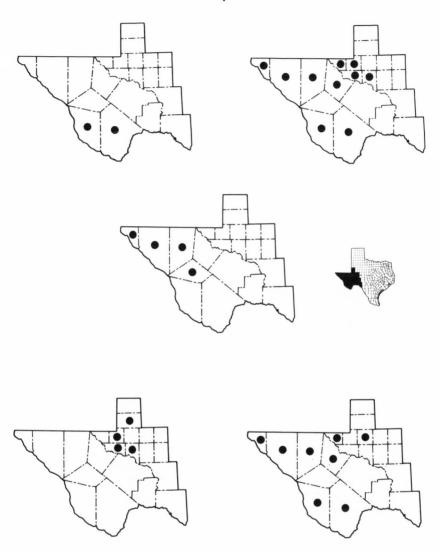

MAP 76. (*Clockwise from upper left*) *Coleonyx reticulatus*, Reticulated Gecko. *Gambelia wislizeni wislezini*, Longnose Leopard Lizard. *Sceloporus magister bimaculosus*, Twin-spotted Spiny Lizard. *Sceloporus graciosus arenicolus*, Dune Sagebrush Lizard. (*Center*) *Phrynosoma douglassi hernandesi*, Mountain Short-horned Lizard.

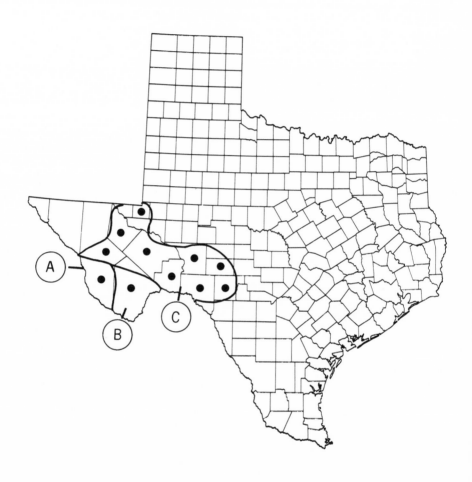

MAP 77.   *Sceloporus merriami longipunctatus* (A), Presidio Canyon Lizard.
Sceloporus merriami annulatus (B), Big Bend Canyon Lizard. *Sceloporus merriami merriami* (C), Merriam's Canyon Lizard.

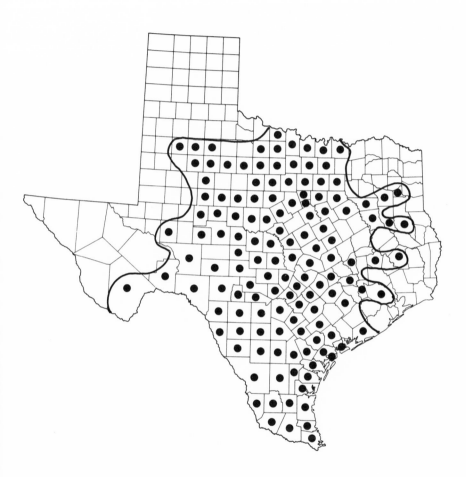

MAP 78. *Sceloporus olivaceus*, Texas Spiny Lizard.

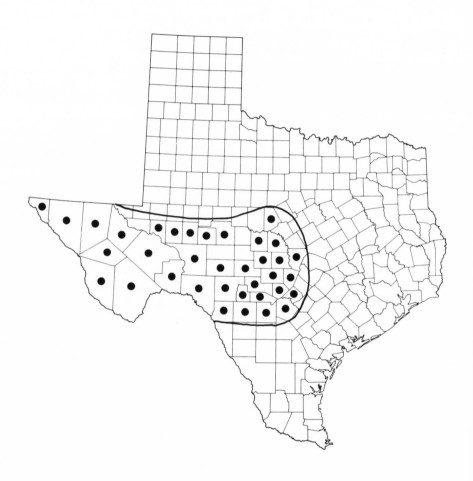

MAP 79. *Sceloporus poinsetti poinsetti,* Crevice Spiny Lizard.

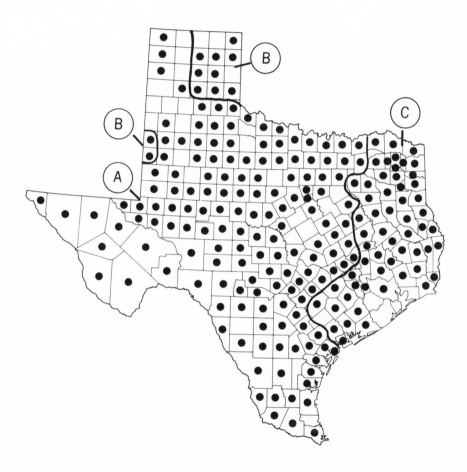

MAP 80. *Sceloporus undulatus consobrinus* (A), Southern Prairie Lizard.
Sceloporus undulatus garmani (B), Northern Prairie Lizard. *Sceloporus undulatus hyacinthinus* (C), Northern Fence Lizard.

MAP 81. *Sceloporus variabilis marmoratus*, Rosebelly Lizard.

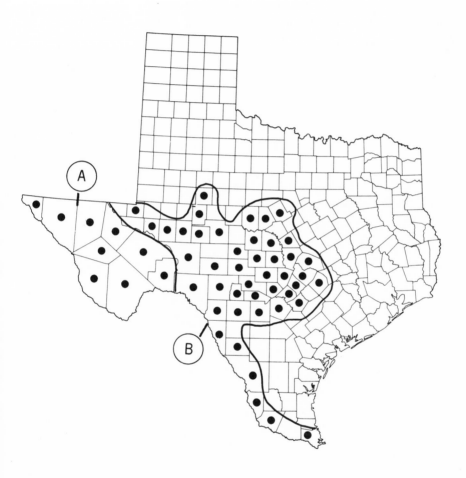

MAP 82. *Urosaurus ornatus schmidti* (A), Big Bend Tree Lizard. *Urosaurus ornatus ornatus* (B), Eastern Tree Lizard.

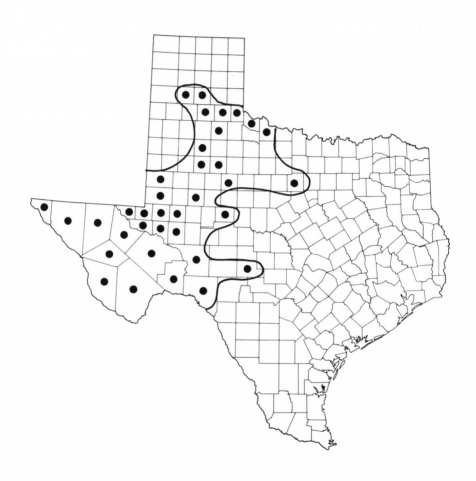

MAP 83. *Uta stansburiana stejnegeri*, Desert Side-blotched Lizard.

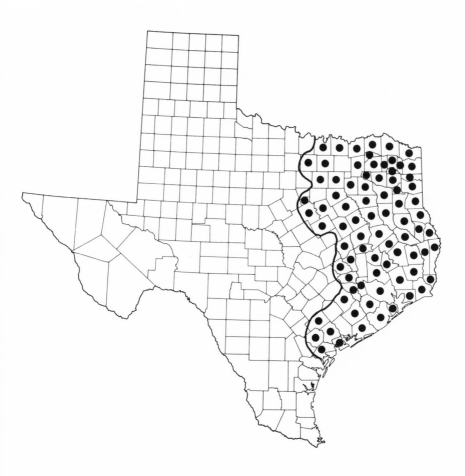

MAP 84. *Eumeces fasciatus,* Five-lined Skink.

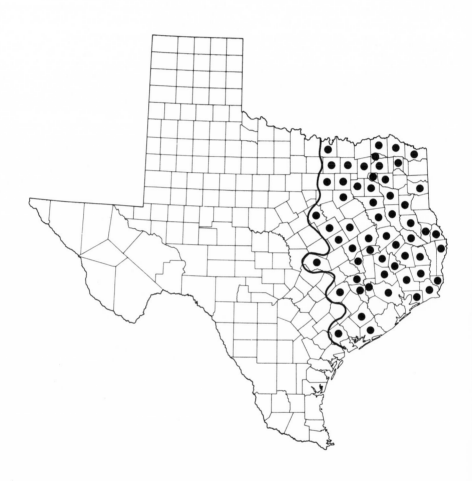

MAP 85. *Eumeces laticeps*, Broadhead Skink.

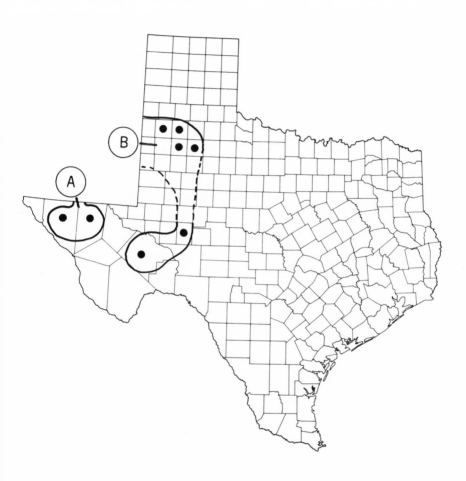

MAP 86. *Eumeces multivirgatus epipleurotus*, Variable Skink.

MAP 87. *Eumeces obsoletus*, Great Plains Skink.

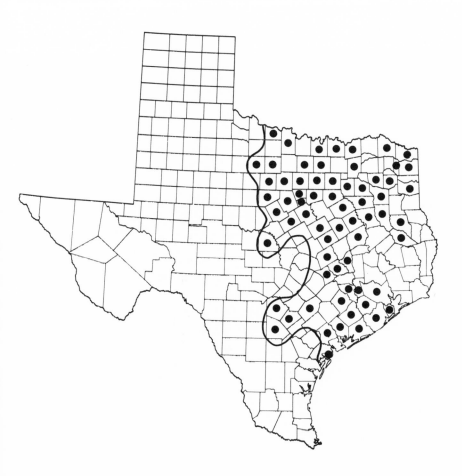

MAP 88. *Eumeces septentrionalis obtusirostris*, Southern Prairie Skink.

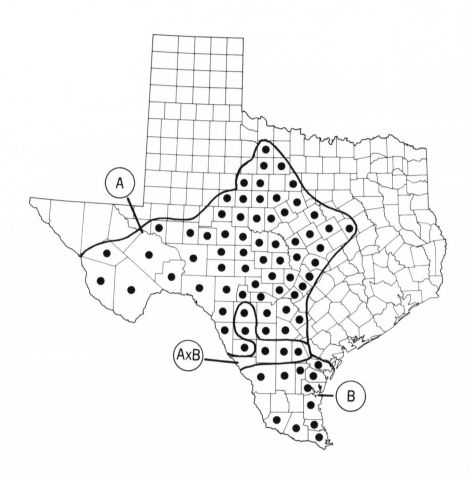

MAP 89. *Eumeces tetragrammus brevilineatus* (A), Short-lined Skink. *Eumeces tetragrammus tetragrammus* (B), Four-lined Skink.

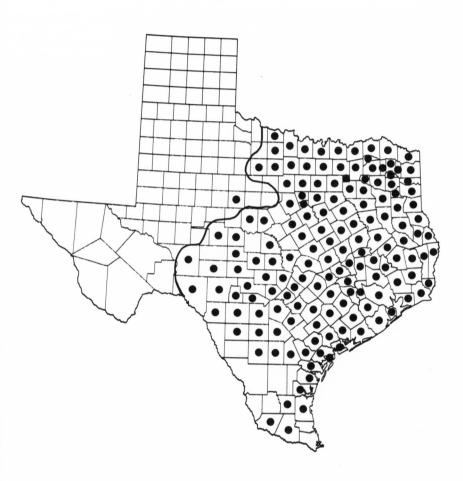

MAP 90. *Scincella lateralis*, Ground Skink.

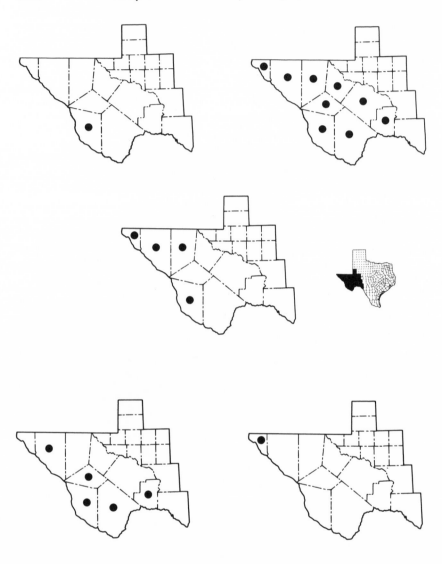

MAP 91. (*Clockwise from upper left*) *Cnemidophorus dixoni*, Gray-checkered Whiptail. *Cnemidophorus exsanguis*, Chihuahuan Spotted Whiptail. *Cnemidophorus uniparens*, Desert Grassland Whiptail. *Cnemidophorus septemvittatus*, Plateau Spotted Whiptail. (*Center*) *Cnemidophorus neomexicanus*, New Mexico Whiptail.

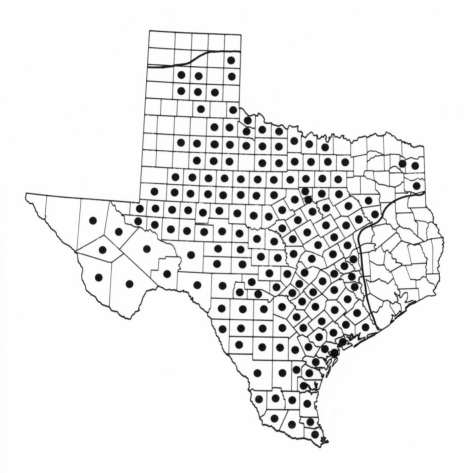

MAP 92. *Cnemidophorus gularis gularis*, Texas Spotted Whiptail.

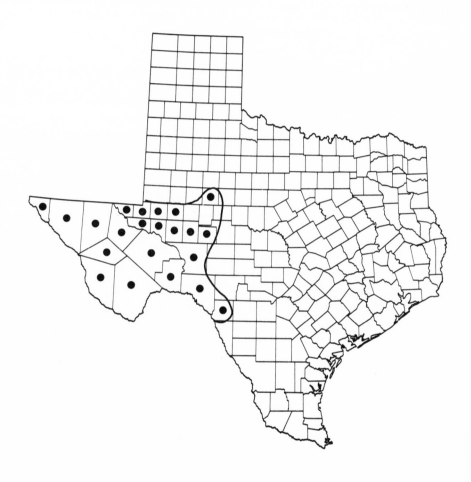

MAP 93. *Cnemidophorus inornatus heptagrammus,* Trans-Pecos Striped Whiptail.

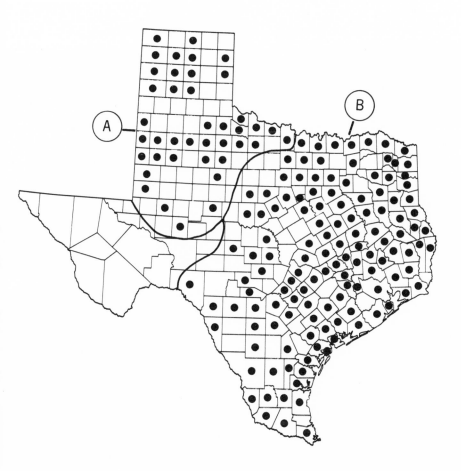

MAP 94. *Cnemidophorus sexlineatus viridis* (A), Prairie-lined Racerunner.
Cnemidophorus sexlineatus sexlineatus (B), Six-lined Racerunner.

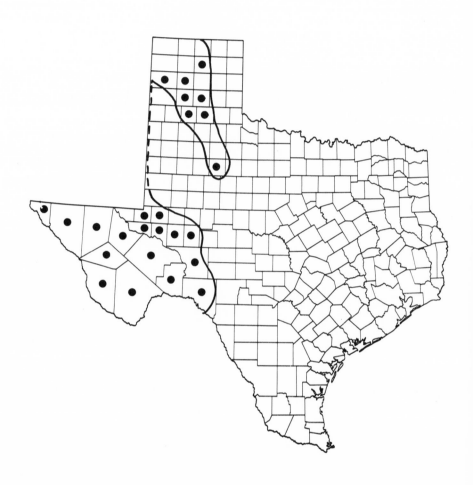

Map 95. *Cnemidophorus tesselatus,* Colorado Checkered Whiptail.

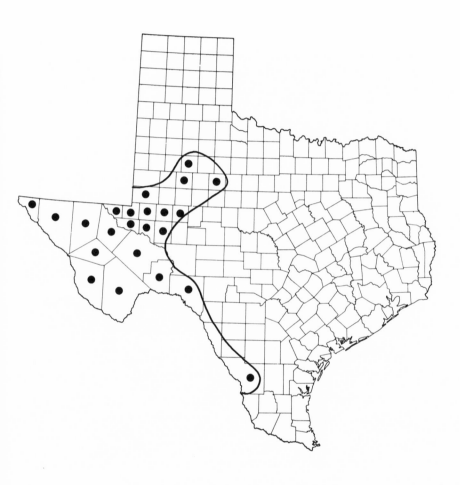

MAP 96. *Cnemidophorus marmoratus*, Marbled Whiptail.

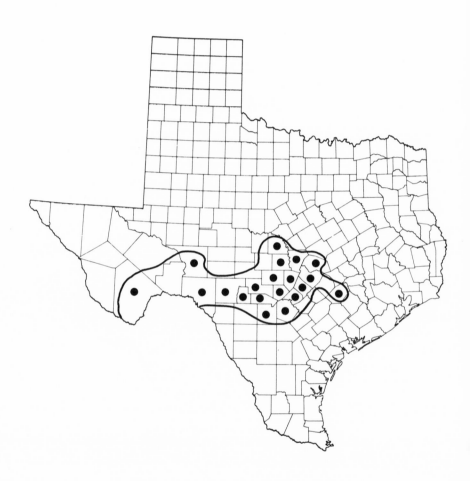

MAP 97. *Gerrhonotus liocephalus infernalis,* Texas Alligator Lizard.

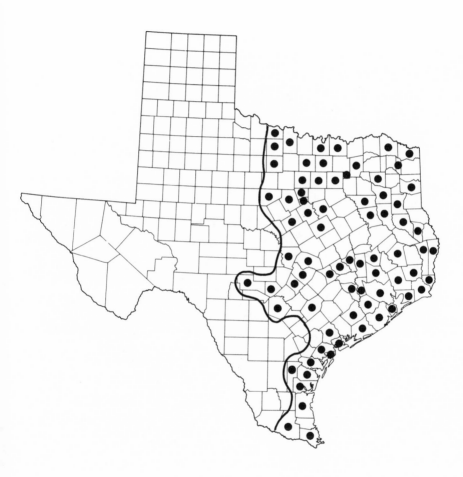

MAP 98. *Ophisaurus attenuatus*, Western Slender Glass Lizard.

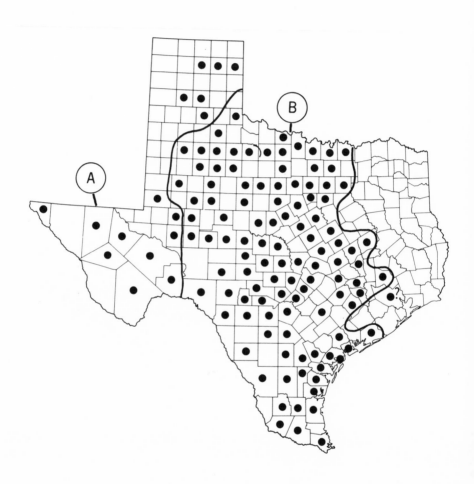

MAP 99. *Leptotyphlops dulcis dissectus* (A), New Mexico Blind Snake. *Leptotyphlops dulcis dulcis* (B), Plains Blind Snake.

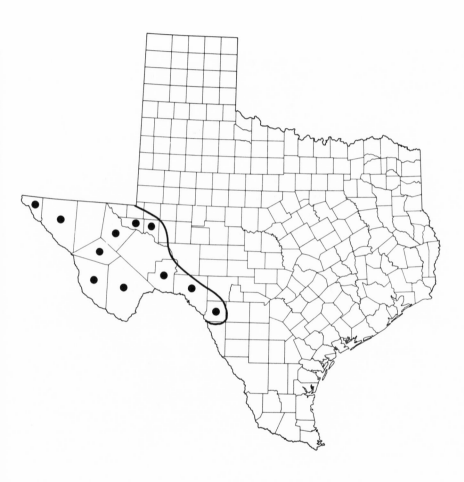

MAP 100. *Leptotyphlops humilis segregus*, Trans-Pecos Blind Snake.

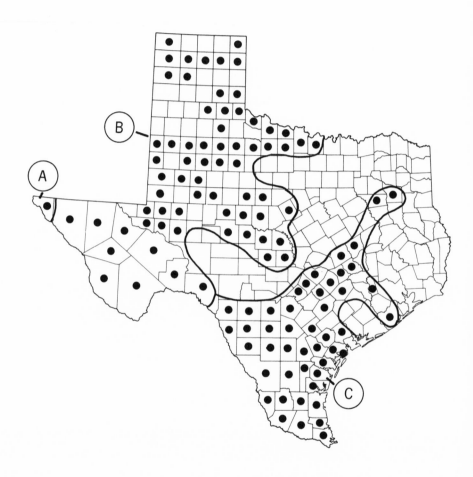

MAP 101. *Arizona elegans philipi* (A), Painted Desert Glossy Snake. *Arizona elegans elegans* (B), Kansas Glossy Snake. *Arizona elegans arenicola* (C), Texas Glossy Snake.

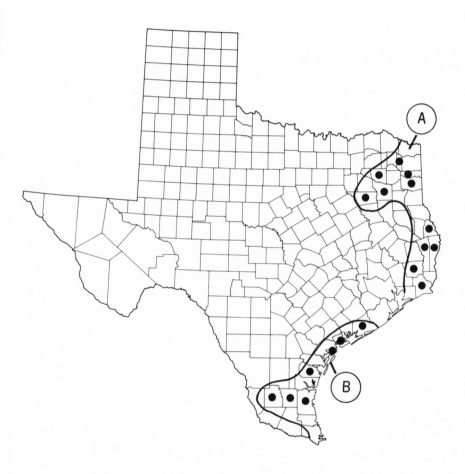

MAP 102. *Cemophora coccinea copei* (A), Northern Scarlet Snake. *Cemophora coccinea lineri* (B), Texas Scarlet Snake.

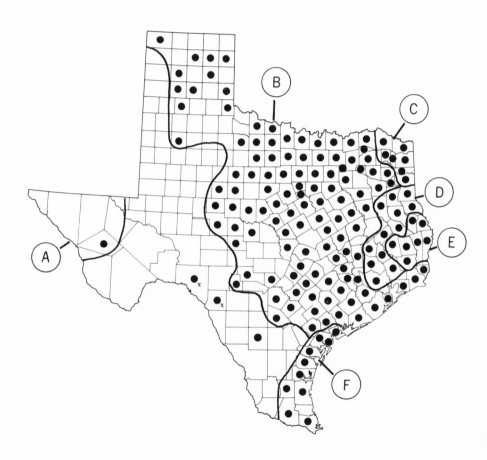

MAP 103. *Coluber constrictor mormon* (A), Western Yellowbelly Racer. *Coluber constrictor flaviventris* (B), Eastern Yellowbelly Racer. *Coluber constrictor priapus* (C), Southern Black Racer. *Coluber constrictor anthicus* (D), Buttermilk Racer. *Coluber constrictor etheridgei* (E), Tan Racer. *Coluber constrictor oaxaca* (F), Mexican Racer.

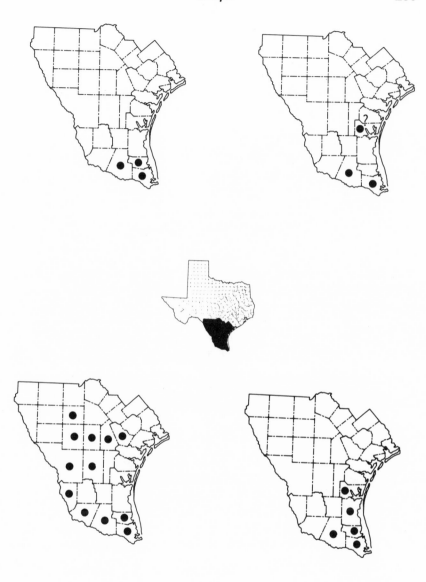

MAP 104. (*Clockwise from upper left*) *Coniophanes imperialis imperialis*, Black-striped Snake. *Drymobius margaritiferus margaritiferus*, Speckled Racer. *Leptodeira septentrionalis septentrionalis*, Northern Cat-eyed Snake. *Ficimia streckeri*, Mexican Hooknose Snake.

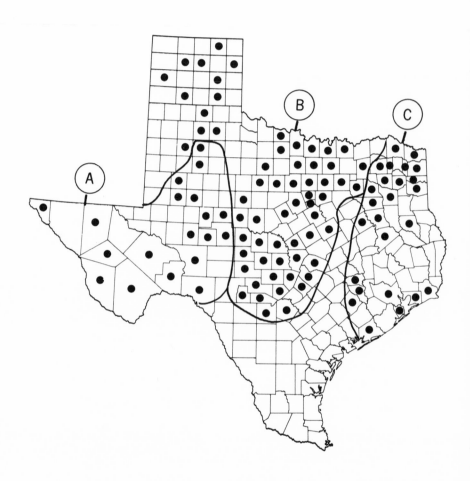

MAP 105. *Diadophis punctatus regalis* (A), Regal Ringneck Snake. *Diadophis punctatus arnyi* (B), Prairie Ringneck Snake. *Diadophis punctatus stictogenys* (C), Mississippi Ringneck Snake.

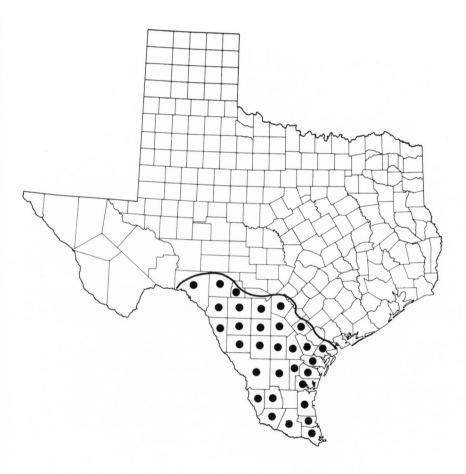

MAP 106. *Drymarchon corais erebennus*, Texas Indigo Snake.

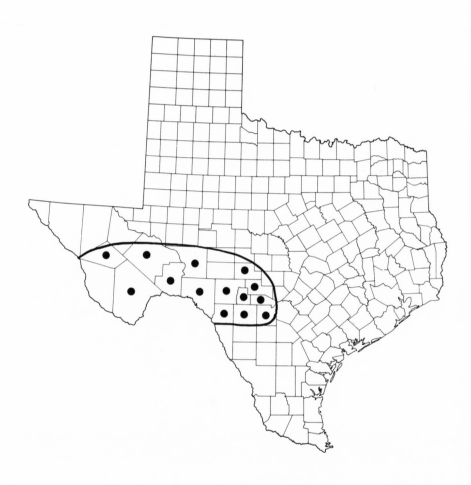

MAP 107. *Elaphe bairdi*, Baird's Rat Snake.

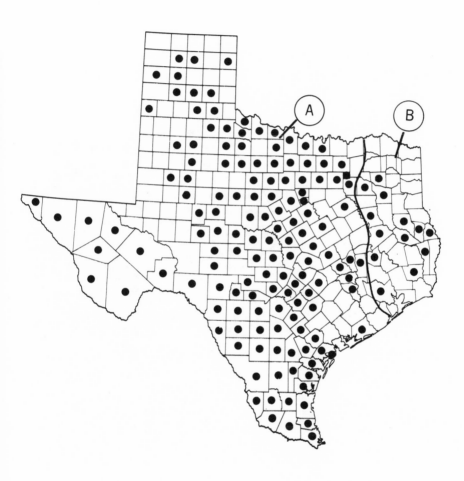

MAP 108. *Elaphe guttata emoryi* (A), Great Plains Rat Snake. *Elaphe guttata guttata* (B), Corn Snake.

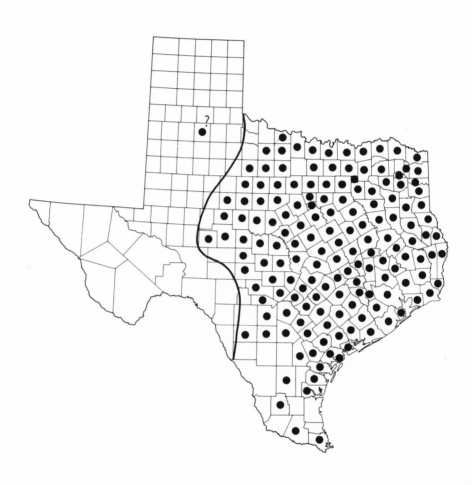

MAP 109. *Elaphe obsoleta lindheimeri*, Texas Rat Snake.

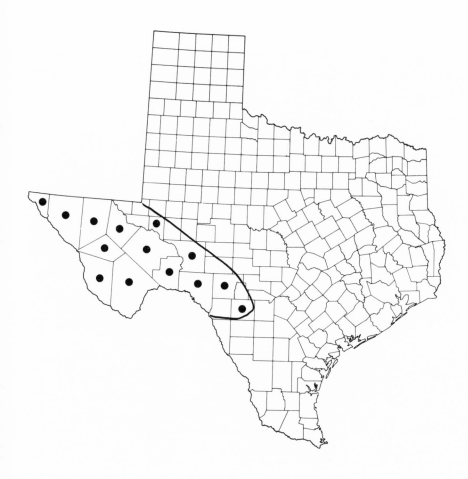

MAP 110. *Elaphe subocularis*, Trans-Pecos Rat Snake.

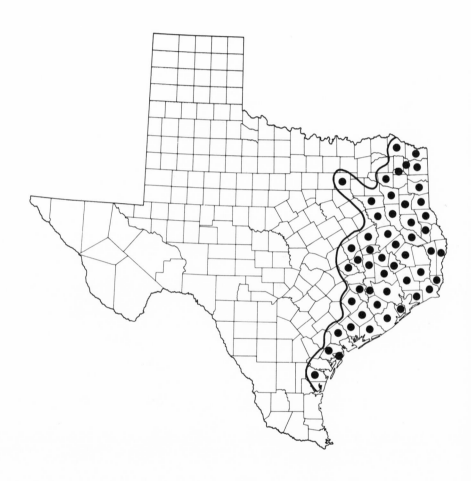

MAP 111. *Farancia abacura reinwardti*, Western Mud Snake.

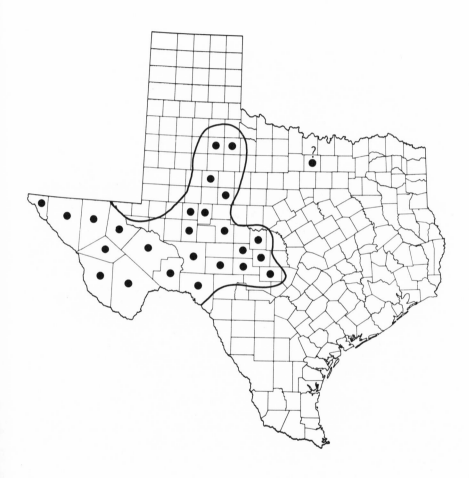

MAP 112. *Gyalopion canum*, Western Hooknose Snake.

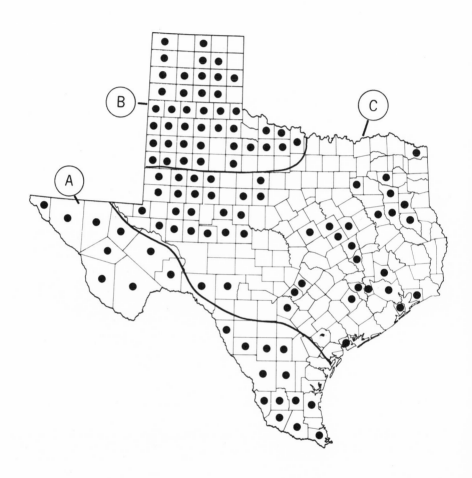

Map 113. *Heterodon nasicus kennerlyi* (A), Mexican Hognose Snake. *Heterodon nasicus nasicus* (B), Plains Hognose Snake. *Heterodon nasicus gloydi* (C), Dusky Hognose Snake.

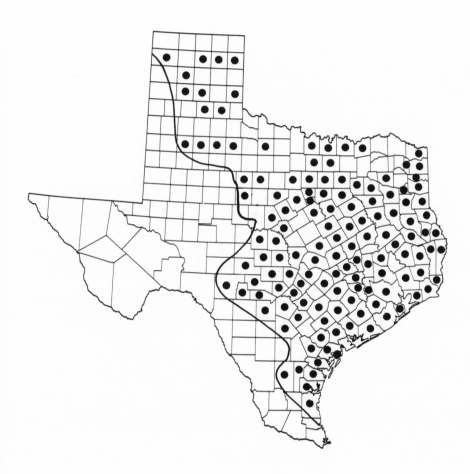

MAP 114. *Heterodon platyrhinos*, Eastern Hognose Snake.

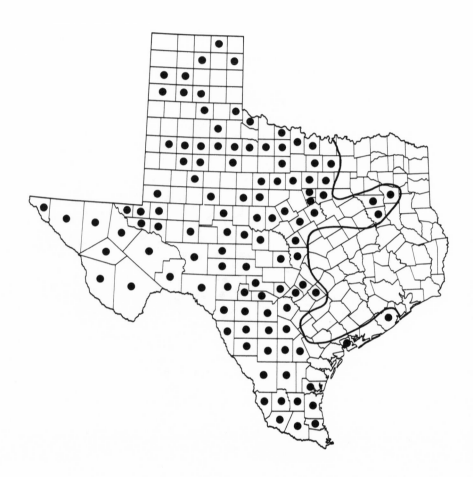

MAP 115. *Hypsiglena torquata jani*, Texas Night Snake.

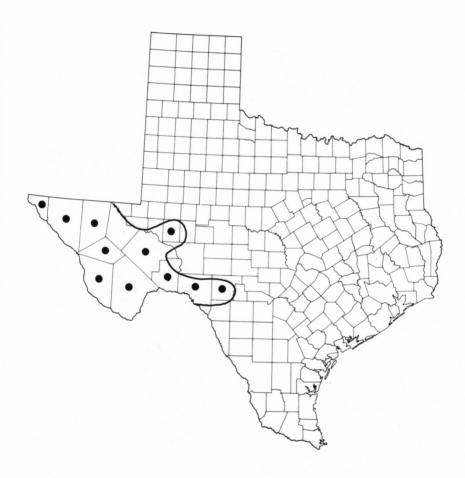

MAP 116. *Lampropeltis alterna*, Gray-banded Kingsnake.

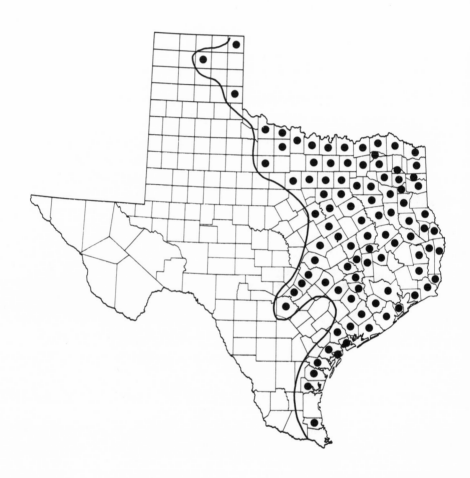

MAP 117. *Lampropeltis calligaster calligaster*, Prairie Kingsnake.

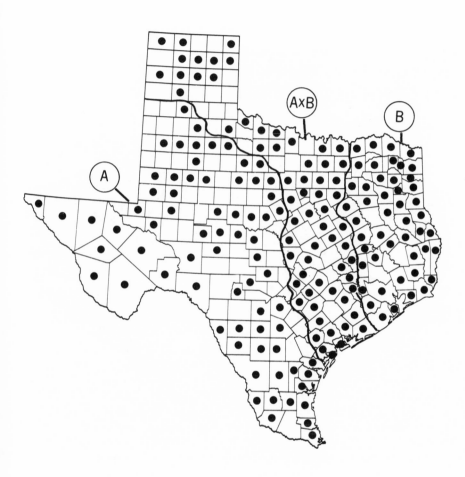

MAP 118. *Lampropeltis getulus splendida* (A), Desert Kingsnake. *Lampropeltis getulus holbrooki* (B), Speckled Kingsnake.

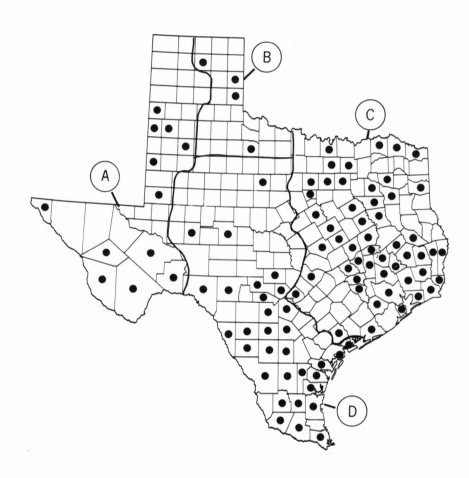

MAP 119. *Lampropeltis triangulum celaenops* (A), New Mexico Milk Snake.
Lampropeltis triangulum gentilis (B), Central Plains Milk Snake. *Lampropeltis
triangulum amaura* (C), Louisiana Milk Snake. *Lampropeltis triangulum annulata* (D), Mexican Milk Snake.

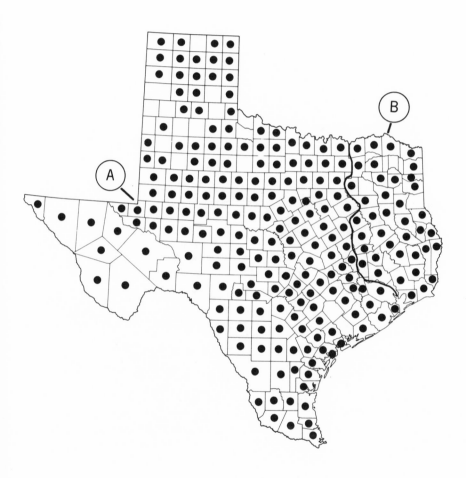

MAP 120. *Masticophis flagellum testaceus* (A), Western Coachwhip. *Masticophis flagellum flagellum* (B), Eastern Coachwhip.

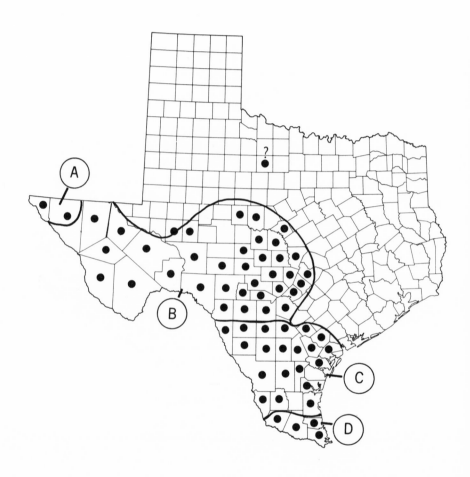

MAP 121. *Masticophis taeniatus taeniatus* (A), Desert Striped Whipsnake. *Masticophis taeniatus girardi* (B), Central Texas Whipsnake. *Masticophis taeniatus schotti* (C), Schott's Whipsnake. *Masticophus taeniatus ruthveni* (D), Ruthven's Whipsnake.

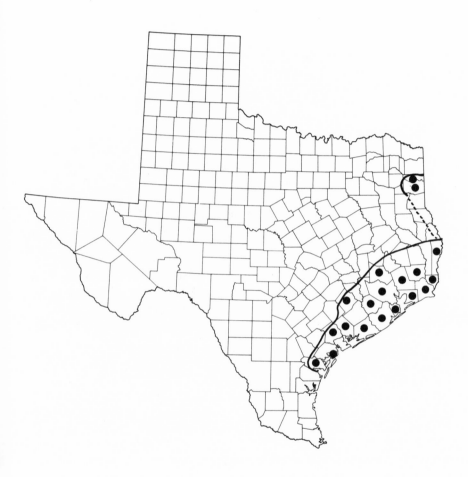

MAP 122. *Nerodia cyclopion*, Green Water Snake.

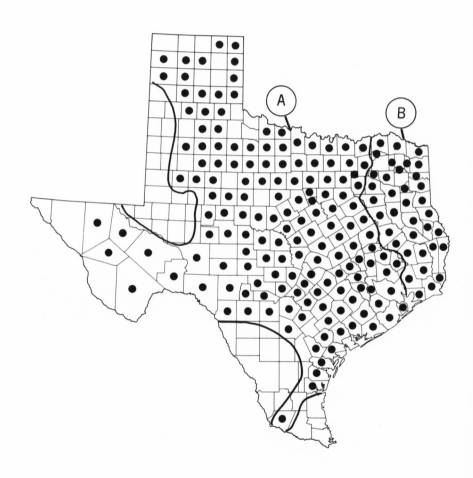

MAP 123. *Nerodia erythrogaster transversa* (A), Blotched Water Snake. *Nerodia erythrogaster flavigaster* (B), Yellowbelly Water Snake.

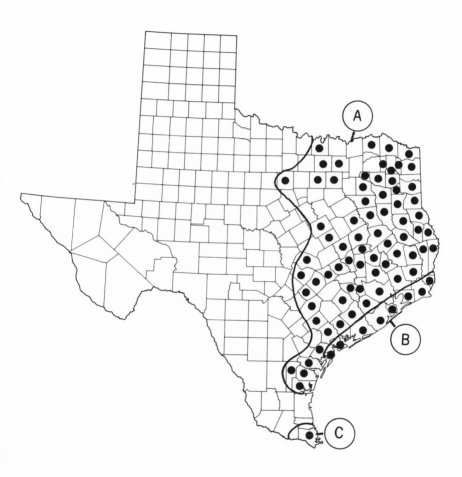

MAP 124. *Nerodia fasciata confluens* (A), Broad-banded Water Snake. *Nerodia fasciata clarki* (B), Gulf Salt Marsh Snake. *Nerodia fasciata pictiventris* (C), Florida Water Snake.

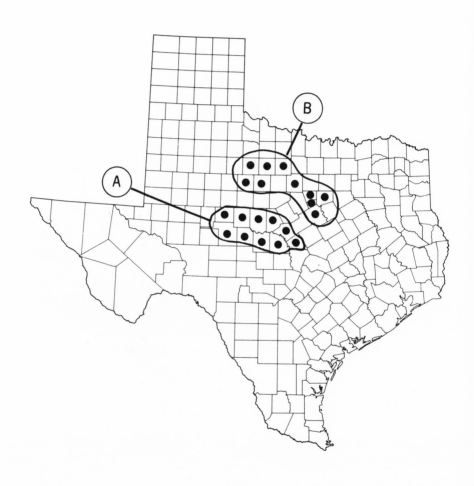

MAP 125. *Nerodia harteri paucimaculata* (A), Concho Water Snake. *Nerodia harteri harteri* (B), Brazos Water Snake.

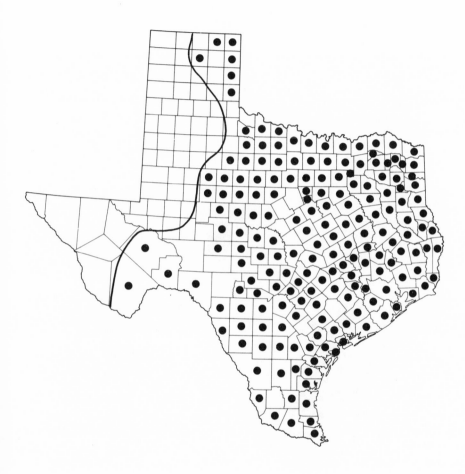

MAP 126. *Nerodia rhombifera rhombifera*, Diamondback Water Snake.

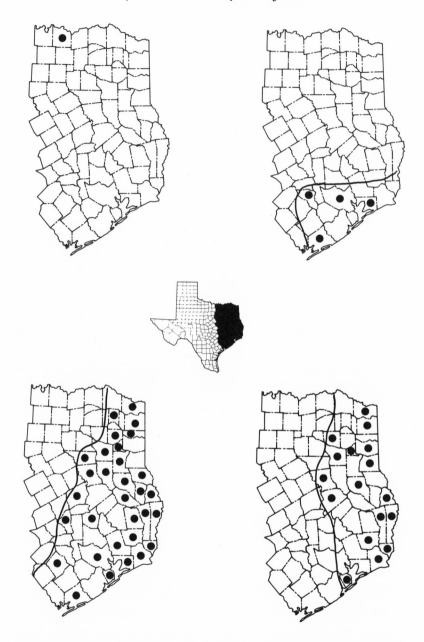

MAP 127. (*Clockwise from upper left*) *Nerodia sipedon pleuralis*, Midland Water Snake. *Opheodrys vernalis blanchardi*, Western Smooth Green Snake. *Storeria occipitomaculata obscura*, Florida Redbelly Snake. *Regina rigida sinicola*, Gulf Crayfish Snake.

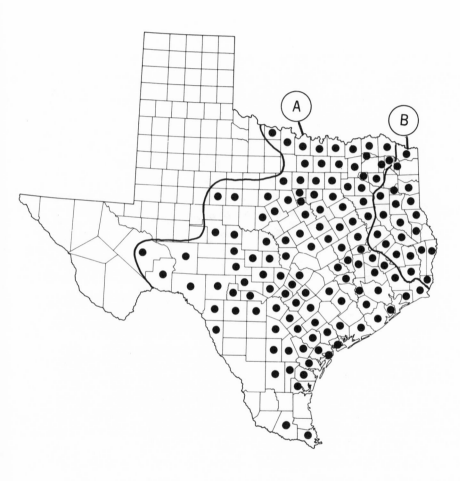

MAP 128.   *Opheodrys aestivus majalis* (A), Western Rough Green Snake.
Opheodrys aestivus aestivus (B), Eastern Rough Green Snake.

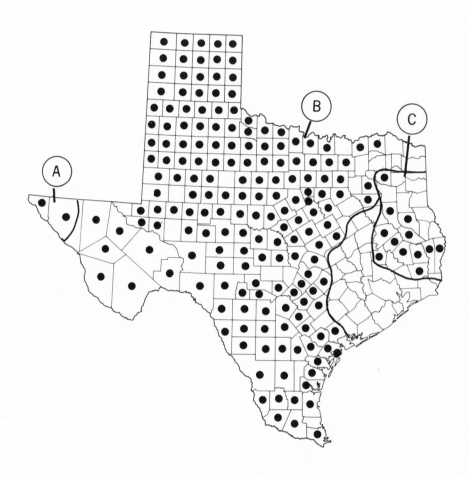

MAP 129. *Pituophis melanoleucus affinis* (A), Sonoran Gopher Snake. *Pituophis melanoleucus sayi* (B), Bullsnake. *Pituophis melanoleucus ruthveni* (C), Louisiana Pine Snake.

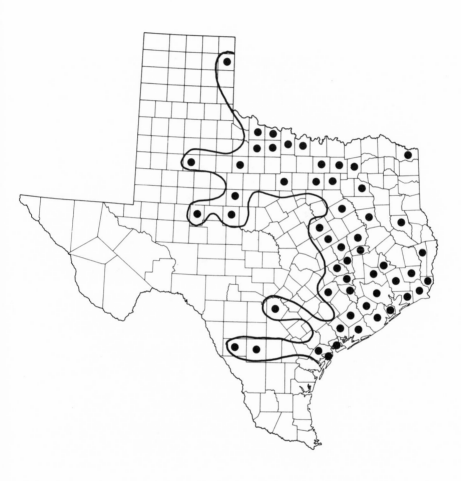

MAP 130. *Regina grahami*, Graham's Crayfish Snake.

MAP 131. *Rhinocheilus lecontei tessellatus*, Texas Longnose Snake.

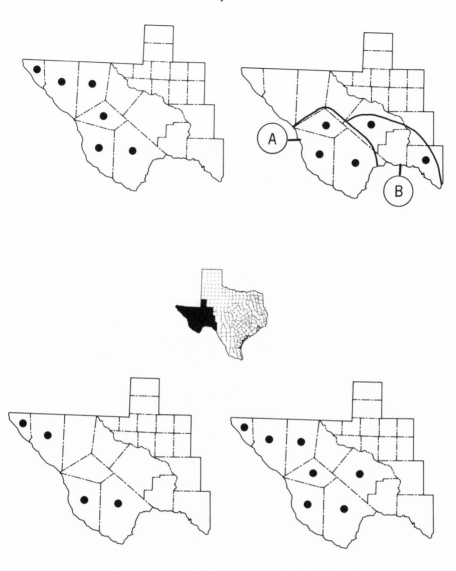

MAP 132. (*Clockwise from upper left*) *Salvadora deserticola*, Big Bend Patchnose Snake. *Tantilla rubra cucullata* (A), Blackhood Snake. *Tantilla rubra diabola* (B), Devil's River Blackhead Snake. *Crotalus scutulatus scutulatus*, Mojave
Rattlesnake. *Trimorphodon biscutatus vilkinsoni*, Texas Lyre Snake.

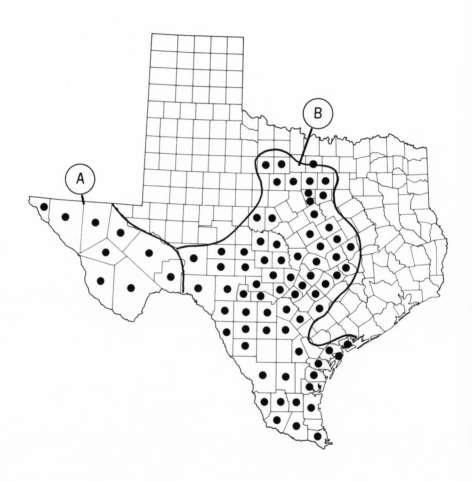

MAP 133. *Salvadora grahamiae grahamiae*, Mountain Patchnose Snake. *Salvadora grahamiae lineata*, Texas Patchnose Snake.

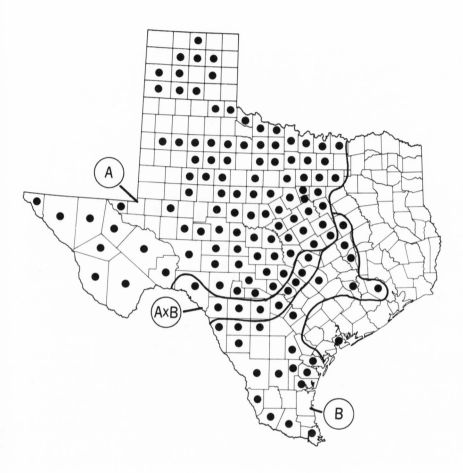

MAP 134. *Sonora semiannulata semiannulata* (A), Ground Snake. *Sonora semiannulata taylori* (B), Taylor's Ground Snake.

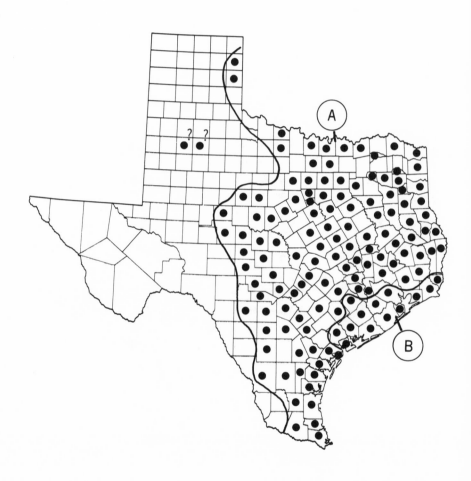

MAP 135. *Storeria dekayi texana* (A), Texas Brown Snake. *Storeria dekayi lim-netes* (B), Marsh Brown Snake.

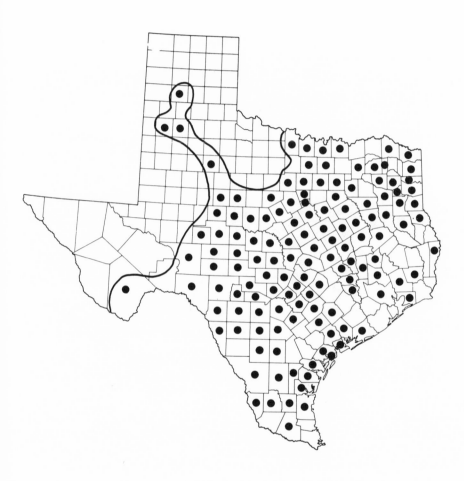

MAP 136. *Tantilla gracilis*, Flathead Snake.

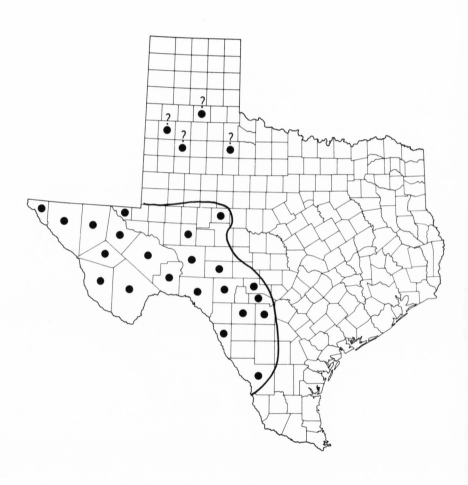

MAP 137. *Tantilla hobartsmithi*, Southwestern Blackhead Snake.

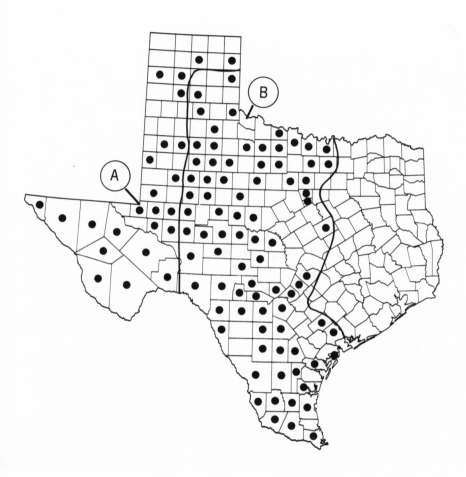

Map 138. *Tantilla nigriceps nigriceps* (A), Plains Blackhead Snake. *Tantilla nigriceps fumiceps* (B), Texas Blackhead Snake.

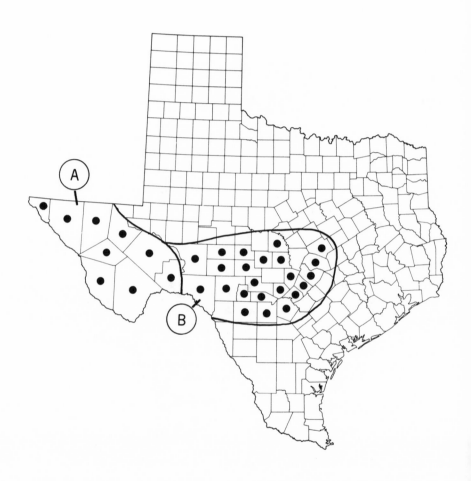

MAP 139. *Thamnophis cyrtopsis cyrtopsis* (A), Western Blackneck Garter Snake. *Thamnophis cyrtopsis ocellatus* (B), Eastern Blackneck Garter Snake.

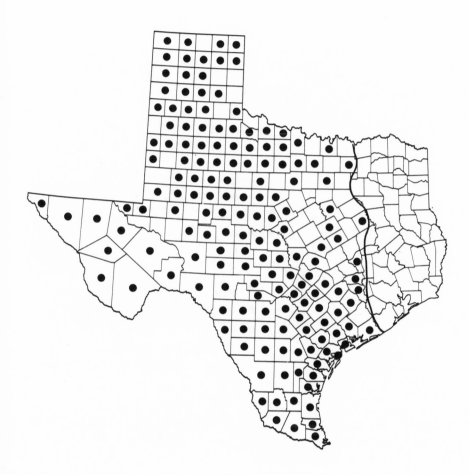

MAP 140. *Thamnophis marcianus marcianus*, Checkered Garter Snake.

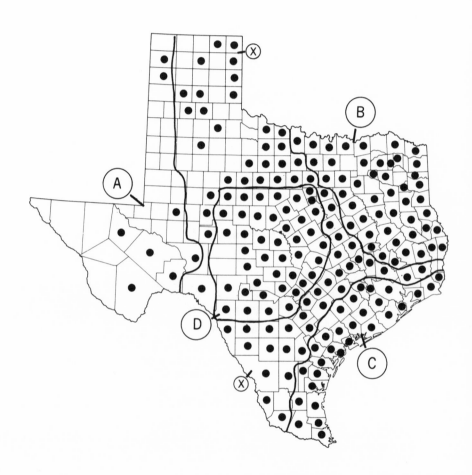

MAP 141. *Thamnophis proximus diabolicus* (A), Arid Land Ribbon Snake. *Thamnophis proximus proximus* (B), Western Ribbon Snake. *Thamnophis proximus orarius* (C), Gulf Coast Ribbon Snake. *Thamnophis proximus rubrilineatus* (D), Redstripe Ribbon Snake.

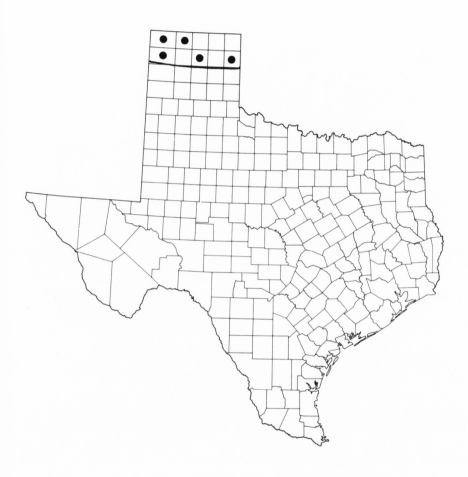

MAP 142. *Thamnophis radix haydeni*, Western Plains Garter snake.

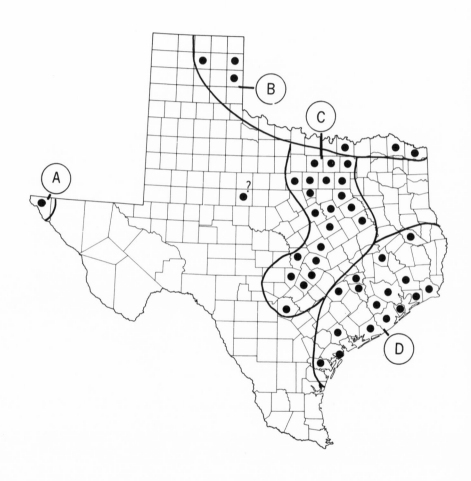

MAP 143. *Thamnophis sirtalis dorsalis* (A), New Mexico Garter Snake. *Thamnophis sirtalis parietalis* (B), Red-sided Garter Snake. *Thamnophis sirtalis annectens* (C), Texas Garter Snake. *Thamnophis sirtalis sirtalis* (D), Eastern Garter Snake.

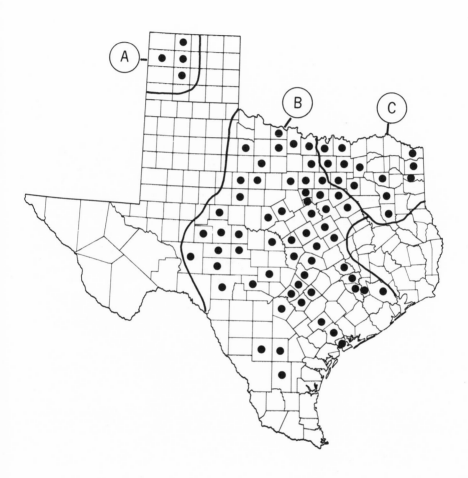

MAP 144. *Tropidoclonion lineatum mertensi* (A), New Mexico Lined Snake. *Tropidoclonion lineatum texanum* (B), Texas Lined Snake. *Tropidoclonion lineatum annectens* (C), Central Lined Snake.

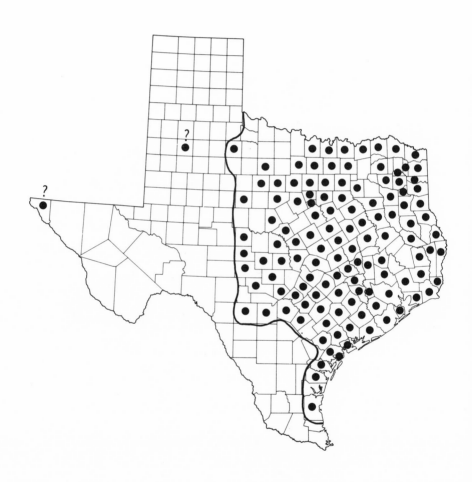

MAP 145. *Virginia striatula*, Rough Earth Snake.

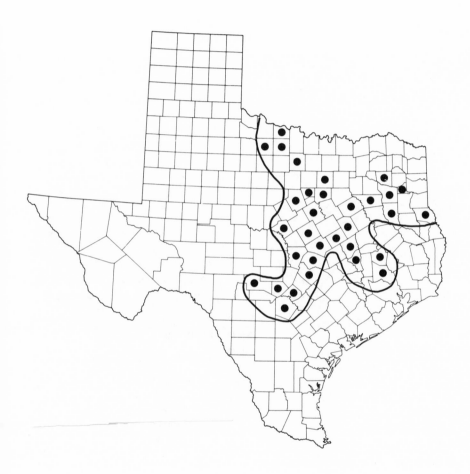

MAP 146. *Virginia valeriae elegans*, Western Earth Snake.

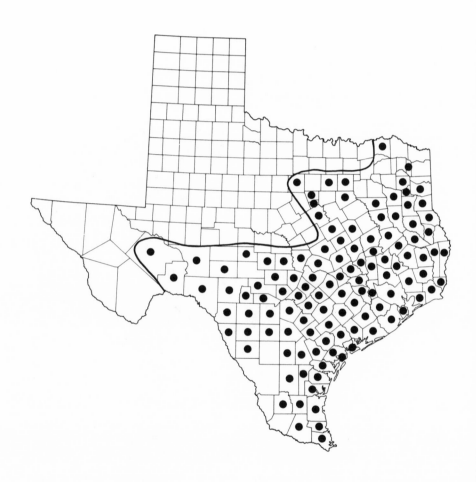

MAP 147. *Micrurus fulvius tenere*, Texas Coral Snake.

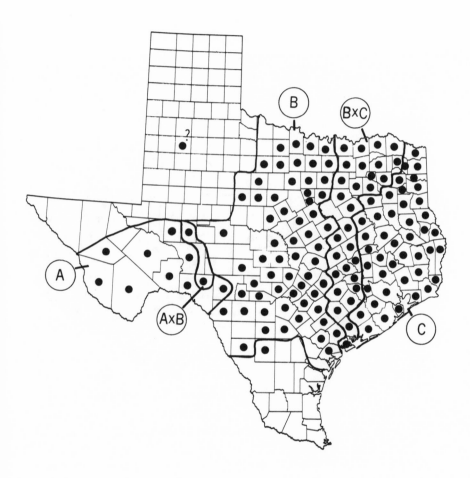

MAP 148. *Agkistrodon contortrix pictigaster* (A), Trans-Pecos Copperhead. *Agkistrodon contortrix laticinctus* (B), Broad-banded Copperhead. *Agkistrodon contortrix contortrix* (C), Southern Copperhead.

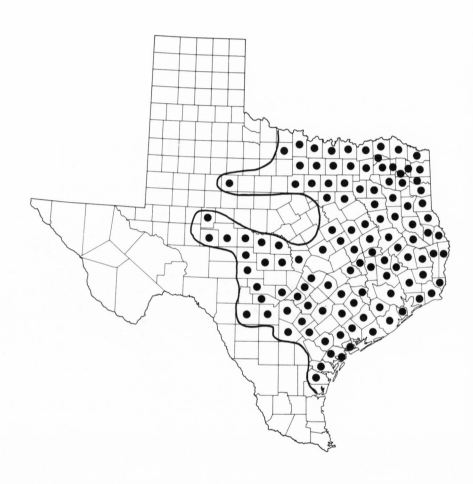

MAP 149.　*Agkistrodon piscivorus leucostoma*, Western Cottonmouth.

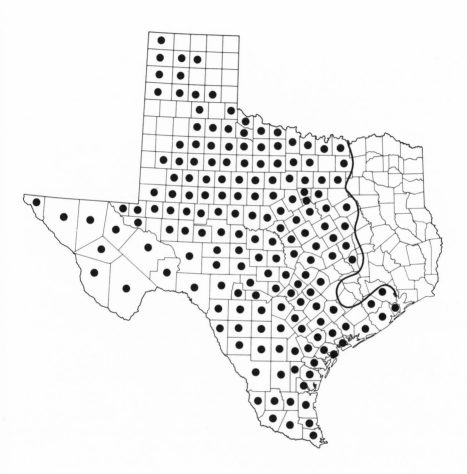

MAP 150. *Crotalus atrox*, Western Diamondback Rattlesnake.

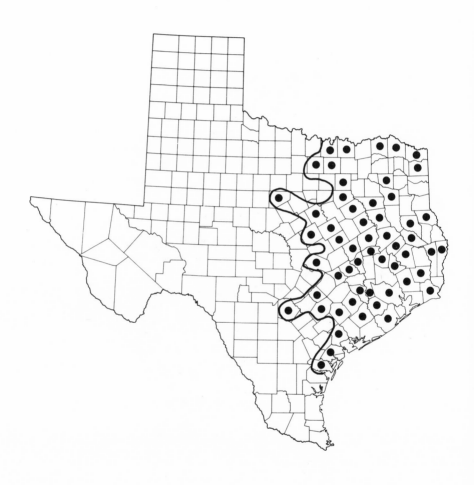

MAP 151. *Crotalus horridus atricaudatus*, Canebrake Rattlesnake.

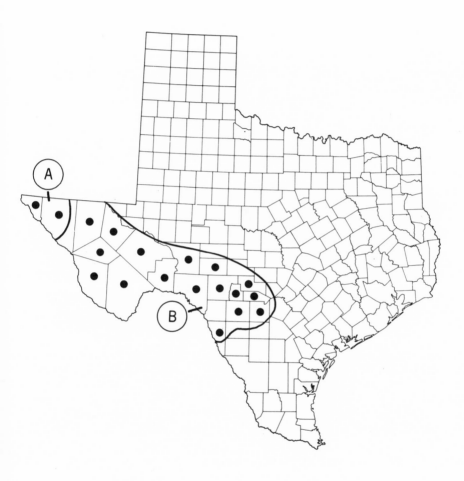

MAP 152. *Crotalus lepidus klauberi* (A), Banded Rock Rattlesnake. *Crotalus lepidus lepidus* (B), Mottled Rock Rattlesnake.

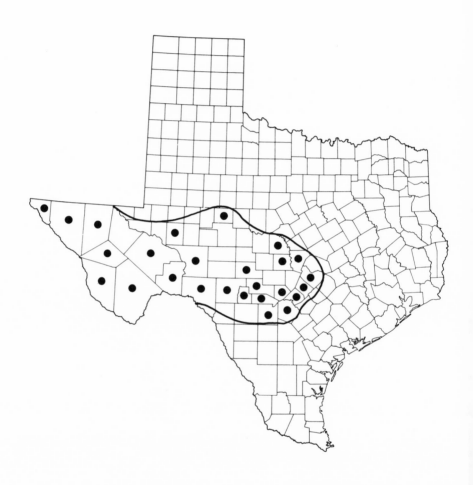

MAP 153. *Crotalus molossus molossus*, Blacktail Rattlesnake.

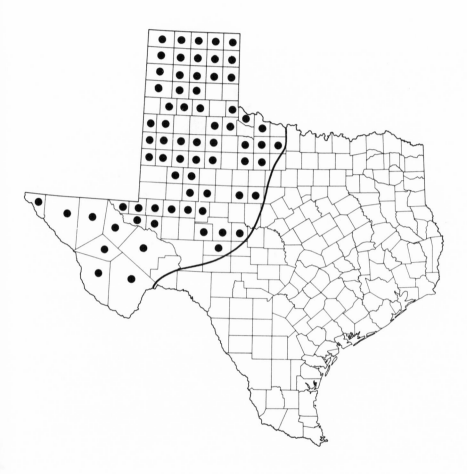

MAP 154. *Crotalus viridis viridis*, Prairie Rattlesnake.

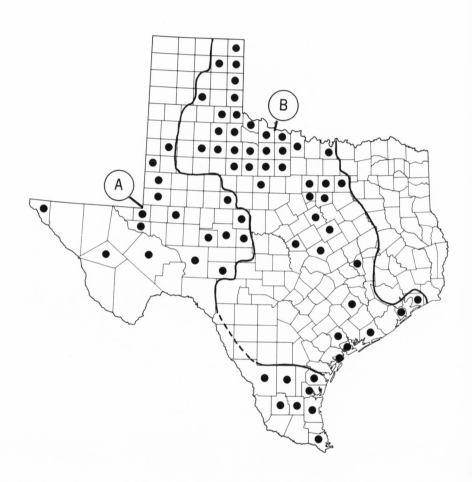

MAP 155. *Sistrurus catenatus edwardsi* (A), Desert Massasauga. *Sistrurus catenatus tergeminus* (B), Western Massasauga.

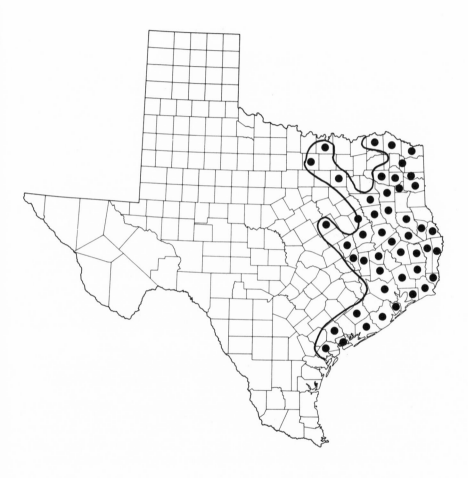

MAP 156. *Sistrurus miliarius streckeri*, Western Pigmy Rattlesnake.

6

Bibliography

Literature on Texas Amphibians and Reptiles from 1852 to 1982 with Selected References from 1983 to 1986

0.1   Adams, D. E. 1966. Operation: Padre Island. *Int. Turtle Tortoise Soc. J.* 1(1):18–20, 40–43, 45.

1.   Adams, H. E. 1963. About rattlesnakes. *Texas Caver* 8(1):4.

2.   Adler, K. K. 1958a. List of specimens of Chelonia and Crocodilia preserved in the author's private collection. *Sp. Publ. Ohio Herp. Soc.* 2:8–21.

3.   ———. 1958b. List of the reptilia preserved in the zoological collections of the Museum of Zoology, Ohio Wesleyan University. *Publ. Dept. Zool. Ohio Wesleyan Univ.* 1–6.

4.   Agassiz, L. 1857. *Contributions to the natural history of the United States of America.* Boston: Little, Brown, and Co.

4.2   Allen, R. F., and J. F. Lhotka, Jr. 1982. *Crotalus atrox:* Notes on the gastric wall. *Copeia* 1982(1):198–200.

5.   Alt, A. 1910. On the histology of the eye of *Typhlotriton spelaeus*, from Marble Cave, Missouri. *Trans. Acad. Sci. St. Louis* 19(6):83–96.

5.1   Altig, R. 1970. A key to the tadpoles of the continental United States and Canada. *Herpetologica* 26(2):180–207.

5.11   Altig, R., and P. H. Ireland. 1984. A key to salamander larvae and larviform adults of the United States and Canada. *Herpetologica* 40(2):212–18.

5.3   Anderson, J. D. 1967a. *Ambystoma texanum. Cat. Amer. Amphib. Rept.* 37.1–37.2.

5.31   ———. 1967b. *Ambystoma opacum. Cat. Amer. Amphib. Rept.* 46.1–46.2.

5.32   ———. 1967c. *Ambystoma maculatum. Cat. Amer. Amphib. Rept.* 51.1–51.4.

6.   Anderson, P. 1942. New record for *Salvadora lineata. Copeia* 1942(2): 127.

7.   Anderson, P. K. 1961. Variation in populations of brown snakes, genus *Storeria*, bordering the Gulf of Mexico. *Amer. Midl. Nat.* 66(1): 235–47.

8.   Anonymous. 1957. Report on Harrel Cave. *Texas Caver* 2(1):11.

9.   Anon. 1959. New salamander discovered. *Texas Caver* 4(5):5.

9.1   Anon. 1969. Escape from extinction. *Time* 93(13):54.

9.11   Anon. 1974. Endangered fauna of the United States. *Bull. Field Mus. Nat. Hist.* 45(12):3–5.

9.12   Anon. 1975. NPCA at work. *Natl. Parks & Conservation* 49(1):25–26.

9.13   Anon. 1977. Endangered and threatened species of the United States and Puerto Rico. *Bull. Field Mus. Nat. Hist.* 48(6):10–11.

9.14   Anon. 1977. New rules proposed for collecting in Texas. *Herpetology* 9(2):18–19.

9.15   Anon. 1978. U.S.-Mexico restoration efforts may be only hope for Kemp's Ridley. *Bull. New York Herp. Soc.* 14(2):27–29.

9.16   Anon. 1978. Species listing for nongame regulations. *Texas Parks & Wildlife Dept. Brochure.* 9000–52:1–22.

9.17   Anon. 1980. Back covers. (Photograph and distributional data of *Eumeces tetragrammus tetragrammus*). *Texas Parks & Wildlife* 38(7):32.

9.18   Anon. 1980. *Bufo marinus* publications. *Herp. Rev.* 11(10):12.

9.19   Anon. 1980. Trans-Pecos ratsnake: Handle with (loving) care. *Chihuahuan Desert Disc.* 8:7.

9.2   Anon. 1980. Selected vertebrate endangered species of the seacoast of the United States—The Houston toad. *USFWS, Biol. Serv. Prog.* FWS/OBS-80/01.38:ii–6.

9.21   Anon. 1980. Selected vertebrate endangered species of the seacoast of the United States. *US FWS, Biol. Serv. Prog.* FWS/OBS-80/01.39: 1–9.

9.22   Anon. 1981. Growling gator awakens Lake Buchanan resident. *Texas Parks & Wildlife* 39(8):21.

9.23   Anon. 1981. Mottled rock rattlesnake: A camouflage artist. *Chihuahuan Desert Disc.* 9:7.

9.4   Armentrout, D., and F. L. Rose, 1971. Some physiological responses to anoxia in the great plains toad, *Bufo cognatus*. *Comp. Biochem. Physiol.* 38A:447–55..

10.   Auffenberg, W. 1948a. Range extension of *Farancia abacura reinwardtii* in Texas. *Herpetologica* 4(5):193.

11.   ———. 1948b. Airplane introduces *Cemphora coccinea* to Texas. *Herpetologica* 4(5):212.

12.   ———. 1949. The racer, *Coluber constrictor stejnegerianus* in Texas. *Herpetologica* 5(2):53–58.

13.   ———. 1955. A reconsideration of the racer, *Coluber constrictor*, in eastern United States. *Tulane Stud. Zool.* 2(6):89–155.

13.1   ———. 1962. A redescription of *Testudo hexagonata* Cope. *Herpetologica* 18(1):25–34.

13.11   ———. 1969. *Tortoise behavior and survival. BSCS Patterns of Life Series. Chicago: Rand McNally & Co.*

13.12   ———. 1974. Checklist of fossil land tortoises. *Bull. Florida St. Mus.* 18(3):121–251.

13.13   ———. 1976. The genus *Gopherus* (Testudinidae): Pt. I. Osteology and relationships of extant species. *Bull. Florida St. Mus.* 20(2):47–110.

13.2   Auffenberg, W., and R. Franz. 1978a. *Gopherus. Cat. Amer. Amphib. Rept.* 211.1–211.2.

13.22   ———. 1978b. *Gopherus berlandieri. Cat. Amer. Amphib. Rept.* 213.1–213.2.

14.   Auffenberg, W., and W. W. Milstead. 1965. Reptiles in the Quaternary of North America. Pp. 557–67 in *The Quaternary of the United States*, edited by H. W. Wright and D. G. Frey. Princeton, N.J.: Princeton University Press.

14.1   Auffenberg, W., and W. G. Weaver. 1969. *Gopherus berlandieri* in southeastern Texas. *Bull. Florida St. Mus.* 13(3):141–203.

15.   Awbrey, F. T. 1963. Homing and home range in *Bufo valliceps. Texas J. Sci.* 15(2):127–41.

15.1   ———. 1968. Call discrimination in female *Scaphiopus couchii* and *Scaphiopus hurterii. Copeia* 1968(2):420–23.

15.5   Axtell, C. A., and R. W. Axtell. 1970. Hibernacula, birth, and young of *Sceloporus grammicus disparilis* (Iguanidae). *Southwest Nat.* 14(3):363–66.

16.   Axtell, R. W. 1950a. Two specimens of the snake *Ficimia streckeri* from Texas. *Copeia* 1950(2):157.

17.   ———. 1950b. Notes on a specimen of *Sceloporus poinsettii* and its young. *Herpetologica* 6(3):80–81.

18.   ———. 1951. An additional specimen of *Lampropeltis blairi* from Texas. *Copeia* 1951(4):313.

19.   ———. 1956. A solution to the long neglected *Holbrookia lacerata* problem, and the description of two new subspecies of Holbrookia. Bull. Chicago Acad. Sci. 10(11):163–79.

20.   ———. 1959a. Female reaction to the male call in two anurans (Amphibia). *Southwest. Nat.* 3(1–4):70–76.

21.   ———. 1959b. Amphibians and reptiles of the Black Gap Wildlife Management Area, Brewster County, Texas. *Southwest. Nat.* 4(2):88–109.

22.   ———. 1960. Orientation by *Holbrookia maculata* (Lacertilia, Iguanidae) to solar and reflected heat. *Southwest. Nat.* 5(1):45–47.

23.   ———. 1961a. *Cnemidophorus inornatus,* the valid name for the little striped whiptail lizard, with the description of an annectant subspecies. *Copeia* 1961(2):148–58.

24.   ———. 1961b. *Eumeces epipleurotus* Cope, a revived name of the southwestern skink *Eumeces multivirgatus gaigei* Taylor. *Texas J. Sci.* 13(3):345–51.

25.   ———. 1963. A reinterpretation of the distribution of *Bufo w. woodhousei.* Girard, especially on the southeastern margin of its range. *Herpetologica* 19(2):115–22.

26.   ———. 1966. Geographic distribution of the unisexual whiptail *Cnemidophorus neomexicanus* (Sauria: Teiidae)—present and past. *Herpetologica* 22(4):241–53.

26.1   ———. 1968. *Holbrookia lacerata. Cat. Amer. Amphib. Rept.* 56.1–56.2

26.11 ———. 1969. Another *Ficimia streckeri* from southern Texas. *Texas J. Sci.* 20(4):381.

26.12 ———. 1977(1978). Ancient playas and their influence on the recent herpetofauna of the northern Chihuahuan desert. Pp. 493–512 in *Transactions of the symposium on the biological resources of the Chihuahuan desert region, United States and Mexico,* edited by R. W. Wauer and D. H. Riskind. Natl. Park Ser. Trans. Proc. Ser. (3).

26.13 ———. 1981. *Holbrookia propinqua:* Type specimens, collector, his route, and restriction of locality, with comments on Baird's *Reptiles of the Boundary* as an important taxonomic reference. *J. Herp.* 15(2): 211–17.

26.14 ———. 1983. Range portrayal and reality: *Heterodon platyrhinos* distribution on the high plains of Texas and Oklahoma. *J. Herp.* 17(2): 191–93.

26.15. ———. 1983. *Holbrookia propinqua. Cat. Amer. Amphib. Rept. 341.1– 341.2.*

26.16 ———. 1986. Interpretive atlas of Texas lizards: *Coleonyx brevis.* 13pp. + unnumbered map. Privately printed and sold by the author.

26.21 Axtell, R. W., and N. Haskell. 1977. An interhiatal population of *Pseudacris streckeri* from Illinois, with an assessment of its postglacial dispersion history. *Chicago Acad. Sci. Nat. Hist. Misc.* 202:1–8.

27. Axtell, R. W., and A. O. Wasserman. 1953. Interesting herpetological records from southern Texas and northern Mexico. *Herpetologica* 9(1):1–6.

27.5 Ayala, S. C., and J. J. Schall. 1977. Apparent absence of blood parasites in southwestern Texas *Cnemidophorus. Southwest. Nat.* 22(1):134–35.

28. Bailey, J. R. 1939. A systematic revision of the snakes of the genus *Coniophanes. Papers Michigan Acad. Sci., Arts, Letters* 24(2):1–48.

29. Bailey, V. 1905. Biological survey of Texas. *N. Amer. Fauna* 25.

30. Baird, S. F. 1854. Descriptions of new genera and species of North American frogs. *Proc. Acad. Nat. Sci. Philadelphia* 7:59–62.

31. ———. 1858. Description of new genera and species of North American lizards in the museum of the Smithsonian Institution. *Proc. Acad. Nat. Sci. Philadelphia* 10:253–65.

32. ———. 1859a. Reptiles of the boundary. *Rept. United States–Mexican Boundary Survey,* vol. 2.

33. ———. 1859b. (Several reports upon reptiles and amphibians). In *General report upon the zoology of the several Pacific railroad routes.* Senate Exec. Doc. 78, 33rd Cong., 2nd sess., vol. 10.

34. Baird, S. F., and C. Girard. 1852a. Reptiles. Pp. 336–53 in H. Stansbury, *Exploration and survey of the valley of the Great Salt Lake, Utah.* Philadelphia: Lippincott, Grambo & Co.

35. ———. 1852b. Characteristics of some new reptiles in the museum of the Smithsonian Institution. *Proc. Acad. Nat. Sci. Philadelphia* 6: 68–70.

36. ———. 1852c. Characteristics of some new reptiles in the museum of the Smithsonian Institution. Second Part. *Proc. Acad. Nat. Sci. Philadelphia* 6:125–29.

37. ———. 1852d. Characteristics of some new reptiles in the museum of the Smithsonian Institution. Third Part. *Proc. Acad. Nat. Sci. Philadelphia* 6:173.

38. ———. 1853. Catalogue of North American reptiles in the museum of the Smithsonian Institute. Part I. Serpents. *Smithsonian Misc. Coll.* 2, art. 5.

39. ———. 1854. Reptiles. Pp. 188–215. in R. B. Marcy and G. B. McClellan, *Exploration of the Red River of Louisiana in the year 1852.* 32nd Cong., 2nd sess., Senate Exec. Doc., Vol. 8, no. 54. Washington, D.C.

40. Baker, C. L. 1947. The species of Amphiumae. *J. Tennessee Acad. Sci.* 2(1):9–21.

41. Baker, J. K. 1956. Frogs of Texas caves. *Texas Caver* 1(10):8–9.

42. ———. 1957a. *Eurycea troglodytes:* A new blind cave salamander from Texas. *Texas J. Sci.* 9(3):328–36.

43. ———. 1957b. Biological notes. *Texas Caver* 2(1):3.

44. ———. 1957c. Some notes on cave salamanders of the Edwards Plateau. *Texas Caver* 2(2):10–11.

45. ———. 1961. Distribution of and key to the neotenic *Eurycea* of Texas. *Southwest Nat.* 6(1):27–32.

45.1 ———. 1966. *Eurycea troglodytes. Cat. Amer. Amphib. Rept.* 23.1–23.2.

45.2 Baker, R. J., J. J. Bull, and G. A. Mengden. 1971. Chromosomes of *Elaphe subocularis* (Reptilia: Serpentes), with description of an *in vivo* technique for preparation of snake chromosomes. *Experientia* 27(10): 1228–29.

45.3 Baker, R. J., G. A. Mengden, and J. J. Bull. 1972. Karyotypic studies of thirty-eight species of North American snakes. *Copeia 1972(2):* 257–65.

46. Baldauf, R. J. 1955. Contributions to the cranial morphology of *Bufo w. woodhousei. Texas J. Sci.* 7(3):275–311.

47. ———. 1957a. Additional studies on the cranial morphology of *Bufo w. woodhousei. Texas J. Sci.* 9(1):84–88.

48.   ———. 1957b. Records of *Agkistrodon piscivorus leucostoma*. *Copeia* 1957(3):229.

49.   ———. 1958. Contributions to the cranial morphology of *Bufo valliceps* Wiegmann. *Texas J. Sci.* 10(2):172–76.

50.   Baldauf, R. J., and R. D. Lord. 1954. Another noteworthy range extension of the toad *Bufo punctatus* in Texas. *Copeia* 1954(2):157.

51.   Baldauf, R. J., and E. C. Tanzer. 1965. Contributions to the cranial morphology of the leptodactylid frog, *Syrrhophus marnocki* Cope. *Texas J. Sci.* 17(1):71–100.

52.   Baldauf, R. J., and J. C. Truett. 1964. First record of *Ambystoma talpoideum* (Holbrook) from Texas. *Copeia* 1964(1):221.

53.   Ballinger, R. E. 1966. Natural hybridization of the toads *Bufo woodhousei* and *B. speciosus*. *Copeia* 1966(2):366–68.

53.1   ———. 1971. Comparative demography of two viviparous lizards (*Sceloporus jarrovi* and *Sceloporus poinsetti*) with consideration of the evolutionary ecology of viviparity in lizards. Ph.D. diss., Texas A&M University. *Diss. Abst. Int.* B32(8):4540–41.

53.11   ———. 1973a. Experimental evidence of the tail as a balancing organ in the lizard, *Anolis carolinensis*. *Herpetologica* 29(1):65–66.

53.12   ———. 1973b. Comparative demography of two viviparous iguanid lizards (*Sceloporus jarrovi* and *Sceloporus poinsetti*). *Ecology* 54(2):269–83.

53.13   ———. 1974. Reproduction in the Texas horned lizard, *Phrynosoma cornutum*. *Herpetologica* 39(4):321–27.

53.14   ———. 1977. Reproductive strategies: Food availability as a source of proximal variation in a lizard. *Ecology* 58(3):628–35.

53.2   Ballinger, R. E., and D. R. Clark. 1973. Energy content of lizard eggs and the measurement of reproductive effort. *J. Herp.* 7(2):129–32.

53.23   Ballinger, R. E., and T. G. Hipp. 1985a. Hematological variations in the collared lizard, *Crotaphytus collaris* (Sauria: Iguanidae). *Copeia* 1985(3):782–84.

53.24   ———. 1985b. Reproduction in the collared lizard, *Crotaphytus collaris*, in west central Texas. *Copeia* 1985(4):976–80.

53.3   Ballinger, R. E., and C. O. McKinney. 1966. Developmental temperature tolerance of certain anuran species. *J. Exp. Zool.* 161(1):21–28.

54.   ———. 1967. Variation and polymorphism in the dorsal color pattern of *Uta stansburiana stejnegeri*. *Amer. Midl. Nat.* 77(2):476.

54.1 ———. 1968. Occurrence of a patternless morph of *Cnemidophorus.* *Herpetologica* 24(3):264–65.

54.2 Ballinger, R. E., and G. D. Schrank. 1970. Acclimation rate and variability of the critical thermal maximum in the lizard *Phrynosoma cornutum.* *Physiol. Zool.* 43(1):19–22.

54.3 ———. 1972. Reproductive potential of female whiptail lizards, *Cnemidophorus gularis gularis.* *Herpetologica* 28(3):217–22.

54.31 ———. 1973. Male reproductive cycles in two species of lizards (*Cophosaurus texanus* and *Cnemidophorus gularis*). *Herpetologica* 29(3): 289–93.

54.4 Ballinger, R. E., and D. W. Tinkle. 1972. Systematics and evolution of the genus *Uta* (Sauria: Iguanidae). *Misc. Publ. Mus. Zool. Univ. Michigan* 145:1–83.

54.41 ———. 1979. On the cost of tail regeneration to body growth in lizards. *J. Herp.* 13(3):374–75.

54.5 Ballinger, R. E., and E. D. Tyler, and D. W. Tinkle. 1972. Reproductive ecology of a west Texas population of the greater earless lizard, *Cophosaurus texanus.* *Amer. Midl. Nat.* 88(2):419–28.

54.7 Banicki, L. H., and R. G. Webb. 1982. Morphological variation of the Texas lyre snake (*Trimorphodon biscutatus vilkinsoni*) from Franklin Mountains, west Texas. *Southwest Nat.* 27(3):321–24.

55. Barbour, T., and A. Loveridge. 1929. Typical reptiles and amphibians in the Museum of Comparative Zoology. *Bull. Mus. Comp. Zool.* 69(10): 205–360.

56. Barden, R. B., and L. J. Kezer. 1944. The eggs of certain plethodontid salamanders obtained by pituitary gland implementation. *Copeia* 1944(1):115–18.

56.2 Barrett, E. P., and C. P. Benjamin. 1977. An analysis of the pigmentation of the epigeal *Eurycea* of the Texas Edwards Plateau. *Copeia* 1977(1):59–65.

56.4 Bartlett, R. D. 1971. The pit vipers of the United States. *Bull. Chicago Herp. Soc.* 6(2):29–39.

57. Barton, A. J. 1948. Snake litters. *Herpetologica* 4(6):198.

58. Baughman, J. L. 1951. The caves of Texas. *Texas Game and Fish* 9(8): 2–7.

58.2 Baur, B. 1979. Leben in der Wüste Krötenechsen (*Phrynosoma* Wiegmann, 1828) 2. Teil: Pflege und Zucht der Rund Schwanz-Krötenechse, *Phrynosoma modestum* Girard, 1852. *Das Aquarium* 125: 528–32.

59.   Baur, G. 1893. Notes on the classification and taxonomy of the Testudinata. *Proc. Amer. Philos. Soc.* 31:210–25.

59.1   Baxter, D. 1971. Lizards. *Texas Parks & Wildlife* 29(11):24–27.

59.2   Bayless, L. E. 1969. Post-metamorphic growth of *Acris crepitans*. *Amer. Midl. Nat.* 81(2):590–92.

59.3   Beasom, S. L. 1974. Selectivity of predator control techniques in South Texas. *J. Wildlife Mgmt.* 38:837–44.

59.4   Beavers, R. A. 1976. Food habits of the western diamondback rattlesnake, *Crotalus atrox,* in Texas (Viperidae). *Southwest. Nat.* 20(4): 503–15.

59.5   Behler, J., and F. W. King. 1978. *The Audubon Society field guide to North American reptiles and amphibians.* New York: Alfred A. Knopf.

59.6   Benefield, G. E. 1979. Geographical distribution. *Tropidoclonion lineatum lineatum. Herp Rev.* 10(3):104.

59.65   Berlandier, J. L. 1980. *Journey to Mexico during the years 1826–1834.* Translated by S. M. Ohlendorf, J. M. Bigelow, and M. M. Standifer. 2 vols. Austin: Texas St. Hist. Assoc.

59.7   Berman, D. S. 1970. Vertebrate fossils from the Lueders formation, Lower Permian of north-central Texas. *Univ. California Publ. Geol. Sci.* 86:1–61.

59.8   Bertl, J., and F. C. Killebrew. 1983. An osteological comparison of *Graptemys caglei* Haynes and McKown and *Graptemys versa* Stejneger (Testudines: Emydidae). *Herpetologica* 39(4):375–82.

60.   Beyer, G. E. 1898. Contributions on the life histories of certain snakes. *Amer. Nat.* 32:17–24.

60.2   Bickham, J. W., C. O. McKinney, and M. F. Mathews. 1976. Karyotypes of the parthenogenetic whiptail lizard *Cnemidophorus laredoensis* and its presumed parental species (Sauria: Teiidae). *Herpetologica* 32(4):395–99.

61.   Bider, J. R. 1962. Dynamics and the temporo-spatial relations of a vertebrate community. *Ecology* 43(4):634–46.

61.3   Bigony, M. 1980. Skimming over the marsh. *Texas Parks & Wildlife* 38(3):10–12.

61.31   ———. 1981. When was the last time you saw a horned lizard? *Texas Parks & Wildlife* 39(2):28–31.

62. Bishop, S. C. 1941. Notes on salamanders with descriptions of several new forms. *Occ. Papers Mus. Zool. Univ. Michigan* 451:1–21.

63. ———. 1947. *Handbook of salamanders.* Ithaca, N.Y.: Comstock Publ. Co.

64. Bishop, S. C., and F. J. W. Schmidt. 1931. The painted turtles of the genus *Chrysemys. Field Mus. Nat. Hist., Zool. Ser.* 18(4):123–39.

65. Bishop, S. C., and M. R. Wright. 1937. A new neotenic salamander from Texas. *Proc. Biol. Soc. Washington* 50:141–43.

66. Blackford, C. M. 1899. A curious salamander. *Nature* 60:389–90.

67. Blair, A. P. 1941. Variation, isolating mechanisms, and hybridization in certain toads. *Genetics* 26:389–417.

68. ———. 1943a. Geographical variation of ventral markings in toads. *Amer. Midl. Nat.* 29(3):615–20.

69. ———. 1943b. The male warning vibration in *Bufo. Amer. Mus. Novitates* 1344:1–7.

70. ———. 1947. Defensive use of parotoid secretion of *Bufo marinus. Copeia* 1947(2):137.

71. ———. 1950. Notes on two anguid lizards. *Copeia* 1950 (1):57.

72. ———. 1957. Amphibians. Pp. 211–71 in W. F. Blair et al., *Vertebrates of the United States.* New York: McGraw-Hill Book Co.

72.5 ———. 1968. Amphibians. Pp. 167–212 in W. F. Blair et al., *Vertebrates of the United States.* 2nd ed. New York: McGraw-Hill Book Co.

73. Blair, W. F. 1949a. Development of the solitary spadefoot in Texas. *Copeia* 1949(1):72.

74. ———. 1949b. The biotic provinces of Texas. *Texas J. Sci.* 2(1):93–117.

75. ———. 1952. Mammals of the Tamaulipan Biotic Province in Texas. *Texas J. Sci.* 4(2):230–50.

76. ———. 1953. Growth, dispersal, and age of sexual maturity of the Mexican toad (*Bufo valliceps* Wiegmann). *Copeia* 1953(4):208–12.

77. ———. 1954. Mammals of the Mesquite Plains Biotic District in Texas and Oklahoma, and speciation in the central grasslands. *Texas J. Sci.* 6(3):235–64.

78. ———. 1955a. Mating call and stage of speciation in the *Microhyla olivacea–M. carolinensis* complex. *Evolution* 9(4):469–80.

79.   ———. 1955b. Differentiation of mating call in spadefoots, genus *Scaphiopus*. *Texas J. Sci.* 7(2):183–88.

80.   ———. 1955c. Size difference as a possible isolation mechanism in *Microhyla*. *Amer. Nat.* 89:297–301.

81.   ———. 1956a. Comparative survival of hybrid toads (*B. woodhousei* X *B. valliceps*) in nature. *Copeia* 1956(4):259–60.

82.   ———. 1956b. Call differences as an isolation mechanism in southwestern toads (genus *Bufo*). *Texas J. Sci.* 8(1):87–106.

83.   ———. 1956c. The mating calls of hybrid toads. *Texas J. Sci.* 8(3):350–55.

84.   ———. 1957. Changes in vertebrate populations under conditions of drought. In *Cold Springs Harbor Symposia on Quantitative Biology* 22:273–75.

85.   ———. 1958a. Mating call in the speciation of anuran amphibians. *Amer. Nat.* 92:27–51.

86.   ———. 1958b. Mating call and stage of speciation of two allopatric populations of spadefoots (*Scaphiopus*). *Texas J. Sci.* 10(4):443–46.

86.1   ———. 1958c. Distributional patterns of vertebrates in the Southwestern United States in relation to past and present environments. Pp. 433–68. In *Zoogeography,* edited by C. L. Hubbs. Washington, D.C.: AAAS Publ. (51).

87.   ———. 1959a. Call structure and species groups in United States tree frogs (*Hyla*). *Southwest Nat.* 3(1–4):77–89.

88.   ———. 1959b. Genetic compatibility and species groups in U.S. toads (*Bufo*). *Texas J. Sci.* 11(4):427–53.

89.   ———. 1960a. Radiation-induced genetic damage in the Mexican toad (*Bufo valliceps*). *Texas J. Sci.* 12(3–4):216–27.

90.   ———. 1960b. Mating calls as evidence of relations in the *Hyla eximia* group. *Southwest. Nat.* 5(3):129–35.

91.   ———. 1960c. A breeding population of the Mexican toad (*Bufo valliceps*) in relation to its environment. *Ecology* 41(1):165–74.

92.   ———. 1960d. *The rusty lizard: A population study.* Austin: University of Texas Press.

93.   ———. 1961a. Further evidence bearing on intergroup and intragroup genetic compatibility in toads (genus *Bufo*). *Texas J. Sci.* 13(2):163–75.

94. ———. 1961b. Calling and spawning seasons in a mixed population of anurans. *Ecology* 42(1):99–110.

95. ———. 1962. Non-morphological data in anuran classification. *Syst. Zool.* 11(2):72–84.

96. ———. 1963a. Intra-group genetic compatibility in the *Bufo americanus* species group of toads. *Texas J. Sci.* 15(1):15–34.

96.1 ———. 1963b. Evolutionary relationships of North American toads of the genus *Bufo:* A progress report. *Evolution* 17(1):1–16.

97. ———. 1964a. Evidence bearing on relationships of the *Bufo boreas* group of toads. *Texas J. Sci.* 16(2) 181–92.

98. ———. 1964b. Isolating mechanisms and interspecies interactions in anuran amphibians. *Quart. Rev. Biol.* 39(4):334–44.

99. ———. 1965. Amphibian speciation. Pp. 543–55 in *The Quaternary of the United States,* edited by H. E. Wright and D. G. Frey. Princeton, N.J.: Princeton University Press.

100. ———. 1966. Genetic compatibility in the *Bufo valliceps* and closely related groups of toads. *Texas J. Sci.* 18(4):333–50.

100.01 Blair, W. F., ed. 1972. *Evolution in the genus* Bufo. Austin: University of Texas Press.

100.02 ———. 1972. Characteristics of the testes. Pp. 324–28 in *Evolution of the genus* Bufo, edited by W. F. Blair. Austin: University of Texas Press.

100.03 ———. 1972. Evidence from hybridization. Pp. 196–232 in *Evolution in the genus* Bufo, edited by W. F. Blair. Austin: University of Texas Press.

100.04 ———. 1974. Character displacement in frogs. *Amer. Zool.* 14(4):1119–25.

100.05 ———. 1976. Some aspects of the biology of the ornate box turtle, *Terrapene ornata. Southwest. Nat.* 21(1):89–104.

101. Blair, W. F., and T. E. Kennerly, Jr. 1959. Effects of x-irradiation on a natural population of the woodmouse (*Peromyscus leucopus*). *Texas J. Sci.* 11(2):137–49.

102. Blair, W. F., and M. J. Littlejohn. 1960. Stage of speciation of two allopatric populations of chorus frogs (*Pseudacris*). *Evolution* 14(1):82–87.

103. Blair, W. F., and C. E. Miller, Jr. 1949. The mammals of the Sierra Vieja Region, southwestern Texas, with remarks on the biogeographic position of the region. *Texas J. Sci.* 1(1):67–92.

104. Blanchard, F. N. 1920. A synopsis of the king snakes: Genus *Lampropeltis* Fitzinger. *Occ. Papers Mus. Zool. Univ. Michigan* 87:1–6.

105. ———. 1921. A revision of the king snakes: Genus *Lampropeltis*. *Bull. U.S. Natl. Mus.* 114:1–260.

106. ———. 1923a. A new North American snake of the genus *Natrix*. *Occ. Papers Mus. Zool. Univ. Michigan* 140:1–7.

107. ———. 1923b. Comments on ring-neck snakes (genus *Diadophis*) with diagnoses of new forms. *Occ. Papers Mus. Zool. Univ. Michigan* 142:1–9.

108. ———. 1924a. A new snake of the genus *Arizona*. *Occ. Papers Mus. Zool. Univ. Michigan* 150:1–3.

109. ———. 1924b. The snakes of the genus *Virginia*. *Papers Michigan Acad. Arts, Sci., Letters* 3(3):343–65.

110. ———. 1924c. The status of *Amphiardus inornatus* (Garman). *Copeia* 1924(1):83.

111. ———. 1925. A key to the snakes of United States, Canada, and Lower California. *Papers Michigan Acad. Arts, Sci., Letters* 4(2):1–65.

112. ———. 1938. Snakes of the genus *Tantilla* in the United States. *Field Mus. Nat. Hist. Zool. Ser.* 20(28):369–76.

113. ———. 1942. The ring-neck snakes, genus *Diadophis*. *Bull. Chicago Acad. Sci.* 7(1):1–142.

113.5 Blaney, R. M. 1973. *Lampropeltis. Cat. Amer. Amphib. Rept.* 150.1–150.2

113.51 ———. 1977. Systematics of the common kingsnake *Lampropeltis getulus* (Linnaeus). *Tulane Stud. Zool. Bot.* 19(3–4):47–103.

113.52 ———. 1979. *Lampropeltis calligaster. Cat. Amer. Amphib. Rept.* 229.1–229.2

113.55 Blaney, R. M., and P. J. Kimmich. 1973. Notes on the young of the Texas horned lizard, *Phrynosoma cornutum. Herp Rev.* 1(4):120.

113.6 Blem, C. 1981. *Heterodon platyrhinos. Cat. Amer. Amphib. Rept.* 282.1–282.2

113.7 Block, E. F. 1967. Parasites of the Texas cricket frog, *Acris crepitans. Texas J. Sci.* 19(4):422.

113.80 Bogart, J. P. 1968. Chromosome number difference in the amphibian genus *Bufo*: The *Bufo regularis* species group. *Evolution* 22(1):42–45.

113.81 ———. 1972. Karyotypes. Pp. 171–95 in *Evolution in the genus* Bufo, edited by W. F. Blair. Austin: University of Texas Press.

113.85 Bogart, J. P., and C. E. Nelson. 1976. Evolutionary implications from karyotypic analysis of frogs of the families Microhylidae and Rhinophrynidae. *Herpetologica* 32(2):199–208.

114. Bogert, C. M. 1939a. Notes on snakes of the genus *Salvadora* with a redescription of a neglected Mexican subspecies. *Copeia* 1939(3): 140–47.

115. ———. 1939b. A study of the genus *Salvadora*, the patch-nosed snakes. *Publ. Biol. Sci., Univ. California at Los Angeles* 1(10):177–236.

116. ———. 1945. Two additional races of the patch-nosed snake, *Salvadora hexalepis. Amer. Mus. Novitates* 1285:1–14.

117. ———. 1960. The influence of sound on the behavior of amphibians and reptiles. In W. Tavolga, *Animal sounds and communication.* Amer. Inst. Biol. Sci. Publ. 7:137–320.

118. ———. 1962. Isolation mechanisms in toads of the *Bufo debilis* group in Arizona and western Mexico. *Amer. Mus. Novitates* 2100:1–37.

119. Bogert, C. M., and J. A. Oliver. 1945. A preliminary analysis of herpetofauna of Sonora. *Bull. Amer. Mus. Nat. Hist.* 83:303–425.

120. Bogush, E. R. 1926. Superstitions of Bexar County. *Publ. Texas Folk-Lore Soc.* 5:112–25.

121. Bolen, E. G., B. McDaniel, and C. Cottam. 1964. Natural history of the black-bellied tree duck (*Dendrocygna autmnalis*) in southern Texas. *Southwest. Nat.* 9(2):78–88.

121.5 Bolt, J. R. 1977. Dissorophoid relationships and ontogeny, and the origin of the Lissamphibia. *J. Paleont.* 51(2):235–49.

122. Bonn, E. W., and W. H. McCarley. 1953. The amphibians and reptiles of the Lake Texoma area. *Texas J. Sci.* 5(4):465–71.

123. Borrell, A. E., and M. D. Bryant. 1942. Mammals of the Big Bend area of Texas. *Univ. California Publ. Zool.* 48(1):1–62.

123.5 Boston, J. D., and C. R. Williams. 1968. Characteristics of proteolytic activity of pepsin from *Rana catesbeiana. Texas J. Sci.* 20(1):77–86.

124. Boucourt, F. 1879. Recherches zoologiques pour servir à l'histoire de la fauna de L'Amérique Centrale et du Mexique; Etudes sur les reptiles et les batraciens. *Miss. Sci. Mexique et L'Amérique Centrale.* Partie Troisième, Livraison IV. Pp. 361–440; pls. 21–22 (A.D.). Paris.

125.   ————. 1881. Recherches zoologiques pour servir à l'histoire de la fauna de L'Amérique Centrale et du Mexique; Etudes sur les reptiles et les batraciens. *Miss. Sci. Mexique et L'Amérique Centrale.* Partie Troisième, Livraison VII. Pp. 441–48; pls. 22(D–J). Paris.

126.   Boulenger, E. G. 1916. A new lizard of the genus *Phrynosoma*, recently living in the Society's gardens. *Proc. Zool. Soc. London* 1916:537.

127.   Boulenger, G. A. 1887. Descriptions of new reptiles and batrachians in the British Museum. Part III. *Ann. Mag. Nat. Hist. Series* 5, 20: 50–53.

128.   ————. 1888. On a rare American newt, *Molge meridionalis*, Cope. *Ann. Mag. Nat. Hist. Series* 6, 1:24.

129.   ————. 1890a. First report on the additions to the lizard collection in the British Museum. *Proc. Zool. Soc. London* 1890:77–85.

130.   ————. 1890b. Second report on additions to the batrachian collection in the Natural History Museum. *Proc. Zool. Soc. London* 1890:323.

131.   ————. 1893. *Catalogue of the snakes in the British Museum.* Vol. I. London.

132.   ————. 1894a. *Catalogue of the snakes in the British Museum.* Vol. II. London.

133.   ————. 1984b. Third report on additions to the lizard collection in the Natural History Museum. *Proc. Zool. Soc. London* 1894:640.

134.   ————. 1896. *Catalogue of the snakes in the British Museum* Vol. III. London.

135.   ————. 1897. A revision of the lizards of the genus *Sceloporus*. *Proc. Zool. Soc. London* 1897:474–522.

136.   ————. 1898. Fourth report on additions to the batrachian collection in the Natural History Museum. *Proc. Zool. Soc. London* 1898:473–82.

137.   ————. 1920. A monograph of the American frogs of the genus *Rana*. *Proc. Amer. Acad. Arts and Sci.* 55(9):413–80.

137.5   Bowen, G. S. 1977. Prolonged western equine encephalitis viremia in the Texas tortoise (*Gopherus berlandieri*). *Amer. J. Trop. Med. Hyg.* 26(1):171–75.

138.   Bowers, C. C., and H. M. Smith. 1947. Hibernation of lizards in western Texas. *Herpetologica* 4(2):80.

139.   Bowers, J. H. 1966. Food habits of the diamond-backed water snake, *Natrix rhombifera rhombifera*, in Bowie and Red River counties, Texas. *Herpetologica* 22(3):225–29.

139.01 ———. 1967a. A record litter of *Thamnophis sirtalis proximus* (Say). *Southwest. Nat.* 12(2):200.

139.02 ———. 1967b. A new record length for the plains hognose snake *Heterodon nasicus nasicus* Baird and Girard. *Herpetologica* 23(1):61.

139.5 Bowker, R. G. 1980. Sound production in *Cnemidophorus gularis*. *J. Herp.* 14(2):187–88.

139.6 Bowman, D. 1984. American alligator reclassified in Texas. *Herp Rev.* 15(1):12.

140. Bragg, A. N. 1954. *Bufo terrestris charlesmithi*, a new subspecies from Oklahoma. *Wasmann J. Biol.* 12(2):245–54.

141. ———. 1960. Feeding in the Houston toad. *Southwest. Nat.* 5(2):106.

142. ———. 1965. *Gnomes of the night*. Philadelphia: University of Pennsylvania Press.

143. Bragg, A. N., and O. Sanders. 1951. A new subspecies of the *Bufo woodhousei* group of toads. *Wasmann J. Biol.* 9(3):363–78.

143.5 Bramble, D. M. 1974. Occurrence and significance of the os transiliens in gopher tortoises. *Copeia* 1974(1):102–109.

143.51 ———. 1982. *Scaptochelys:* Generic revision and evolution of gopher tortoises. *Copeia* 1982(4):852–67.

144. Brame, A. H., Jr., 1962. A survey of albinism in salamanders. *Abh. Berichte Natur. Vorgeschichte* 11(3):65–81.

144.01 ———. 1967. A list of the world's recent and fossil salamanders. *Herpetologica* 2(1):1–26.

145. Brattstrom, B. H. 1954. The fossil pit-vipers (Reptilia: Crotalidae) of North America. *Trans. San Diego Soc. Nat. Hist.* 12(3):31–46.

145.01 ———. 1961. Some new fossil tortoises from western North America with remarks on the zoogeography and paleoecology of tortoises. *J. Paleontol.* 35(3):543–60.

146. ———. 1963. A preliminary review of the thermal requirements of amphibians. *Ecology* 44(2):238–55.

147. ———. 1964. Evolution of the pit vipers. *Trans. San·Diego Soc. Nat. Hist.* 13(11):185–268.

148. ———. 1965. Body temperatures of reptiles. *Amer. Midl. Nat.* 73(2):376–422.

148.01 ———. 1967. A succession of Pliocene and Pleistocene snake faunas from the high plains of the United States. *Copeia* 1967(1):188–202.

148.5 Brecke, B. J., J. B. Murphy, and W. Seifert. 1976. An inventory of reproduction and social behavior in captive Baird's ratsnakes *Elaphe obsoleta bairdi* (Yarrow). *Herpetologica* 32(4):389–95.

149. Breckenridge, W. J. 1943. The life history of the black-banded skink *Eumeces septentrionalis septentrionalis* (Baird). *Amer. Midl. Nat.* 29(3):591–606.

149.4 Brimley, C. S. 1904. The box tortoises of southeastern North America. *J. Elisha Mitchell Sci. Soc.* 20(1):27–34.

149.41 ———. 1907. Notes on some turtles of the genus *Pseudemys*. *J. Elisha Mitchell Sci. Soc.* 23(2):76–84.

149.42 ———. 1910. Records of some reptiles and batrachians from the southeastern United States. *Proc. Biol. Soc. Washington.* 23:9–18.

149.7 Brodie, E. D. 1977. Salamander antipredator postures. *Copeia* 1977(3):523–35.

150. Brooks, B. 1906. The anatomy of the internal urogenital organs of certain North American lizards. *Trans. Texas Acad. Sci.* 8:23–38.

150.5 Brooks, G. R. 1972. Intestinal parasites of the lizard *Lygosoma laterale*. *Quart. J. Florida Acad. Sci.* 35(1):8–14.

150.51 ———. 1975. *Scincella lateralis* (Say). *Cat. Amer. Amphib. Rept.* 169.1–169.4.

151. Brown, A. E. 1901a. A review of the genera and species of American snakes north of Mexico. *Proc. Acad. Nat. Sci. Philadelphia* 53:10–110.

152. ———. 1901b. A new species of *Coluber* from western Texas. *Proc. Acad. Nat. Sci. Philadelphia* 53:492–95.

153. ———. 1901c. A new species of *Ophibolus* from western Texas. *Proc. Acad. Nat. Sci. Philadelphia* 53:612–13.

154. ———. 1903a. The variations of *Eutaenia* in the Pacific subregion. *Proc. Acad. Nat. Sci. Philadelphia* 55:286–97.

155. ———. 1903b. Texas reptiles and their faunal relations. *Proc. Acad. Nat. Sci. Philadelphia* 55:543–58.

156. ———. 1903c. Note on *Crotalus scutulatus*. *Proc. Acad Nat. Sci. Philadelphia* 55:625.

157.　　Brown, B. C. 1937. Notes on *Coniophanes imperialis* (Baird). *Copeia*
　　　　1937(4):234.

158.　　———. 1939. The effect of *Coniophanes* poisoning in man. *Copeia*
　　　　1939(2):109.

159.　　———. 1942a. Notes on *Eurycea neotenes. Copeia* 1942(3):176.

160.　　———. 1942b. Notes on *Crotaphytus reticulatus. Copeia* 1942(3):176.

161.　　———. 1947. *Natrix rigida* in Texas. *Herpetologica* 3(1):23.

162.　　———. 1950. *An annotated check list of the reptiles and amphibians of
　　　　Texas.* Waco, Tex.: Baylor Univ. Studies.

163.　　———. 1951a. *Diemictylus viridescens louisianensis* in north-eastern
　　　　Texas. *Herpetologica* 7(2):64.

164.　　———. 1951b. A range extension of the southern prairie skink in Texas.
　　　　Herpetologica 7(2):72.

165.　　———. 1951c. *Eumeces antracinus* in Texas. Herpetologica 7(2):76.

166.　　———. 1951d. The Texas hooded snake in the lower Rio Grande Valley
　　　　of Texas. *Herpetologica* 7(4):175.

167.　　———. 1952. A notable specimen of the Pecos skink. *Herpetologica*
　　　　8(3):101–102.

167.01　———. 1967a. *Eurycea latitans. Cat. Amer. Amphib. Rept.* 34.1–34.2.

167.02　———. 1976b. *Eurycea nana. Cat. Amer. Amphib. Rept.* 35.1–35.2.

167.03　———. 1967c. *Eurycea neotenes. Cat. Amer. Amphib. Rept.* 36.1–36.2.

167.04　———. 1967d. *Trionyx muticus muticus* in the Texas Panhandle. *South-
　　　　west Nat.* 12(4):487.

168.　　Brown, B. C., and J. Haver. 1952. An unusually large congregation of
　　　　turtles. *Herpetologica* 8(1):2.

169.　　Brown, B. C., and M. B. Mittleman. 1947. A range extension for *Cro-
　　　　talus m. molossus* B. and G. in Texas. *herpetologica* 4(1): 23–24.

170.　　Brown, D. A. 1964. Nesting of a captive *Gopherus berlandieri* (Agassiz).
　　　　Herpetologica 20(3):209–10.

170.2　Brown, H. A. 1976. California and Arizona populations of the western
　　　　spadefoot toads (genus *Scaphiopus*). *Nat. Hist. Mus. Los Angeles Co.,
　　　　Contr. Sci.* 286:1–15.

170.3   Brown, L. E. 1968. The significance of natural hybridization in certain aspects of the speciation of some North American toads (genus *Bufo*). *Diss. Abst. Int.* B28(10):4343B.

170.31   ———. 1970. Interspecies interactions as possible causes of racial size differences in the toads *Bufo americanus* and *Bufo woodhousei*. *Texas J. Sci.* 21(3):261–67.

170.32   ———. 1971. Natural hybridization and trends toward extinction in some relict Texas toad populations. *Southwest Nat.* 16(2):185–99.

170.33   ———. 1973. *Bufo houstonensis*. *Cat. Amer. Amphib. Rept.* 133.1–133.2.

170.34   ———. 1974. Behavioral reactions of bullfrogs while attempting to eat toads. *Southwest. Nat.* 19(3):335–37.

170.35   ———. 1975. The status of the near-extinct Houston toad (*Bufo houstonensis*) with recommendations for its conservation. *Herp Rev.* 6:37–40.

170.36   ———. 1979. Houston toad recovery team meets in Houston. *Herp Rev.* 10(3):100.

170.37   Brown, L. E., and M. J. Littlejohn. 1972. Male release call in the *Bufo americanus* group. Pp. 310–23 in *Evolution in the genus* Bufo, edited by W. F. Blair. Austin: University of Texas Press.

170.38   Brown, L. E., and R. A. Thomas. 1982. Misconceptions about the endangered Houston toad (*Bufo houstonensis*). *Herp Rev.* 13(2):37.

170.4   Brown, R. 1968. Alligator snapping turtles *Macroclemys temmincki*. *Herpetology* 2(4):13–14.

170.5   Brown, T. L., and R. V. Lucchino. 1972. A record-sized specimen of the Texas horned lizard (*Phrynosoma cornutum*). *Texas J. Sci.* 24(3):353–54.

170.6   Brownell, J. A. 1971. Effects of the interaction between a hybrid toad and parental species, *Bufo valliceps* and *B. woodhousei*. Ph.D. diss., University of Texas at Austin. *Diss. Abst. Int.* B33(12):152B.

170.7   Bruce, R. C. 1976. Population structure, life history, and evolution of paedogenesis in the salamander *Eurycea neotenes*. *Copeia* 1976(2):242–56.

171.   Buck, H. D. 1946. Food of *Farancia abacura* in Texas. *Herpetologica* 3(4):111.

172.   Bundy, R. E., D. Meyers, and J. Neess. 1955. Observations on two species of lizards in the Chihuahuan desert. *Copeia* 1955(4):312.

172.5   Burchfield, P. M., T. F. Beimler, and C. S. Doucette. 1982. An unusual precoital head-biting behavior in the Texas patchnosed snake, *Salvadora grahamae lineata* (Reptilia: Serpentes: Colubridae). *Copeia* 1982(1):192–93.

173.   Burger, W. L. 1950. New, revised, and reallocated names for North American whiptailed lizards, genus *Cnemidophorus*. *Chicago Acad. Sci. Nat. Hist. Misc.* 65:1–9.

174.   Burger, W. L., H. M. Smith, and F. E. Potter, Jr. 1950. Another neotenic *Eurycea* from the Edwards Plateau. *Proc. Biol. Soc. Washington* 63:51–58.

175.   Burger, W. L., P. W. Smith, and H. M. Smith. 1949. Notable records of reptiles and amphibians in Oklahoma, Arkansas, and Texas. *J. Tennessee Acad. Sci.* 24(2):130–34.

176.   Burkett, R. D. 1962. Two clutches of eggs in the lizard *Gerrhonotus liocephalus infernalis*. *Herpetologica* 18(3):211.

177.   ———. 1964. A new locality record in Texas for the lizard *Eumeces anthracinus pluvialis* Cope. *Trans. Kansas Acad. Sci.* 67(1):98.

178.   ———. 1966. Natural history of cottonmouth moccasin, *Agkistrodon piscivorus* (Reptilia). *Univ. Kansas Publ. Mus. Nat. Hist.* 17(9):435–91.

178.01   ———. 1967. An extension of the known range in Texas for the stinkpot turtles, *Sternothaerus odoratus*. *Trans. Kansas Acad. Sci.* 69(3–4):361.

178.2   Burr, B. M., and M. A. Morris. 1975. Geographic distribution: *Storeria dekayi limnetes*. *Herp Rev.* 6(4):116.

179.   Burt, C. E. 1928. The synonymy, variation, and distribution of the collared lizard, *Crotaphytus collaris* (Say). *Occ. Papers Mus. Zool. Univ. Michigan* 196:1–19.

180.   ———. 1929. The synonymy, variation, and distribution of the Sonoran skink, *Eumeces obsoletus* (Baird and Girard). *Occ. Papers Mus. Zool. Univ. Michigan* 201:1–12.

181.   ———. 1931a. The status of the spotted racerunner, *Cnemidophorus sexlineatus gularis* (Baird and Girard). *Proc. Biol. Soc. Washington* 44:73–78.

182.   ———. 1931b. A report on some amphibians and reptiles from Kansas, Nebraska, and Oklahoma. *Proc. Biol. Soc. Washington* 44:11–16.

183.   ———. 1931c. On the occurrence of a throat-fan in *Callisaurus ventralis gabbii* and two species of *Crotaphytus*. *Copeia* 1931(2):58.

184. ———. 1931d. A study of the teiid lizards of the genus *Cnemidophorus* with special reference to their phylogenetic relationships. *Bull. United States Natl. Mus.* 154:1–286.

185. ———. 1932. The status of the horned lizard *Phrynosoma brevicornis*, described from Texas by E. G. Boulenger (1916). *Proc. Biol. Soc. Washington* 45:73–74.

186. ———. 1935a. Contributions to Texas herpetology. II. Some observations and an experiment on the worm snake, *Leptotyphlops*. *Ecology* 16(3):530–31.

187. ———. 1935b. Contributions to Texas herpetology. III. Bullsnakes of the genera *Arizona* and *Pituophis*. *J. Washington Acad. Sci.* 25(8): 380–83.

188. ———. 1935c. A key to the lizards of the United States and Canada. *Trans. Kansas Acad. Sci.* 38:255–305.

189. ———. 1936a. Contributions to the herpetology of Texas. I. Frogs of the genus *Pseudacris*. *Amer. Midl. Nat.* 17(4):770–75.

190. ———. 1936b. Contributions to Texas herpetology. IV. Sand snakes of the genus *Tantilla*. *Trans. Amer. Micro. Soc.* 55(2):239–42.

191. ———. 1937a. Contributions to Texas herpetology. V. Spiny and Scaly lizards (*Sceloporus*). *Papers Michigan Acad. Sci, Arts, Letters* 22: 535–36.

192. ———. 1937b. Lizards of the southeastern United States. *Trans. Kansas Acad. Sci.* 40:353–54.

193. ———. 1938a. Contributions to Texas herpetology. VI. Narrowmouthed froglike toads (*Microhyla* and *Hypopachus*). *Papers Michigan Acad. Sci. Arts, Letters* 23:607–10.

194. ———. 1938b. Contributions to Texas herpetology. VII. The salamanders. *Amer. Midl. Nat.* 29(2):374–80.

195. Burt, C. E., and M. D. Burt. 1929a. A collection of amphibians and reptiles from the Mississippi Valley with field observations. *Amer. Mus. Novitates* 381.

196. ———. 1929b. Field notes and locality records on a collection of amphibians and reptiles chiefly from the western half of the United States. I. Amphibians. *J. Washington Acad. Sci.* 19(19):428–34.

197. ———. 1929c. Field notes and locality records on a collection of amphibians and reptiles chiefly from the western half of the United States. II. Reptiles. *J. Washington Acad. Sci.* 19(20):448–60.

198.   ———. 1932. A brief review of Texas herpetological history with comments on the zoogeographic importance of the state. *Bio-Log* 2(1):1–2.

198.5   Buth, D. G., G. C. Gorman, and C. S. Lieb. 1980. Genetic divergence between *Anolis carolinensis* and its Cuban progenitor, *Anolis porcatus*. *J. Herp.* 14(3):279–84.

199.   Byrd, E. E., and J. F. Denton. 1938. New trematodes of the subfamily Reniferinae, with a discussion of the systematics of the genera and species assigned to the subfamily group. *J. Parasit.* 24(5):379–99.

200.   Cagle, F. R. 1950. Notes on *Halbrookia texana* in Texas. *Copeia* 1950(3): 230.

201.   ———. 1954a. Two new subspecies of *Graptemys pseudogeographica*. *Occ. Papers Mus. Zool. Univ. Michigan* 546:1–17.

202.   ———. 1954b. A Texas population of the cricket frog, *Acris*. *Copeia* 1954(3):227–28.

203.   ———. 1957. Reptiles. Pp. 273–358 in W. F. Blair et al., *Vertebrates of the United States*. New York: McGraw-Hill Book Co.

203.1   ———. 1968. Reptiles. Pp. 214–68 in W. F. Blair et al., *Vertebrates of the United States*. 2nd ed. New York: McGraw-Hill Book Co.

204.   Cahn, A. R. 1962. The breeding habits of the Texas horned toad, *Phrynosoma cornutum*. *Amer. Nat.* 60:546–51.

204.1   Cain, B. W., and S. R. Utesch. 1976. An unusual color pattern of the green treefrog, *Hyla cinerea*. *Southwest. Nat.* 21(2):235–36.

204.2   Calmonte, A. 1978. Die Schwarzschwanz-Klapperschlange-in der Freiheit-und im Terrarium beobachtet. *Das Aquarium* 107:221–23.

204.3   Campbell, J. A. 1972. Reproduction in captive Trans-Pecos ratsnakes, *Elaphe subocularis*. *Herp Rev.* 4:129–30.

204.31   ———. 1973. A captive hatching of *Micrurus fulvius tenere* (Serpentes, Elapidae). *J. Herp.* 7(3):312–15.

204.4   Campbell, P. M., and W. K. Davis. 1968. Vertebrates in stomachs of *Bufo valliceps*. *Herpetologica* 24(4):327–28.

204.41   ———. 1971. The effects of various combinations of temperature and relative humidity on the evaporative water loss of *Bufo valliceps*. *Texas J. Sci.* 22(4):389–402.

205.   Campbell, T. N. 1958. Archeological remains from the Live Oak Point Site, Aransas County, Texas. *Texas J. Sci.* 10(4):423–42.

205.01 Carl, G. 1978. Notes on worm-eating in the prairie ringneck snake, *Diadophis punctatus arnyi. Bull. Maryland Herp. Soc.* 14(2):95–97.

205.11 ———. 1980. Distributional records for Johnson County, Texas. *Herp Rev.* 11(4):116–17.

205.12 ———. 1981. Reproduction in the captive Brazos water snake, *Nerodia harteri. Texas J. Sci.* 33(1):77–78.

205.15 Carl, G., and R. Hudson. 1983. Life history notes: *Lampropeltis getulus holbrooki* X *splendida. Herp Rev.* 14(1):20.

206.   Carpenter, C. C. 1961. Patterns of social behavior of Merriam's canyon lizard (*Sceloporus m. merriami-Iguanidae*). *Southwest. Nat.* 6(3–4): 138–48.

206.1   ———. 1978. Comparative display behavior in the genus *Sceloporus* (Iguanidae). *Milwaukee Publ. Mus. Contr. Biol. Geol.* 18:1–71.

207.   Carpenter, C. C., et al. 1961. A *Uta* invasion of Oklahoma. *Southwest. Nat.* 6(3–4):192–93.

208.   Carr, A. F., Jr. 1938a. A new subspecies of *Pseudemys floridana*, with notes on the *floridana* complex. *Copeia* 1938(3):105–109.

209.   ———. 1938b. Notes on the *Pseudemys scripta* complex. *Herpetologica* 1(5):131–35.

210.   ———. 1946. Status of the mangrove terrapin. *Copeia* 1946(3):170–72.

211.   ———. 1949. The identity of *Malacoclemmys kohni* Baur. *Herpetologica* 5(1):9–10.

212.   ———. 1952. *Handbook of turtles.* Ithaca, N.Y.: Comstock Publ. Co.

212.5   Carr, J. L., and T. W. Houseal. 1981. Post-hibernation behavior in *Terrapene triunguis* (Emydidae). *Southwest Nat.* 26(2):199–200.

212.6   Case, T. J. 1983. Sympatry and size similarity in *Cnemidophorus.* Pp. 297–325 in *Lizard ecology: Studies of a model organism*, edited by R. B. Huey, E. R. Pianka, and T. W. Schoener. Cambridge, Mass.: Harvard University Press.

212.7   Cash, M. N., and J. P. Bogart. 1978. Cytological differentiation of the diploid-tetraploid species pair of North American treefrogs (Amphibia, Anura, Hylidae). *J. Herp.* 12(4):555–58.

213.   Cavazos, L. F. 1951. Spermatogenesis of the horned lizard *Phrynosoma cornutum. Amer. Nat.* 85:373–79.

213.5   Cei, J. M., V. Erspamer, and M. Roseghini. 1968. Taxonomic and evolutionary significance of biogenic amines and polypeptides in amphibian skin. II. Toads of the genera *Bufo* and *Melanophtyniscus. Syst. Zool.* 17(3):232–45.

214.   Chamberlin, E. B. 1937. Clark's water snake on the mid-Texas coast. *Copeia* 1947(2):140.

214.5   Chambers, R. C. 1977. Energetics in different life histories of *Ambystoma tigrinum. Herp Rev.* 8(3), suppl. 4.

214.9   Chaney, A. H. 1982. *Keys to the vertebrates of Texas.* Kingsville, Tex.: Caesar Kleberg Wildlife, Res. Inst.

215.   Chaney, A. H., and R. E. Gordon. 1954. Notes on a population of *Sceloporus merriami merriami* Stejneger. *Texas J. Sci.* 6(1):78–82.

216.   Chantell, C. J. 1966. Late Cenozoic hylids from the Great Plains. *Herpetologica* 22:259–64.

216.2   Chatterjee, S. 1983. An ictidosaur fossil from North America. *Science* 220(4602):1151–53.

216.5   Cherfas, J. 1978. A tale of two turtles. *New Scient.* 78(1104):513–16.

217.   Chrapliwy, P. S., and E. V. Malnate. 1961. The systematic status of the spadefoot toad *Spea laticeps* Cope. *Texas J. Sci.* 13(2):160–62.

218.   Chrapliwy, P. S., and A. J. Ward, Jr. 1963. New records of the western hooknosed snake, *Ficimia cana* (Cope), in west Texas. *Southwest. Nat.* 8(1):52–53.

219.   Clark, D. R. 1964. Reproduction and sexual dimorphism in a population of the rough earth snake, *Virginia striatula* (Linnaeus). *Texas J. Sci.* 16(3):265–95.

220.   ———. 1966. Notes on sexual dimorphism in tail length in American snakes. *Trans. Kansas Acad. Sci.* 69(3–4):226–32.

220.11   ———. 1968. Experiments into selection of soil type, soil moisture level, and temperature by five species of small snakes. *Trans. Kansas Acad. Sci.* 70(4):490–96.

220.12   ———. 1970. Loss of the left oviduct in the Colubrid snake genus *Tantilla. Herpetologica* 26(1):130–33.

220.13   ———. 1971. Branding as a marking technique for amphibians and reptiles. *Copeia* 1971(1):148–51.

220.14   ———. 1974. The western ribbon snake (*Thamnophis proximus*): Ecology of a Texas population. *Herpetologica* 30(4):372–79.

220.15   ———. 1976. Ecological observations on a Texas population of six-lined racerunners, *Cnemidophorus sexlineatus* (Reptilia, Lacertilia, Teiidae). *J. Herp.* 10(2):133–38.

220.2   Clark, D. R., and R. R. Fleet. 1976. The rough earth snake (*Virginia striatula*): Ecology of a Texas population. *Southwest. Nat.* 20(4): 467–78.

220.3   Clark, D. R., and J. C. Kroll. 1974. Thermal ecology of anoline lizards: Temperate versus tropical strategies. *Southwest. Nat.* 19(1): 9–19.

220.4   Clark, D. R., and C. S. Lieb. 1973. Notes on reproduction in the night snake (*Hypsiglena torquata*). *Southwest. Nat.* 18(2): 248–52.

221.   Clarke, R. F. 1965. An ethnological study of the iguanid lizard genera *Callisaurus*, *Cophosaurus*, and *Holbrookia*. *Emporia State Res. Stud.* 8(4): 1–66.

222.   Clay, W. M. 1938. A synopsis of the North American water snakes of the genus *Natrix*. *Copeia* 1932(4): 173–82.

223.   Cochran, D. M. 1961. Type specimens of reptiles and amphibians in the United States National Museum. *Bull. United States Natl. Mus.* 220: 1–291.

223.1   Cole, C. J. 1970. Karyotypes and evolution of the *spinosus* group of lizards in the genus *Sceloporus*. *Amer. Mus. Novitates* 2431: 1–47.

223.11   ———. 1971. Karyotypes of the five monotypic species groups of lizards in the genus *Sceloporus*. *Amer. Mus. Novitates* 2450: 1–17.

223.12   ———. 1972. Chromosome variation in North American fence lizards (genus *Sceloporus; undulatus* species group). *Syst. Zool.* 21(4): 357–63.

223.13   ———. 1975. Karyotype and systematic status of the sand dune lizard (*Sceloporus graciosus arenicolus*) of the American southwest. *Herpetologica* 31(3): 288–93.

223.14   ———. 1978. Karyotypes and systematics of the lizards in the *variabilis, jalapae,* and *scalaris* species groups of the genus *Sceloporus*. *Amer. Mus. Novitates* 2653: 1–13.

223.2   Cole, C. J., and L. M. Hardy. 1981. Systematics of North American colubrid snakes related to *Tantilla planiceps* (Blainville). *Bull. Amer. Mus. Nat. Hist.* 171(3): 199–284.

223.3   Cole, C. J., Charles H. Lowe, and J. W. Wright. 1968. Karyotypes of eight species of toads (genus *Bufo*) in North America. *Copeia* 1968(1): 96–100.

223.5   Collins, J. T., and J. C. Knight. 1980. *Crotalus horridus. Cat. Amer. Amphib. Rept.* 253.1–253.2.

224.   Conant, R. 1942. Notes on the young of three recently described snakes, with comments upon their relationships. *Bull. Chicago Acad. Sci.* 6(10): 193–200.

225.   ———. 1949. Two new races of *Natrix erythrogaster*. *Copeia* 1949(1): 1–15.

226.   ———. 1955. Notes on three Texas reptiles, including an addition to the fauna of the state. *Amer. Mus. Novitates* 1726:1–6.

227.   ———. 1956. A review of two rare pine snakes from the Gulf coastal plain. *Amer. Mus. Novitates* 1781:1–31.

228.   ———. 1958. *A field guide to reptiles and amphibians of the United States and Canada east of the 100th meridian.* Boston: Houghton Mifflin Co.

229.   ———. 1960. The queen snake, *Natrix septemvittata,* in the interior highlands of Arkansas and Missouri, with comments upon similar disjunct distributions. *Proc. Acad. Nat. Sci. Philadelphia* 112(2):25–40.

230.   ———. 1963. Evidence for the specific status of the water snake *Natrix fasciata. Amer. Mus. Novitates* 2122:1–38.

230.1   ———. 1969. A review of the water snakes of the genus *Natrix* in Mexico. *Bull. Amer. Mus. Nat. Hist.* 142(1):3–140.

230.11 ———. 1973. Reviews and comments: Amphibians and reptiles in Texas. *Copeia* 1973(1):184–85.

230.12 ———. 1975. *A field guide to the reptiles and amphibians of eastern and central North Ameirca.* Boston: Houghton Mifflin Co.

230.13 ———. 1977. The Florida water snake (Reptilia, Serpentes, Colubridae) established at Brownsville, Texas, with comments on other herpetological introductions in the area. *J. Herp.* 11(2):217–20.

230.14 ———. 1977(1978)a. Semiaquatic reptiles and amphibians of the Chihuahuan desert and their relationships to drainage patterns of the region. Pp. 455–91 in *Transactions of the symposium on the biological resources of the Chihuahuan desert region, United States and Mexico,* edited by R. W. Wauer, D. H. Riskind. Natl. Park. Ser. Trans. Proc. Ser. (3).

230.15 ———. 1978b. Distribution patterns of North American snakes: Some examples of the effects of Pleistocene glaciation and subsequent climatic changes. *Bull. Maryland Herp. Soc.* 14(4):241–59.

230.2   Conant, R., and J. F. Berry. 1978. Turtles of the family Kinosternidae in the southwestern United States and adjacent Mexico: Identification and distribution. *Amer. Mus. Novitates* 2642:1–18.

231.   Conant, R., and W. Bridges. 1939. *What snake is that?* New York: D. Appleton-Century Co.

232.   Conant, R., et al. 1956. Common names for North American amphibians and reptiles. *Copeia* 1956(3):172–85.

232.9   Cook, M. L., and B. C. Brown. 1974. Variation in the genus *Desmog-nathus* (Amphibia: Plethodontidae) in the western limits of its range. *J. Herp.* 8(1):93–105.

233.   Cook, R. S., et al. 1965. A serological study of infectious diseases of wild populations in south Texas. *Trans. N. Amer. Wildlife Natl. Res. Conf.* 13:142–55.

233.41   Cooper, W. E., Jr. 1985. Female residency and courtship intensity in a territorial lizard, *Holbrookia propinqua*. *Amphib.-Rept.* 6(1):63–69.

233.5   Cooper, W. E., Jr., and R. F. Clarke. 1982. Steroidal induction of female reproductive coloration in the keeled earless lizard, *Holbrookia propinqua*. *Herpetologica* 38(3):425–29.

234.   Cope, E. D. 1859. Catalogue of the venomous serpents in the Museum of the Academy of Natural Sciences of Philadelphia, with notes on the families, genera and species. *Proc. Acad. Nat. Sci. Philadelphia* 11:332–47.

235.   ———. 1860a. Catalogue of the Colubridae in the Museum of the Academy of Natural Sciences of Philadelphia, with notes and descriptions of new species. Part 2. *Proc. Acad. Nat. Sci. Philadelphia* 12:242–66.

236.   ———. 1860b. Notes and descriptions of new and little known species of American reptiles. *Proc. Acad. Nat. Sci. Philadelphia* 12:339–44.

237.   ———. 1860c. Descriptions of reptiles from tropical America. *Proc. Acad. Nat. Sci. Philadelphia* 12:368–74.

238.   ———. 1860d. Catalogue of the Colubridae in the Museum of the Academy of Natural Sciences of Philadelphia. Part 3. *Proc. Acad. Nat. Sci. Philadelphia* 12:553–56.

239.   ———. 1863. On *Trachycephalus*, *Scaphiopus* and other American Batrachia. *Proc. Acad. Nat. Sci. Philadelphia* 14:43–54.

240.   ———. 1867. A review of the species of the Amblystomidae. *Proc. Acad. Nat. Sci. Philadelphia* 18:166–211.

241.   ———. 1872. Synopsis of the species of the Chelydrinae. *Proc. Acad. Nat. Sci. Philadelphia* 24:22–29.

242.   ———. 1875. Check-list of North American Batrachia and Reptilia; with a systematic list of the higher groups, and an essay on geographic distribution. *Bull. United States Natl. Mus.* 1:1–104.

243.   ———. 1878a. A Texas cliff frog. *Amer. Nat.* 12:186.

244.   ———. 1878b. A new genus of Cystignathidae from Texas. *Amer. Nat.* 12:253.

245.   ———. 1880. On the zoological position of Texas. *Bull. United States Natl. Mus.* 17:1–51.

246.   ———. 1883. Notes on the geographic distribution of Batrachia and Reptilia in western North America. *Proc. Acad. Nat. Sci. Philadelphia* 35:10–35.

247.   ———. 1886a. The habits of *Eublepharis variegatus. Amer. Nat.* 20: 735–36.

248.   ———. 1886b. Synonymic list of the North American species of *Bufo* and *Rana*, with descriptions of some new species of Batrachia from specimens in the National Museum. *Proc. Amer. Philos. Soc.* 23: 514–26.

249.   ———. 1888a. On a new species of *Bufo* from Texas. *Proc. United States Natl. Mus.* 11:317–18.

250.   ———. 1888b. Catalogue of Batrachia and Reptilia brought by William Taylor from San Diego, Texas. *Proc. United States Natl. Mus.* 11: 395–98.

251.   ———. 1889. The Batrachia of North America. *Bull. United States Natl. Mus.* 34:1–525.

252.   ———. 1891. A critical review of the characters and variations of the snakes of North America. *Proc. United States Natl. Mus.* 14:589–694.

252.1   ———. 1892a. A synopsis of the species of the teiid genus *Cnemidophorus. Trans. Amer. Philos. Soc.* 17(1):27–52.

253.   ———. 1892b. The Batrachia and Reptilia of northwestern Texas. *Proc. Acad. Nat. Sci. Philadelphia* 44:331–37.

254.   ———. 1893. On a new spadefoot from Texas. *Amer. Nat.* 27:155–56.

255.   ———. 1895a. Classification of the Ophidia. *Trans. Amer. Philos. Soc.* 18:186–219.

256.   ———. 1895b. On some new North American snakes. *Amer. Nat.* 29: 676–80.

257.   ———. 1900. The crocodilians, lizards, and snakes of North America. *Ann. Rept. United States Natl. Mus.* 1898:155–1294.

257.5   Cover, J. F. 1985. *Tropidoclonion lineatum annectens* X *texanum* (Central X Texas Lined Snake). Coloration. *Herp Rev.* 16(3):81.

258.   Craun, V. S. 1948. Commercial caves of Texas. *Bull. Nat. Speleol. Soc.* 10:33–45.

259.   Creel, G. C. 1963. Bat as a food item of *Rana pipiens. Texas J. Sci.*
        15(1):104–106.

260.   Crimmins, M. L. 1925. An addition to the herpetological fauna of the
        United States. *Copeia* 1925(1):7.

261.   ———. 1926. Collecting rattlesnake venom to be used in making anti-
        venin serum. *J. Amer. Med. Assoc.* 87:1645.

261.1   ———. 1927a. Notes on Texas rattlesnakes. *Bull. Antivenin Inst. Amer.*
        1(1):23–24.

262.   ———. 1927b. Facts about Texas snakes and their poison. *Texas State J.
        Med.* 23(3):198–203.

263.   ———. 1931. Rattlesnakes and their enemies in the southwest. *Bull.
        Antivenin Inst. Amer.* 5(2):46–47.

264.   ———. 1946. The treatment of poisonous snake bites in Texas. *Proc.
        Trans. Texas Acad. Sci.* 24:54–61.

264.5   Crouch, G. E. 1978. An ecological study of the American alligator in a
        reservoir receiving thermal effluents. *Masters Abstr.* 16(2):78.

265.   Crouse, H. W. 1902. The venomous snakes and spiders of Texas. *Trans.
        State Med. Assoc.* (unpaged reprint).

265.3   Crum, C. 1983. Notes concerning locality data of Texas reptiles. *Trans.
        Dallas Herp. Soc.* 5:1–2.

265.8   Cuellar, H. S. 1971. Levels of genetic compatibility of *Rana areolata*
        with southwestern members of the *Rana pipiens* complex (Anura:
        Ranidae). *Evolution* 25(2):399–409.

266.   Cuellar, O. 1966a. Delayed fertilization in the lizard *Uta stansburiana.
        Copeia* 1966(3):549–57.

267.   ———. 1966b. Oviducal anatomy and sperm storage structures in liz-
        ards. *J. Morph.* 119(1):7–20.

267.5   Culley, D. D., and H. G. Applegate. 1967. Pesticides at Presidio. IV.
        Reptiles, birds, and mammals. *Texas J. Sci.* 19(3):301–10.

268.   Curran, C. H., and C. Kauffeld. 1937. *Snakes and their ways.* New York:
        Harper and Bros.

269.   Curtis. L. 1949a. The snakes of Dallas County, Texas. *Field and Lab.*
        17(1):1–13.

270.   ———. 1949b. A key to the snakes of Dallas County, Texas. *Field and
        Lab.* 17(4):146–50.

271. ———. 1950a. Distribution of some Texas reptiles and amphibians. *Field and Lab.* 18(1):47.

272. ———. 1950b. A case of twin hatching in the rough green snake. *Copeia* 1950(3):232.

273. ———. 1951a. An additional record of the salamander *Amphiuma* in Texas. *Field and Lab.* 19(2):84.

274. ———. 1951b. Physiographic influence of the Edwards Plateau on its endemic amphibian fauna—a resume. *Field and Lab.* 19(3):119–24.

275. ———. 1952. Cannibalism in the Texas coral snake. *Herpetologica* 8(2):27.

276. Curtis, L., and D. Sellers. 1952. Range extension of *Natrix grahami* B. and G. in Texas. *Field and Lab.* 20(1):34.

277. Curtis. L., and D. W. Tinkle. 1951. The striped water snake, *Natrix rigida* (Say), in Texas. *Field and Lab.* 19(2):72–74.

277.4 Cutting, R. H., and L. R. Irby. 1970. A radioecological study of White Creek, Brazos County, Texas. *TASCA* 24(3):3–8.

277.8 Cys, J. M. 1976. New county records and range extensions of some west Texas reptiles. *Herp Rev.* 7(3):126.

278. Dalquest, W. W. 1962. Tortoises from the Pliocene of Texas. *Texas J. Sci.* 14(2):192–96.

279. Dana, S. W., and D. W. Tinkle. 1965. Effects of x-radiation on the testes of the lizard, *Uta stansburiana stejnegeri. Int. J. Radiation Biol.* 9(1):67–80.

280. Daugherty, A. E. 1942. A record of *Graptemys pseudogeographica versa. Copeia* 1942(1):51.

281. Davenport, J. W. 1943. *Field book of the snakes of Bexar County, Texas, and vicinity.* San Antonio, Tex.: Witte Mem. Mus.

282. Davis, D. D. 1948. Flash display of aposematic colors in *Farancia* and other snakes. *Copeia* 1948(3):208–11.

282.2 Davis, H. T., and C. S. Brimley. 1944. *Poisonous snakes of the eastern United States with first aid guide.* Raleigh: North Carolina St. Mus.

283. Davis, W. B. 1938. White-throated sparrow killed by copperhead. *Condor* 40(4):183.

284. ———. 1945. The hatching of *Leiolopisma laterale. Copeia* 1945(2):115–16.

285.   ———. 1949. The smooth green snake in Texas. *Copeia* 1949(3):233.

286.   ———. 1951. Food of the black-banded snake, *Coniophanes imperialis imperialis* Baird. *Copeia* 1951(4):314.

287.   ———. 1953. Another record of the smooth green snake in Texas. *Herpetologica* 9(2):165.

288.   Davis, W. B., and J. R. Dixon. 1958. A new *Coleonyx* from Texas. *Proc. Biol. Soc. Washington* 71:149–52.

289.   Davis, W. B., and F. T. Knapp. 1953. Notes on the salamander *Siren intermedia*. *Copeia* 1953(2):119–21.

289.4   Davis, W. K. 1974. The Mediterranean gecko, *Hemidactylus turcicus*, in Texas. *J. Herp.* 8(1):77–80.

289.6   Dean, R. H., and D. W. Steinbach. 1981. Endangered marine turtles of the Gulf Coast. *Tex. Ag. Ext. Ser.* L-1867.

290.   Degenhardt, W. G. 1966. A method of counting some diurnal ground lizards of the genera *Holbrookia* and *Cnemidophorus* with results from the Big Bend National Park. *Amer. Midl. Nat.* 75(1):61–100.

290.1   ———. 1967. Reptilian distribution in Big Bend National Park, Texas. *Bull. Ecol. Soc. Amer.* 48(2):82.

290.11 ———. 1977(1978). A changing environment: Documentation of lizards and plants over a decade. Pp. 533–55. in *Transactions of the symposium on the biological resources of the Chihuahuan desert region, United States and Mexico, edited by R. H. Wauer and D. H. Riskind. Natl. Park Ser. Trans. Proc. Ser. (3).*

290.12 ———. 1984. Geographic distribution. *Leptotyphlops dulcis dulcis*. *Herp Rev.* 15(4):114–15.

290.2   Degenhardt. W. G., T. L. Brown, and D. A. Esterla. 1976. The taxonomic status of *Tantilla cucullata* and *Tantilla diabola*. *Texas J. Sci.* 17(1):225–34.

291.   Degenhardt, W. G., and P. B. Degenhardt. 1965. The host-parasite relationship between *Elaphe subocularis* (Reptilia: Colubridae) and *Aponomma elaphensis* (Acarina: Ixodidae). *Southwest. Nat.* 10(3):167–78.

291.5   Degenhardt, W. G., and K. L. Jones. 1972. A new sagebrush lizard, *Sceloporus graciosus*, from New Mexico and Texas. *Herpetologica* 28(3):212–17.

292.   Degenhardt, W. G., and W. W. Milstead. 1959. Notes on a second specimen of the snake *Tantilla cucullata* Minton. *Herpetologica* 15(3):158–59.

293.   Degenhardt, W. G., and G. E. Steele. 1957. Additional specimens of *Trimorphodon vilkinsoni* from Texas. *Copeia* 1957(4):309–10.

293.3   Delisle, K., and F. L. Rose. 1973. Serum protein changes during metamorphosis in *Ambystoma tigrinum*. *Comp. Biochem. Physiol.* 44A: 1015–20.

293.6   Delnicki, D., and E. Bolen. 1977. Use of black-bellied duck nest sites by other species. *Southwest. Nat.* 22(2):275–77.

293.8   DeMar, R. E. 1967. Two new species of *Broiliellus* (Amphibians) from the Permian of Texas. *Fieldiana-Geology* 16(5):117–29.

294.   Detrie, A. J. 1950. Osteology of the skull of *Phrynosoma cornutum* (Harlan). *Field and Lab.* 18(4):146–55.

295.   Dial, B. E. 1965a. Distributional notes on reptiles and amphibians from northeastern Texas. *Southwest. Nat.* 10(2):143–44.

296.   ———. 1965b. Pattern and coloration in juveniles of two west Texas *Elaphe. Herpetologica* 21(1):75–78.

296.1   ———. 1978a. Aspects of the behavioral ecology of two Chihuahuan desert geckos (Reptilia; Lacertilia; Gekkonidae). *J. Herp.* 12(2): 209–16.

296.11   ———. 1978b. The thermal ecology of two sympatric, nocturnal *Coleonyx* (Lacertilia: Gekkonidae). *Herpetologica* 34(2):194–201.

296.3   Dial, B. E., and L. C. Fitzpatrick. 1981. The energetic costs of tail autotomy to reproduction in the lizard *Coleonyx brevis* (Sauria: Gekkonidae). *Oecologia* 51:310–17.

296.31   ———. 1982. Evaporative water loss in sympatric *Coleonyx* (Sauria: Gekkonidae). *Comp. Biochem. Physiol.* 71A(4) 623–25.

297.   Dickerson, M. C. 1931. *The frog book.* Garden City, N.Y.: Doubleday, Doran and Co.

298.   Diener, R. A. 1957. An ecological study of the plain-bellied water snake. *Herpetologica* 13(3):202–11.

299.   ———. 1965. The occurrence of tadpoles of the green treefrog *Hyla cinerea cinerea* (Schneider) in Trinity Bay, Texas. *British J. Herp.* 3(8):198–99.

300.   Ditmars, R. L. 1922. *The reptile book.* Garden City, N.Y.: Doubleday, Page and Co.

300.1   ———. 1927. Occurrence and habits of our poisonous snakes. *Bull Antivenin Inst. Amer.* 1(1):3–5.

301. ———. 1930. The poisonous snakes of the New World. *Bull. New York Zool. Soc.* 33(3):79–132.

302. ———. 1931. *Snakes of the world.* New York: Macmillan.

303. ———. 1934. A review of the box turtles. *Zoologica* 17(1):1–44.

304. ———. 1946. *The reptiles of North America.* New York: Doubleday and Co.

305. Dixon, J. R. 1952. A large bull snake, *Pituophis catenifer sayi*, from Texas. *Copeia* 1952(3):193.

306. ———. 1956. The mottled rock rattlesnake, *Crotalus lepidus lepidus*, in Edwards County, Texas. *Copeia* 1956(2):126–27.

307. ———. 1957. Notes on the glossy snakes, *Arizona elegans*, in Texas. *Southwest. Nat.* 2(3):132–33.

308. ———. 1958. The warty gecko from Laredo, Texas. *Herpetologica* 13(4):256.

308.5 ———. 1959a. *Arizona elegans* in southeastern Texas. *Herpetologica* 15(2):72.

309. ———. 1959b. Geographic variation and distribution of the long-tailed group of the glossy snake, *Arizona elegans* Kennicott. *Southwest. Nat.* 4(1):20–29.

310. ———. 1960a. A new name for the snake *Arizona elegans arizonae*. *Southwest. Nat.* 5(4):226.

311. ———. 1960b. Epizoophytic algae on some turtles of Texas and Mexico. *Texas J. Sci.* 12(1–2):36–38.

312. ———. 1965. A taxonomic reevaluation of the night snake, *Hypsiglena ochrohyncha* and relatives. *Southwest. Nat.* 10(2):125–31.

312.1 ———. 1970a. *Coleonyx brevis*. *Cat. Amer. Amphib. Rept.* 88.1–88.2.

312.11 ———. 1970b. *Coleonyx reticulatus*. *Cat. Amer. Amphib. Rept.* 89.1–89.2.

312.12 ———. 1970c. *Coleonyx*. *Cat. Amer. Amphib. Rept.* 95.1–95.2.

312.13 ———. 1970d. A noteworthy record of *Eumeces multivirgatus* from Texas. *Southwest. Nat.* 15(4):502.

312.3 Dixon, J. R., and R. R. Fleet. 1976. *Arizona elegans* Kennicott. *Cat. Amer. Amphib. Rept.* 179.1–179.4.

313. Dixon, J. R., M. Sabath, and R. Worthington. 1962. Comments on snakes from central and western Mexico. *Herpetologica* 18(2):91–100.

314. do Amaral, A. 1927a. Notes on nearctic poisonous snakes and treatment of their bites. *Bull. Antivenin Inst. Amer.* 1(3):61–76.

315. ———. 1927b. The anti-snake bite campaign in Texas and in the sub-tropical United States. *Bull. Antivenin Inst. Amer.* 1(3):77–85.

315.1 ———. 1929a. Key to the rattlesnakes of the genus *Crotalus* Linne, 1758. *Bull. Antivenin Inst. Amer.* 3(1):4–6.

315.11 ———. 1929b. Studies on nearctic ophidia. V. On *Crotalus confluentus* Say, 1823 and its allied forms. *Bull. Antivenin Inst. Amer.* 2(4):86–97.

316. Dowling, H. G. 1951. A taxonomic study of the ratsnakes, genus *Elaphe* Fitzinger. I. The status of the name *Scotophis laetus* Baird and Girard (1853). *Copeia* 1951(1):39–44.

317. ———. 1952. A taxonomic study of the ratsnakes, genus *Elaphe* Fitzinger. IV. A check list of the American forms. *Occ. Papers Mus. Zool. Univ. Michigan* 541:1–12.

318. ———. 1956. Geographic relations of Ozarkian amphibians and reptiles. *Southwest. Nat.* 1(4):174–89.

319. ———. 1957. A taxonomic study of the ratsnakes, genus *Elaphe* Fitzinger. V. The *rosalie* section. *Occ. Papers Mus. Zool. Univ. Michigan* 583:1–22.

319.1 Dowling, H. G., ed. 1975. Snake venoms and venomous snakes. Pp. 203–12 in *1974 yearbook of herpetology*. New York: HISS Publ.

319.5 Dronen, N., and H. T. Underwood. 1977. The life cycle of *Cephalogonimus vesicaudus* (Digenea: Cephalogonimidae) from *Trionyx spiniferus* from Texas. *Proc. Helminth. Soc. Washington* 44(2):198–200.

319.6 Dryden, L. S. 1985. Geographic distribution. *Cnemidophorus laredoensis. Herp Rev.* 16(2):60.

320. Duellman, W. E. 1958. A monographic study of the colubrid snake genus *Leptodeira. Bull. Amer. Mus. Nat. Hist.* 114:1–152.

320.1 ———. 1967. Additional studies of chromosomes of anuran amphibians. *Syst. Zool.* 16(1):38–43.

320.11 ———. 1968a. *Smilisca. Cat. Amer. Amphib. Rept.* 58.1–58.2.

320.12 ———. 1968b. *Smilisca baudinii. Cat. Amer. Amphib. Rept.* 59.1–59.2.

321. Duellman, W. E., and B. Berg. 1962. Type specimens of amphibians and reptiles in the Museum of Natural History, the University of Kansas. *Univ. Kansas Publ. Mus. Nat. Hist.* 15(4):183–204.

322. Duellman, W. E., and R. G. Zweifel. 1962. A synopsis of the lizards of the *sexlineatus* group (genus *Cnemidophorus*). *Bull. Amer. Mus. Nat. Hist.* 123:159–210.

322.1 Duffield, L. F. 1970. Some Panhandle aspect sites: Their vertebrates and paleoecology. *Diss. Abst. Int.* B31(6):3123-B.

322.2 Dukes, R. 1983. Innate food preferences based on tongue flick rates of two sympatric species of the genus *Nerodia. Trans. Dallas Herp. Soc.* 4:1–4.

323. Dundee, H. A. 1957. Partial metamorphosis induced in *Typhlomolge rathbuni. Copeia* 1957(1):52–53.

323.1 ———. 1974. Evidence for specific status of *Graptemys pseudogeographica. Copeia* 1974(2):540–42.

323.2 Dunham, A. E. 1978. Food availability as a proximate factor influencing individual growth rates in the iguanid lizard *Sceloporus merriami. Ecology* 59(4):770–78.

323.21 ———. 1981. Populations in a fluctuating environment: The comparative population ecology of the iguanid lizards *Sceloporus merriami* and *Urosaurus ornatus. Univ. Michigan Misc. Pub. Mus. Zool.* 158:1–62.

323.22 ———. 1982. Demographic and life-history variation among populations of the iguanid lizard *Urosaurus ornatus:* Implications for the study of life-history phenomena in lizards. *Herpetologica* 38(1):209–21.

324. Dunkle, D. H., and H. M. Smith. 1937. Notes on some Mexican ophidians. *Occ. Papers Mus. Zool. Univ. Michigan* 363:1–15.

325. Dunn, E. R. 1918. The collection of Amphibia Caudata of the Museum of Comparative Zoology. *Bull. Mus. Comp. Zool.* 62:445–71.

326. ———. 1926. *The salamanders of the family Plethodontidae.* Northampton, Mass.: Smith College.

327. ———. 1932. The status of *Tropidoclonion lineatum. Proc. Biol. Soc. Washington* 45:195–98.

328. ———. 1936. Notes on North American *Leptodeira. Proc. Natl. Acad. Sci.* 22(12):689–98.

329. ———. 1938. Notes on frogs of the genus *Acris. Proc. Acad. Nat. Sci. Philadelphia* 90:153–54.

330.   ———. 1940. The races of *Ambystoma tigrinum*. *Copeia* 1940(3): 154–62.

330.5   Dutton, R. H., and L. D. Fitzpatrick. 1975. Metabolic compensation to seasonal temperatures in the rusty lizard (*Sceloporus olivaceus*). *Comp. Biochem. Physiol.* 51A:309–18.

330.9   Dyrkacz, S. 1974. Western diamondback rattlesnake, *Crotalus atrox*, from Brewster Co., Texas. (photograph and caption) *Herp Rev.* 5(2):41.

330.91   ———. 1981. Recent instances of albinism in North American amphibians and reptiles. *SSAR Herp. Circ.* 11:1–32.

331.   Eads, R. B., G. C. Menzies, and B. G. Hightower. 1956. The ticks of Texas, with notes on their medical significance. *Texas J. Sci.* 8(1): 7–24.

332.   Eads, R. B., J. S. Wiseman, and G. C. Menzies. 1957. Observations concerning the Mexican free-tailed bat, *Tadarida mexicana*, in Texas. *Texas J. Sci.* 9(2):227–42.

332.01   Easterla, D. A. 1975. Giant desert centipede preys upon snake. *Southwest. Nat.* 20(3):411.

332.02   ———. 1975. Reproductive and ecological observations on *Tantilla cucullata* from Big Bend National Park, Texas (Serpentes, Colubridae). *Herpetologica* 31(2):234–36.

332.03   ———. 1978. The Mediterranean gecko, *Hemidactylus turcicus*, at Big Bend National Park. *Texas J. Sci.* 30(2):199.

332.1   Easterla, D. A., and R. C. Reynolds. 1975. Additional records and ecological notes on the reticulated gecko, *Coleonyx reticulatus* (Davis and Dixon), from the southern Trans-Pecos of western Texas. *J. Herp.* 9(2):233–36.

333.   Eaton, T. H., and R. M. Imagawa. 1948. Early development of *Pseudacris clarkii*. *Copeia* 1948(4):263–66.

333.1   Eberle, W. G. 1972. Comparative chromosomal morphology of the new world natricine snake genera *Natrix* and *Regina*. *Herpetologica* 28(2): 98–105.

334.   Eddleman, C. D., and W. A. Akersten. 1966. Margay from the post-Wisconsin of southeastern Texas. *Texas J. Sci.* 18(4):378–85.

335.   Edgren, R. A. 1952. A synopsis of the snakes of the genus *Heterodon*, with the diagnosis of a new race of *Heterodon nasicus* Baird and Girard. *Chicago Acad. Sci. Nat. Hist. Misc.* 112:1–4.

336.   ———. 1957. Melanism in hog-nosed snakes. *Herpetologica* 13(2): 131–35.

337.   ———. 1961. A simplified method for analysis of clines; geographic variation in the hognose snake *Heterodon platyrhinos* Latreille. *Copeia* 1961(2):125–32.

338.   Edwards, C. L. 1896a. Notes on the biology of *Phrynosoma cornutum* Harlan. *Zool. Anzeiger* 19:108–11.

339.   ———. 1896b. Life habits of *Phrynosoma*. *Science* n.s. 3:763–65.

340.   ———. 1903. A note on *Phrynosoma*. *Science* n.s. 17:826–27.

340.5   Ehrenfield, D. W. 1976. The conservation of non-resources. *Amer. Scient.* 64(6):648–56.

341.   Eifrig, C. W. G. 1929. Texas bird habitats. *Auk* 46(1):70–78.

342.   Eigenmann, C. H. 1899. The eye of *Typhlomolge* from the artesian wells of San Marcos, Texas. *Proc. Indiana Acad. Sci.* 8:251.

343.   ———. 1900a. Degeneration in the eyes of the cold-blooded vertebrates of the North American caves. *Proc. Indiana Acad. Sci.* 9:31–46.

344.   ———. 1900b. Degeneration in the eyes of the cold-blooded vertebrates of the North American caves. *Science* n.s. 11(274):492–503.

345.   ———. 1900c. The blind fishes of North America. *Pop. Sci. Monthly* 56:-437–86.

346.   ———. 1900d. The eyes of the blind vertebrates of North America. II. The eyes of *Typhlomolge rathbuni* Stejneger. *Trans. Amer. Micro. Soc.* 21:49–61.

347.   ———. 1900e. A contribution to the fauna of the caves of Texas. *Proc. Amer. Assoc. Adv. Sci.* 49:228–30.

348.   ———. 1900f. A contribution to the fauna of the caves of Texas. *Science* n.s. 12:301–302.

349.   ———. 1901. Description of a new cave salamander, *Sperlerpes stejnegeri*, from the caves of southwestern Missouri. *Trans. Amer. Micro. Soc.* 22:189–92.

350.   ———. 1909. Cave vertebrates of America: A study in degenerative evolution. *Publ. Carnegie Inst. Washington* 104:1–241.

351.   Ellis, T. K. 1940. Notes on behavior in *Anolis*. *Copeia* 1940(3):162–64.

352.   Emerson, E. T. 1905. General anatomy of *Typhlomolge rathbuni*. *Proc. Boston Soc. Nat. Hist.* 32:43–76.

353.   Englehardt, G. P. 1932. Notes on poisonous snakes in Texas. *Copeia* 1932(1):37–38.

353.5   Ernst, C. H. 1971. *Chrysemys picta. Cat. Amer. Amphib. Rept.* 106.1–106.4.

353.6   Ernst, C. H., and R. W. Barbour. 1972. *Turtles of the United States.* Lexington: University Press of Kentucky.

353.7   Ernst, C. H., and E. M. Ernst. 1979. Synopsis of protozoans parasitic in native turtles of the United States. *Bull. Maryland Herp. Soc.* 15(1):1–15.

353.8   Ernst, E. M., and C. H. Ernst. 1977. Synopsis of helminths endo-parasites in native turtles of the United States. *Bull. Maryland Herp. Soc.* 13(1):1–75.

353.9   Estes, R. 1969. The Batrachrosauroididae and Scapherpetontidae, Late Cretaceous and early Cenozoic salamanders. *Copeia* 1969(2):225–34.

353.91   ———. 1983. *Handbuch de Paläoherpetologie* (Encyclopedia of Paleo-herpetology). Stuttgart and New York: Gustav Fischer Verlag.

354.   Etheridge, R. E. 1948. Range extension of the faded snake *Arizona e. elegans* in Texas. *Herpetologica* 4(6):194.

355.   ———. 1952. The southern range of the racer *Coluber constrictor stejnegerianus* (Cope), with remarks on the Guatemalan species *Coluber ortenbergeri. Copeia* 1952(3):189–90.

355.3   Everhart, B. 1958. Notes on the helminths of *Pseudemys scripta elegans* (Wied, 1838) in areas of Texas and Oklahoma. *Proc. Oklahoma Acad. Sci.* 38:38–43.

355.4   Everitt, C. T. 1971. Courtship and mating of *Eumeces multivirgatus* (Scincidae). *J. Herp.* 5(3–4):189–90.

355.5   Everitt, J. H. 1974. Distribution: *Phrynosoma modestum. Herp Rev.* 5(4):108.

356.   Falck, E. G. 1940. Food of an eastern rock rattlesnake in captivity. *Copeia* 1940(4):135.

356.2   Falko, J. 1973. The Texas banded gecko. *Bull. Canadian Amphib. Rept. Conserv. Soc.* 11(2):4–5.

357.   Ferguson, G. W. 1965. Verification of a population of *Ficimia cana* in north-central Texas. *Herpetologica* 21(2):156–57.

358.   ———. 1966a. Effect of follicle-stimulating hormone and testosterone proprionate on the reproduction of the side-blotched lizard, *Uta stansburiana. Copeia* 1966(3):495–98.

359.   ———. 1966b. Releasers of courtship and territorial behavior in the side-blotched lizard, *Uta stansburiana. Anim. Behav.* 14(1):89–92.

359.01   ———. 1969a. Geographic variation and evolution of stereotyped behavioral patterns of the side-blotched lizards of the genus *Uta* (Iguanidae). *Diss. Abst. Int.* 30:2466-B.

359.02   ———. 1969b. Interraciál discrimination in male side-blotched lizards, *Uta stansburiana. Copeia* 1969(1):188–89.

359.03   ———. 1971. Variation and evolution of the push-up displays of the side-blotched lizard genus *Uta* (Iguanidae). *Syst. Zool.* 20(1):79–101.

359.1   Ferguson, G. W., and T. Brockman. 1980. Geographic differences of growth rate of *Sceloporus undulatus* (Sauria: Iguanidae). *Copeia* 1980(2):259–64.

359.2   Ferguson, G. W., K. L. Brown, and V. G. DeMarco. 1982. Selective basis for the evolution of variable egg and hatchling size in some iguanid lizards. *Herpetologica* 38 (1):178–88.

359.3   Fetzer, A. 1982. The glossy snake (*Arizona elegans*). *San Diego Herp. Soc. Newsltr.* 4(5):1–2.

359.4   Fichter, L. S. 1969. Geographical distribution and osteological variation in fossil and recent specimens of two species of *Kinosternon* (Testudines). *J. Herp.* 3(3–4):113–19.

360.   Finch, R. C. 1962. S. S. S. reports on the Bat-Well. *Texas Caver* 7(12): 139–42.

361.2   Finnley, D., ed. 1978a. Critical habitat determined for Houston toad. *Endangered Spec. Tech. Bull.* 3(2):1, 3.

361.21.   ———. 1978b. U.S.-Mexico restoration efforts may be only hope for Kemp's Ridley. *Endangered Spec. Tech. Bull.* 3(10):6–8.

361.22   ———. 1978c. Rulemaking actions—July 1978. San Marcos gambusia and salamander. *Endangered Spec. Tech. Bull.* 3(8):8.

361.   Fitch, H. S. 1954. Life history and ecology of the five-lined skink, *Eumeces fascitus. Univ. Kansas Publ. Mus. Nat. Hist.* 8(1):1–156.

362.   ———. 1955. Habits and adaptations of the great plains skink (*Eumeces obsoletus*). *Ecol. Monogr.* 25(1):59–83.

363.   ———. 1956a. An ecological study of the collared lizard (*Crotaphytus collaris*). *Univ. Kansas Publ. Mus. Nat. Hist.* 8(3):213–74.

364.   ———. 1956b. A field study of the Kansas ant-eating frog, *Gastrophryne olivacea. Univ. Kansas Publ. Mus. Nat. Hist.* 8(4):275–306.

365.   ———. 1958. Natural history of the six-lined race-runner, (*Cnemidophorus sexlineatus*). *Univ. Kansas Publ. Mus. Nat. Hist.* 11(2):11–62.

366. ———. 1960. Autecology of the copperhead. *Univ. Kansas Publ. Mus. Nat. Hist.* 13(4):85–288.

367. ———. 1963. Natural history of the racer *Coluber constrictor. Univ. Kansas Publ. Mus. Nat. Hist.* 15(8):351–468.

368. ———. 1965. An ecological study of the garter snake, *Thamnophis sirtalis. Univ. Kansas Publ. Mus. Nat. Hist.* 15(10):493–564.

368.1 ———. 1978. Sexual size differences in the genus *Sceloporus. Univ. Kansas Sci. Bull.* 51(13):441–61.

368.2 ———. 1980. *Thamnophis sirtalis. Cat. Amer. Amphib. Rept.* 270.1–270.4.

369. Fitch, H. S., and H. W. Greene. 1965. Breeding cycle in the ground skink, *Lygosoma laterale. Univ. Kansas Publ. Mus. Nat. Hist.* 15(11):565–75.

369.2 Fitch, H. S., and D. M. Hillis. 1984. The *Anolis* dewlap: Interspecific variability and morphological associations with habitat. *Copeia* 1984(2):315–23.

370. Fitch, H. S., and T. P. Maslin. 1961. Occurrence of the garter snake, *Thamnophis sirtalis*, in the Great Plains and Rocky Mountains. *Univ. Kansas Publ. Mus. Nat. Hist.* 13(5):289–308.

371. Fitch, H. S., and W. W. Milstead. 1961. An older name for *Thamnophis cyrtopsis* (Kennicott). *Copeia* 1961(1):112.

372. Fitch, H. S., and W. W. Tanner. 1951. Remarks concerning the systematics of the collared lizard (*Crotaphytus collaris*), with a description of a new subspecies. *Trans. Kansas Acad. Sci.* 54(4):548–59.

372.1 Fitzgerald, K. T., H. M. Smith, and L. J. Guillette, Jr. 1981. Nomenclature of the diploid species of the diploid-tetraploid *Hyla versicolor* complex. *J. Herp.* 15(3):356–60.

372.2 Fleet, R. R. 1972. Notes on the blind snake, *Leptotyphlops dulcis dulcis*, in eastern Texas. *Southwest. Nat.* 17(3):309.

372.3 Fleet, R. R., D. R. Clark, and F. W. Plapp. 1972. Residues of DDT and dieldrin in snakes from two Texas agro-systems. *Bioscience* 22(11):664–65.

372.4 Fleet, R. R., and J. R. Dixon. 1971. Geographic variation within the long-tailed group of the glossy snake, *Arizona elegans. Herpetologica* 27(3):295–302.

372.5 Fleet, R. R., and J. Kroll. 1978. Litter size and parturition behavior in *Sistrurus miliarius streckeri. Herp Rev.* 9(1):11.

372.6   Fleet, R. R., and F. W. Plapp. 1978. DDT residues in snakes decline since DDT ban. *Bull. Environ. Contam. Toxicol.* 19(4):383–87.

372.7   Flickinger, E. L. 1981. Wildlife mortality at petroleum pits in Texas. *J. Wildlife Mgt.* 45(2):560–64.

372.8   Flickinger, E. L., and B. M. Mulhern. 1980. Aldrin persists in yellow mud turtle. *Herp Rev.* 11(2):29–30.

373.   Flury, A. 1949a. *Gerrhonotus liocephalus infernalis* Baird in Texas. *Herpetologica* 5(3):65–67.

374.   ———. 1949b. Range extension for two west Texas snakes. *Copeia* 1949 (3):293.

375.   ———. 1950. A new king snake from Trans-Pecos Texas. *Copeia* 1950(3): 215–17.

376.   Fontaine, P. 1944. *Natrix* as a predator of fish in the Dallas area. *Field and Lab.* 12(1):17–18.

377.   Fontaine, P., and L. Curtis. 1948. The coral snake *Micrurus fulvius tenere* (B. and G.) in Dallas County, Texas. *Field and Lab.* 16(2):93.

377.1   Foote, R., and J. A. MacMahon. 1977. Electrophoretic studies of rattlesnake (*Crotalus* and *Sistrurus*) venom: Taxonomic implications. *Comp. Biochem. Physiol.* 57B(3):235–41.

377.2   Forestor, D. C. 1973. Mating call as a reproductive isolating mechanism between *Scaphiopus bombifrons* and *S. hammondi*. *Copeia* 1973(1): 60–67.

377.23 Foreyt, W. J., C. W. Leathers, and E. N. Smith. 1985. *Trichoderma* sp. infection in the alligator (*Alligator mississippiensis*). *J. Herp.* 19(4): 530–31.

377.3   Forks, T. P., and J. E. Forks. 1982. Defensive display of the Texas rat snake, *Elaphe obsoleta lindheimeri*. *Bull. Chicago Herp. Soc.* 17(4): 100.

378.   Fouquette, M. J., Jr. 1954. Food competition among four sympatric species of garter snakes, genus *Thamnophis*. *Texas J. Sci.* 5(2):172–88.

379.   ———. 1960. Call structure in frogs of the family Leptodactylidae. *Texas J. Sci.* 12(3–4):201–15.

379.1   ———. 1969. Rhinophrynidae. *Cat. Amer. Amphib. Rept.* 78.1–78.2.

379.11 ———. 1980. Effect of environmental temperatures on body temperatures of aquatic-calling anurans. *J. Herp.* 14(4):347–52.

380. Fouquette, M. J., Jr., and H. L. Lindsay, Jr. 1955. An ecological survey of reptiles in parts of northwestern Texas. *Texas J. Sci.* 7(4):402–21.

381. Fouquette, M. J., Jr., and M. J. Littlejohn. 1960. Patterns of oviposition in two species of hylid frogs. *Southwest. Nat.* 5(2):92–96.

382. Fouquette, M. J., Jr., and F. E. Potter, Jr. 1961. A new black-headed snake from southwestern Texas. *Copeia* 1961(2):144–48.

383. Fowler, H. W., and E. R. Dunn. 1917. Notes on salamanders. *Proc. Acad. Nat. Sci. Philadelphia* 69:7–28.

384. Fowler, J. A. 1948. A Texas snake den. *Bull. Natl. Speleo. Soc.* 10:118.

384.1 Fox, S. F. 1974. Natural selection in the lizard *Uta stansburiana*. *Diss. Abst. Int.* B34(12):5498.

384.11 ———. 1975. Natural selection on morphological phenotypes of the lizard *Uta stansburiana*. *Evolution* 29(1):95–107.

384.12 ———. 1978. Natural selection on behavioral phenotypes of the lizard *Uta stansburiana*. *Ecology* 59(4):834–47.

384.13 ———. 1983. Fitness, home-range quality, and aggression in *Uta stansburiana*. Pp. 149–68 in *Lizard ecology: Studies of a model organism*, edited by R. B. Huey, E. R. Pianka, and T. W. Schoener. Cambridge, Mass.: Harvard University Press.

384.2 Francis, K. 1978. Kemp's Ridley sea turtle conservation programs at South Padre Island, Texas, and Rancho Nuevo, Tamaulipas, Mexico. Pp. 51–62 in *Proc. Florida and Interregional Conf. on Sea Turtles, July 1976, Jensen Beach, Florida*, edited by G. E. Henderson. Mar. Res. Publ. 33.

384.25 Freed, P. S. 1983a. Geographic distribution. *Tropidoclonion lineatum texanum. Herp Rev.* 14(1):29.

384.26 ———. 1983b. *Nerodia erythrogaster flavigaster* (yellowbelly water snake). Coloration. *Herp Rev.* 14(3):75.

384.3 Frierson, L. 1927. *Phrynosoma cornutum* (Harlan) in Louisiana. *Copeia* 1927(165):114.

384.34 Fritts, T. H., W. Hoffman, and M. A. McGehee. 1983. The distribution and abundance of marine turtles in the Gulf of Mexico and nearby Atlantic waters. *J. Herp.* 17(4):327–44.

384.4 Frost, D. R., and T. R. Van Devender. 1979. The relationship of the ground snakes *Sonora semiannulata* and *S. episcopa* (Serpentes: Colubridae). *Occ. Papers Mus. Zool. Louisiana St. Univ.* 52:1–9.

385.   Fugler, C. M. 1955. New locality records for the Louisiana pine snake, *Pituophis catenifer ruthveni* Stull. *Herpetologica* 11(1):24.

386.   Gadow, H. 1901. *Amphibia and reptiles.* London: Macmillan and Co.

387.   ———. 1905. The distribution of Mexican amphibians and reptiles. *Proc. Zool. Soc. London* 2:191–244.

387.5   Gaffney, F. G., and Fitzpatrick, L. C. 1973. Energetics and lipid cycles in the lizard, *Cnemidophorus tigris. Copeia* 1973(3):446–52.

388.   Gaige, H. T. 1931. Notes on *Syrrhophus marnocki* Cope. *Copeia* 1931(2):63.

388.2   Gallaway, B. J. 1968. A habitat study of the Brazos water snake, *Natrix harteri harteri*, in Texas. *TASCA* 23(2):13–15.

388.4   Gallo, J. F., Jr., and K. Reese. 1978. Notes on the hatching of eggs and description of the hatchlings of the reticulated gecko, *Coleonyx reticulatus* Davis and Dixon (Lacertilia: Eublepharidae). *Southwest. Nat.* 23(2):308–309.

388.6   Gambs, R. D., and M. J. Littlejohn. 1979. Acoustic behavior of males of the Rio Grande leopard frog (*Rana berlandieri*): An experimental analysis through field playback trials. *Copeia* 1979(4):643–50.

389.   Garman, S. W. 1883(1884). The reptiles and batrachians of North America, pt. 1, Ophidia. *Mem. Mus. Comp. Zool.* 8(3):1–185.

390.   ———. 1887. Reptiles and batrachians from Texas and Mexico. *Bull. Essex. Inst.* 19:119–38.

391.   ———. 1892. On Texas reptiles. *Bull. Essex Inst.* 24:1–12.

391.4   Garriott, J. 1978. Observations on the Mediterranean gecko (*Hemidactylus turcicus*). *Occ. Papers Dallas Herp. Soc.* 1:11–12.

391.6   Garstka, W. R. 1982. Systematics of the *mexicana* species group of the colubrid genus *Lampropeltis*, with a hypothesis mimicry. *Breviora* 466:1–35.

391.8   Gartside, D. F., J. S. Rogers, and H. C. Dressaur. 1977. Speciation with little genic and morphological differentiation in the ribbon snakes *Thamnophis proximus* and *T. sauritus* (Colubridae). *Copeia* 1977(4):697–705.

392.   Gehlbach, F. R. 1956. Annotated records of southwestern amphibians and reptiles. *Trans. Kansas Acad. Sci.* 59(3):364–72.

393.   ———. 1965. Herpetology of the Zuni Mountains region, northwestern New Mexico. *Proc. United States Natl. Mus.* 116:243–332.

393.01 ———. 1967a. *Ambystoma tigrinum. Cat. Amer. Amphib. Rept.* 51.1–52.4.

393.02 ———. 1967b. *Lampropeltis mexicana. Cat. Amer. Amphib. Rept.* 55.1–55.2.

393.03 ———. 1970. Death-feigning and erratic behavior in leptotyphlopid, colubrid, and elapid snakes. *Herpetologica* 26(1):24–34.

393.04 ———. 1971. Lyre snakes of the *Trimorphodon biscutatus* complex: A taxonomic resume. *Herpetologica* 27(2):200–11.

393.05 ———. 1972. Coral snake mimicry reconsidered. The strategy of self-mimicry. *Forma et Function* 5:311–20.

393.06 ———. 1974. Evolutionary relations of southwestern ringneck snakes (*Diadophis punctatus*). *Herpetologica* 30(2):140–48.

393.07 ———. 1979. Biomes of the Guadalupe escarpment: Vegetation, lizards and human impact. *Natl. Park Serv. Trans. Proc. Ser.* (4):427–39.

394. Gehlbach, F. R., and J. K. Baker. 1962. Kingsnakes allied with *Lampropeltis mexicana:* Taxonomy and natural history. *Copeia* 1962(2):291–300.

394.1 Gehlbach, F. R., et al. 1975. TOES watch-list of endangered, threatened, and peripheral vertebrates of Texas. *Texas Orgn. Endangered Spec. Publ.* 1:1–12.

394.2 Gehlbach, F. R., R. Gordon, and J. B. Gordon. 1973. Aestivation of the salamander, *Siren intermedia. Amer. Midl. Nat.* 89(5):455–63.

394.4 Gehlbach, F. R., and J. A. Holman. 1974. Paleoecology of amphibians and reptiles from Pratt Cave, Guadalupe Mountains National Park, Texas. *Southwest. Nat.* 19(2):191–98.

394.5 Gehlbach, F. R., and S. E. Kennedy. 1978. Population ecology of a highly productive aquatic salamander (*Siren intermedia*). *Southwest. Nat.* 23(3):423–30.

395. Gehlbach, F. R., and C. J. McCoy, Jr. 1965. Additional observations on variation and distribution of the grey-banded kingsnake, *Lampropeltis mexicana* (Garman). *Herpetologica* 21(1):35–38.

395.1 Gehlbach, F. R., and B. Walker. 1970. Acoustic behavior of the aquatic salamander *Siren intermedia. Bioscience* 20(2):1107–1108.

395.2 Gehlbach, F. R., J. F. Watkins, and J. C. Kroll. 1971. Pheromone trail-following studies of typhtopid, leptotyplopid, and colubrid snakes. *Behavior* 90(19):282–94.

395.21   Gehlbach, F. R., J. F. Watkins, and H. W. Reno. 1968. Blind snake defensive behavior elicted by ant attacks. *Bioscience* 18(8):784–85.

395.3   Gehrmann, W. H. 1973. Serum proteins and nutritional state in immature *Natrix erythrogaster transversa*. *Copeia* 1973(1):176–78.

395.4   Gehrmann, W. H., and C. C. Carpenter. 1973. Evidence for a central cholinoceptive component in despotic behavior in the male collared lizard *Crotaphytus collaris*. *Proc. Oklahoma Acad. Sci.* 53:38–40.

396.   Geiser, S. W. 1941. Dr. Benno Matthes: An early herpetologist. *Field and Lab.* 9(2):37–45.

397.   Gentry, A. F. 1885. A review of the genus *Phrynosoma*. *Proc. Acad. Nat. Sci. Philadelphia* 37:138–48.

398.   George, J. E. 1960. Notes on the parasitic mites of some west Texas reptiles. *Southwest Nat.* 5(2):105–106.

399.   George, J. L., and W. H. Stickel. 1949. Wildlife effects of DDT dust used for tick control on a Texas prairie. *Amer. Midl. Nat.* 42(1):228–37.

399.2   Gerhardt, H. C. 1974. Mating call differences between eastern and western populations of the treefrog *Hyla chrysoscelis*. *Copeia* 1974(2): 534–36.

399.4   Gillette, D. D. 1974. A proposed revision of the evolutionary history of *Terrapene carolina triunguis*. *Copeia* 1974(2):537–39.

400.   Gilmore, C. W. 1938. Fossil snakes of North America. *Geol. Soc. Amer. Spec. Papers* 9:viii–96.

401.   Girard, C. 1852. A monographic essay on the genus *Phrynosoma*. Pp. 345–65 in *Stansbury's exploration and survey of the valley of the Great Salt Lake of Utah*. Philadelphia: Lippincott, Grambo and Co.

402.   ———. 1854. A list of North American bufonids, with diagnoses of new species. *Proc. Acad. Nat. Sci. Philadelphia* 7:86–88.

403.   ———. 1858. Herpetology. In *United States exploring expedition during the years 1838, 1840, 1841, 1842, under the command of Charles Wilkes, U.S.N.* Vol. 20. Philadelphia: J. B. Lippincott and Co.

404.   ———. 1859. Herpetological notices. *Proc. Acad. Nat. Sci. Philadelphia* 11:169–70.

405.   Glass, B. P. 1946a. A new *Hyla* from south Texas. *Herpetologica* 3(3): 101–103.

406.   ———. 1946b. *Hyla crucifer* in Texas. *Copeia* 1946(2):103.

407. ———. 1951. Age of maturity of neotenic *Ambystoma tigrinum mavortium* Baird. *Amer. Midl. Nat.* 46:391–94.

408. Glass, B. P., and N. Hartweg. 1951. *Kinosternon murrayi,* a new musk turtle of the *hirtipes* group from Texas. *Copeia* 1951(1):50–52.

408.2 Glenn, J. L., et al. 1983. Geographical variation in *Crotalus scutulatus scutulatus* (Mojave rattlesnake) venom properties. *Toxicon* 21(1): 119–30.

408.5 Glidewell, J. 1974. Records of the snake *Coluber constrictor* (Reptilia: Colubridae) from New Mexico and the Chihuahuan desert of Texas. *Southwest. Nat.* 19(2):215–17.

409. Gloyd, H. K. 1935a. The cane-brake rattlesnake. *Copeia* 1935(4):175–78.

410. ———. 1935b. Some aberrant color patterns in snakes. *Papers Michigan Acad. Sci., Arts, Letters* 20:661–68.

411. ———. 1935c. The subspecies of *Sistrurus miliarius. Occ. Papers Mus. Zool. Univ. Michigan* 322:1–7.

412. ———. 1936. The subspecies of *Crotalus lepidus. Occ. Papers Mus. Zool. Univ. Michigan* 337:1–5.

413. ———. 1938. A case of poisoning from the bite of a black coral snake. *Herpetologica* (5):121–25.

414. ———. 1940. The rattlesnakes, genera *Sistrurus* and *Crotalus. Spec. Publ. Chicago Acad. Sci.* 4:1–270.

415. ———. 1944. Texas snakes. *Texas Geogr.* 8:1–18.

416. ———. 1948. Another account of the "dance" of the western diamond rattlesnake. *Chicago Acad. Sci. Nat. Hist. Misc.* 34:1–3.

417. ———. 1955. A review of the massasaugas, *Sistrurus catenatus,* of the southwestern United States (Serpentes: Crotalidae). *Bull. Chicago Acad. Sci.* 10(6):83–98.

418. ———. 1958. Aberrations in the color pattern of some crotalid snakes. *Bull. Chicago Acad. Sci.* 10(12):185–95.

418.1 ———. 1969. Two additional subspecies of North American crotalid snakes, genus Agkistrodon. *Proc. Biol. Soc. Washington* 82:219–32.

419. Gloyd, H. K., and R. Conant. 1934a. The broad-banded copperhead: A new subspecies of *Agkistrodon mokasen. Occ. Papers Mus. Zool. Univ. Michigan* 283:1–5.

420. ———. 1934b. The taxonomic status, range, and natural history of Schott's racer. *Occ. Papers Mus. Zool. Univ. Michigan* 287:1–17.

421.   ———. 1938. The subspecies of the copperhead *Agkistrodon mokasen* Beauvois. *Bull. Chicago Acad. Sci.* 6:163–66.

422.   ———. 1943. A synopsis of the American forms of *Agkistrodon* (copperheads and moccasins). *Bull. Chicago Acad. Sci.* 7(2):147–70.

423.   Goff, C. C. 1936. Distribution and variation of a new subspecies of water snake, *Natrix cyclopion floridana*, with a discussion of its relationships. *Occ. Papers Mus. Zool. Univ. Michigan* 327:1–9.

423.5   Goff, M. L., and R. B. Loomis. 1978. A genus *Odontacarus* (Acari: Trombiculidae) in North America. *J. Med. Ento. Honolulu* 14(3):370–73.

424.   Goin, C. J. 1942. Description of a new race of *Siren intermedia*. *Ann. Carnegie Mus.* 29:211–17.

425.   ———. 1957. Description of a new salamander of the genus *Siren* from the Rio Grande. *Herpetologica* 13(1):37–42.

426.   Goin, C. J., and M. G. Netting. 1940. A new gopher frog from the Gulf Coast, with comments on the *Rana areolata* group. *Ann. Carnegie Mus.* 38:137–68.

426.2   Gollob, R. 1978. Bullfrogs preying on cedar waxwings. *Herp. Rev.* 9(2):47–48.

426.4   Goodwin, H. A. 1974. Here today . . . gone tomorrow? *Natl. Wildlife* 12(3):29–31.

427.   Graham, A. B. 1957. The thyroid gland of *Typhlomolge rathbuni*. *Copeia* 1957(1):41–43.

428.   Grant, C. 1936. The southwestern desert tortoise, *Gopherus agassizi*. *Zoologica* 21:225–29.

429.   ———. 1956. Alligators in western Texas. *Herpetologica* 12(2):90.

430.   ———. 1960. Differentiation of the southwestern tortoises (genus *Gopherus*), with notes on their habits. *Trans. San Diego Soc. Nat. Hist.* 12(27):441–48.

431.   Greding, E. J., Jr. 1964a. Food of *Ancistrodon c. contortrix* in Houston and Trinity counties, Texas. *Southwest. Nat.* 9(2):105.

432.   ———. 1964b. Food of *Natrix* in Hunt County, Texas. *Southwest. Nat.* 9(3):206.

432.1   Greenberg, N. 1977. An ethogram of the blue spiny lizard, *Sceloporus cyanogenys* (Reptilia: Lacertilia: Iguanidae). *J. Herp.* 11(2):177–95.

432.2   Greene, H. W. 1969. Fat storage in females of an introduced lizard, *Hemidactylus turcicus*, from Texas. *Texas J. Sci.* 21(2):233–35.

432.23 ———. 1984. Taxonomic status of the western racer, *Coluber constrictor mormon. J. Herp.* 18(2):210–11.

433. Greene, H. W., and B. E. Dial. 1966. Brooding behavior by a female Texas alligator lizard. *Herpetologica* 22(4):303.

434. Greene, H. W., and G. V. Oliver, Jr. 1965. Notes on the natural history of the western massasauga. *Herpetologica* 21(3):225–28.

435. Grobman, A. B. 1941. A contribution to the knowledge of variation in *Opheodrys aestivus* (Harlan), with the description of a new subspecies. *Misc. Publ. Mus. Zool. Univ. Michigan* 50:1–38.

436. ———. 1944. The distribution of the salamanders of the genus *Plethodon* in eastern United States and Canada. *Ann. New York Acad. Sci.* 45(7):261–316.

437. ———. 1950a. The problem of the natural range of a species. *Copeia* 1950(3):231–32.

438. ———. 1950b. The distribution of the races of *Desmognathus fuscus* in the southern states. *Chicago Acad. Sci. Nat. Hist. Misc.* 70:1–8.

438.1 ———. 1984. Scutellation variation in *Opheodrys aestivus. Bull. Florida St. Mus.* 29(4):153–70.

438.4 Grubb, J. C. 1970. Orientation in post-reproductive Mexican toads, *Bufo valliceps. Copeia* 1970(4):674–80.

438.41 ———. 1971. Selected aspects of olfactory and visual orientation in anuran amphibians. *Diss. Abst. Int.* B33(1):154–B.

438.42 ———. 1973a. Orientation in newly metamorphosed Mexican toads, *Bufo valliceps. Herpetologica* 29(2):95–100.

438.43 ———. 1973b. Olfactory orientation in breeding Mexican toads, *Bufo valliceps. Copeia* 1973(3):490–97.

438.44 ———. 1975. Olfactory orientation in southern leopard frogs, *Rana utricularia. Herpetologica* 31(2):219–22.

438.6 Grunwaldt, P. H. 1980. Liste der Schildkröten in der herpetologischen Sammlung des Zoologischen Instituts und Zoologischen Museums der Universität Hamburg. (Testudines, Reptilia). *Bestandslisten der herpetologischen Sammlung des Zoologischen Instituts und Zoologischen Museums der Universität Hamburg (ZMH)*, 1.

439. Guidry, E. B. 1953. Herpetological notes from southeastern Texas. *Herpetologica* 9(1):49–56.

439.2 Guillette, L. J., J. Weigel, and G. Flater. 1983. Unilateral testicular pigmentation in the Mexican lizard *Sceloporus variabilis. Copeia* 1983(1):155–61.

440.   Gunter, G. 1941. A plague of toads. *Copeia* 1941(4):226.

441.   ———. 1945. The northern range of Berlandier's turtle. *Copeia* 1945(3): 175.

442.   Gunther, A. 1858. Catalogue of colubrine snakes in the collection of the British Museum. London. 24:231.

443.   Guttman, S. I. 1965. An electrophoretic analysis of the blood proteins of the genus *Siren*. *Texas J. Sci*. 17(3):267–77.

443.01   ———. 1969. Blood protein variation in the *Bufo americanus* species group of toads. *Copeia* 1969(2):243–49.

443.02   ———. 1971. An electrophoretic analysis of the hemoglobins of old and new world lizards. *J. Herp*. 5(1–2):11–16.

443.03   ———. 1972. Blood proteins. Pp. 265–78 in *Evolution in the genus* Bufo, edited by W. F. Blair. Austin: University of Texas Press.

443.2   Gwynne, P. 1975. Wildlife in danger. *Newsweek* 85(1):36–41.

443.3   Hahn, D. E. 1979a. Leptotyphlopidae, *Leptotyphlops*. *Cat. Amer. Amphib. Rept*. 230.1–230.4.

443.31   ———. 1979b. *Leptotyphylops dulcis*. *Cat. Amer. Amphib. Rept*. 231.1– 231.2.

443.32   ———. 1979c. *Leptotyphlops humilis*. *Cat. Amer. Amphib. Rept*. 232.1– 232.4.

444.   Hahn, W. E. 1962. Serum protein and erythrocyte changes during metamorphosis in paedogenic *Ambystoma tigrinum mavortium*. *Comp. Biochem. Physiol*. 7:55–61.

445.   Hahn, W. E., and D. W. Tinkle. 1965. Fat body cycling and experimental evidence for its adaptive significance to ovarian follicle development in the lizard *Uta stansburiana*. *J. Exp. Zool*. 158(1):79–86.

445.2   Hall, R. J. 1976. *Eumeces obsoletus* (Baird and Girard). *Cat. Amer. Amphib. Rept*. 186.1–186.3.

446.   Hallowell, E. 1852a. Descriptions of new species of reptiles inhabiting North America. *Proc. Acad. Nat. Sci. Philadelphia* 6:177–82.

447.   ———. 1852b. On a new genus and three new species of reptiles inhabiting North America. *Proc. Acad. Nat. Sci. Philadelphia* 6:206–209.

448.   ———. 1854. Notices of new reptiles from Texas. *Proc. Acad. Nat. Sci. Philadelphia* 7:192–93.

449. ———. 1856a. Notice of a collection of reptiles from Kansas and Nebraska, presented to the Academy of Natural Sciences, by Dr. Hammond, USA. *Proc. Acad. Nat. Sci. Philadelphia* 8:238–53.

450. ———. 1856b. Note on the collection of reptiles from the neighborhood of San Antonio, Texas, recently presented to the Academy of Natural Sciences by Dr. A. Heerman. *Proc. Acad. Nat. Sci. Philadelphia* 8:306–10.

451. ———. 1859. Report on reptiles collected on the survey. In *Report of Lieutenant J. G. Parke. Pacific R.R. Rept.* Vol. 10.

451.5 Hambrick, P. S. 1975. New county records and range extensions of Texas amphibians and reptiles. *Herp Rev.* 6(3):79–80.

451.51 ———. 1976. Additions to the Texas herpetofauna, with notes on peripheral range extensions and new records of Texas amphibians and reptiles. *Texas J. Sci.* 27(2):291–99.

452. Hamilton, R. D. 1944. Notes on mating and migration in Berlandier's turtle. *Copeia* 1944(1):62.

453. ———. 1947. The range of *Pseudemys scripta gaigei*. *Copeia* 1947(1):65–66.

454. Hamilton, W. J. 1947. Hibernation of the lined snake. *Copeia* 1947(3):209–10.

454.1 Hampton, N. 1976. Annotated checklist of the amphibians and reptiles of Travis County, Texas. Pp. 84–101 in *A bird finding and naturalist's guide for Austin, Texas, area*, edited by E. Kutac and S. Caran. Austin, Tex.: Oasis Press.

454.3 Hardy, L. M. 1975a. A systematic revision of the colubrid snake genus *Gyalopion. J. Herp.* 9(1):107–32.

454.31 ———. 1975b. A systematic revision of the colubrid snake genus *Ficimia. J. Herp.* 9(2):133–68.

454.32 ———. 1976a. *Ficimia streckeri* Taylor. *Cat. Amer. Amphib. Rept.* 181.1–181.2.

454.33 ———. 1976b. *Gyalopion* Cope. *Cat. Amer. Amphib. Rept.* 182.1–182.4.

455. Harper, F. 1932. A new Texas subspecies of the lizard genus *Holbrookia. Proc. Biol. Soc. Washington* 45:15–18.

456. ———. 1935. The name of the gopher frog. *Proc. Biol. Soc. Washington* 48:79–82.

457. ———. 1947. A new cricket frog (*Acris*) from the middle western states. *Proc. Biol. Soc. Washington* 60:39–40.

458. Harrington, J. W. 1953. A fossil Pleistocene snake from Denton County, Texas. *Field and Lab.* 21(1):20.

458.2 Harris, A. H. 1977(1978). Wisconsin age environments in the northern Chihuahuan desert: Evidence from the higher vertebrates. Pp. 23–52 in *Transactions of the symposium on the biological resources of the Chihuahuan desert region, United States and Mexico,* edited by R. W. Wauer, D. N. Riskin. Natl. Park Ser. Trans. Proc. Ser. (3).

458.4 Harris, H. S., and R. S. Simmons. 1978. A preliminary account of the rattlesnakes with the description of four new subspecies. *Bull. Maryland Herp. Soc.* 14(3):105–211.

459. Hartman, C. 1922. A brown rat kills a rattler. *J. Mamm.* 3(2):116–17.

460. Hartweg, N. 1939a. A new American *Pseudemys. Occ. Papers Mus. Zool. Univ. Michigan* 397:1–4.

461. ———. 1939b. Further notes on the *Pseudemys scripta* complex. *Copeia* 1939(1):55.

462. ———. 1940. Description of *Salvadora intermedia,* new species, with remarks on the *grahamiae* group. *Copeia* 1940 (4):256–59.

463. Harwood, P. D. 1930. A new species of *Oxysomatium* (Nematoda) with some remarks on the genera *Oxysomatium* and *Aplectana,* and observations on the life history. *J. Parasit.* 17(2):61–73.

464. ———. 1932. The helminths parasitic in the Amphibia and Reptilia of Houston, Texas, and vicinity. *Proc. United States Natl. Mus.* 81, art. 17.

465. ———. 1936. The effects of soil types on the helminths parasitic in the ground lizard, *Leiolopisma laterale* (Say). *Ecology* 17(4):694–98.

466. Hay, O. P. 1892. On the ejection of blood from the eyes of horned toads. *Proc. United States Natl. Mus.* 15:375–78.

467. ———. 1908. The fossil turtles of North America. *Publ. Carnegie Inst. Washington* (75):1–568.

468. ———. 1911. A fossil specimen of alligator snapper (*Macrochelys temmenckii*) from Texas. *Proc. Amer. Philos. Soc.* 50:452–55.

469. ———. 1916. Descriptions of some fossil vertebrates found in Texas. *Bull. Univ. Texas* (71):1–24.

470. ———. 1924. The Pleistocene of the middle region of North America and its vertebrated animals. *Publ. Carnegie Inst. Washington* (332A): 1–385.

470.2   Haynes, D. 1976. *Graptemys caglei* Haynes and McKown. *Cat. Amer. Amphib. Rept.* 184.1–184.2.

470.3   Haynes, D., and McKown, R. R. 1974. A new species of map turtle (genus *Graptemys*) from the Guadalupe river system in Texas. *Tulane Stud. Zool. Bot.* 18(4):143–52.

470.4   Heaton, M. J. 1979. Cranial anatomy of the primitive captorhinid reptiles from the late Pennsylvania and Early Permian Oklahoma and Texas. *Oklahoma Geol. Survey Bull.* 127:1–84.

471.   Hecht, M. K. 1958. A synopsis of the mud puppies of eastern North America. *Proc. Staten Is. Inst. Arts, Sci.* 21(1):3–38.

472.   Hecht, M. K., and B. L. Matalas. 1946. A review of middle North American toads of the genus *Microhyla*. *Amer. Mus. Novitates* 1315:1–21.

473.   Henderson, G. G. 1961. Reproductive potential of *Microhyla olivacea*. *Texas J. Sci.* 13(3):355–56.

473.2   Hendricks, A. C., J. T. Wyatt, and D. E. Henley. 1971. Infestation of a Texas red-eared turtle by leeches. *Texas J. Sci.* 22(2–3):247.

473.4   Hendricks, F. S. 1973. Geographic distribution. *Coleonyx reticulatus*. *HISS News-J.* 1(1):21.

473.41 ———. 1975. Biogeography, natural history and systematics of *Cnemidophorus tigris* (Sauria: Teiidae) east of the continental divide. *Diss. Abst. Int.* 36(5):2105–2106.

473.42 ———. 1985. Intrapopulational variation in the caudal osteology of *Cnemidophorus tigris marmoratus* Baird and Girard (Reptilia: Teiidae). *Texas J. Sci.* 37(1):33–47.

473.43 Hendricks, F. S., and J. R. Dixon. 1984. Population structure of *Cnemidophorus tigris* (Reptilia: Teiidae) east of the continental divide. *Southwest. Nat.* 29(1):137–40.

474.   Hensley, M. 1959. Albinism in North American amphibians and reptiles. *Publ. Mus. Michigan St. Univ. Biol. Ser.* 1(4):135–59.

474.1   ———. 1968. Another albino lizard, *Sceloporus undulatus hyacinthinus* (Green). *J. Herp.* 1(1–4):92–93.

475.   Herald, E. S. 1952. Texas blind salamander in the aquarium. *Aquarium J.* 23(8):149–52.

476.   ———. 1955. A longevity record for the Texas blind salamander. *Herpetologica* 11(3):192.

477.   Herreid, C. F., II. 1961. Snakes as predators of bats. *Herpetologica* 17(4):271–72.

478.   Hewatt, W. G. 1937. Courting and egg-laying habits of *Phrynosoma cornutum. Copeia* 1937(4):234.

478.2   Heyer, W. R. 1971. *Leptodactylus labialis. Cat. Amer. Amphib. Rept.* 104.1–104.3.

478.21   ———. 1978. Systematics of the *fuscus* group of the frog genus *Leptodactylus* (Amphibia: Leptodactylidae). *Nat. Hist. Mus. Los Angeles Co. Sci. Bull.* 29:1–85.

479.   Heyl, D. H., and H. M. Smith. 1957. Another unicolor many-lined skink from Nebraska. *Herpetologica* 13(1):12–14.

480.   Hibbard, C. W., and W. W. Dalquest. 1966. Fossils from the Seymour formation of Knox and Baylor counties, Texas, and their bearing on the late Kansan climate of that region. *Contrib. Mus. Paleontol. Univ. Michigan* 21:1–66.

480.2   Hibbitts, T. 1978. Techniques for collecting the common salamanders of Texas. *Occ. Papers Dallas Herp. Soc.* 1:4–7.

481.   Highton, R. 1962. Revision of North American salamanders of the genus *Plethodon. Bull. Florida St. Mus.* 6(3):235–367.

482.   Hill, I. R. 1954. The taxonomic status of the mid-Gulf Coast *Amphiuma. Tulane Stud. Zool.* 1(12):191–215.

482.2   Hill, W. H. 1971. Pleistocene snakes from a cave in Kendall County, Texas. *Texas J. Sci.* 22(2–3):209–16.

482.3   Hiller, I. 1973. Birth of snakes. *Texas Parks and Wildlife* 31(3):30–31.

482.4   Hillis, D. M. 1977. An incident of death-feigning in *Sonora semiannulata blanchardi. Bull. Maryland Herp. Soc.* 13(2):116–17.

482.41   ———. 1981. Premating isolating mechanisms among three species of the *Rana pipiens* complex in Texas and southern Oklahoma. *Copeia* 1981(2):312–19.

482.42   ———. 1982. Morphological differentiation and adaptation of the larvae of *Rana berlandieri* and *R. sphenocephala* (*Rana pipiens* complex) in sympatry. *Copeia* 1982(1):168–74.

482.5   Hillis, D. M., and S. L. Campbell. 1982. New localities for *Tantilla rubra cucullata* (Colubridae) and the distribution of its two morphotypes. *Southwest. Nat.* 27(2):220–21.

482.6   Hillis, D. M., A. M. Hillis, and R. F. Martin. 1984. Reproductive ecology and hybridization of the endangered Houston toad (*Bufo houstonensis*). *J. Herp.* 18(1):56–72.

483.   Hilman, J. L., and R. W. Strandtmann. 1960. The incidence of *Hepato-zooa serpentium* in some west Texas snakes. *Southwest. Nat.* 5(4): 226–28.

484.   Hilton, W. A. 1956. Eye muscles of salamanders. *Herpetologica* 12(4): 273–76.

484.5   Hinderstein, B., and J. Boyce. 1977. The Miocene salamander *Batra-chosauroides dissimulans* (Amphibia: Urodela) from east Texas. *J. Herp.* 11(3):369–72.

485.   Hoddenbach, G. A. 1966. Reproduction in western Texas *Cnemidopho-rus sexlineatus* (Sauria: Teiidae). *Copeia* 1966 (1):110–13.

485.5   Hoff, G., and D. O. Trainer. 1973. Arboviruses in reptiles: Isolation of a bunyamwera group virus from a naturally infected turtle. *J. Herp.* 7(2):55–62.

486.   Hoffman, C. H., and J. P. Linduska. 1949. Some considerations of the biological effects of DDT. *Sci. Monthly* 69:104–14.

487.   Hoffpauir, C. H., and E. P. Morrison. 1966. *Rhabdias ranae* from *Bufo valliceps*. *Southwest. Nat.* 11(2):302.

487.5   Holbrook, J. 1842. *North American herpetology*. Misc. Publ., SSAR Fac-simile reprint 1976, five volumes in one.

487.7   Hollis, P. 1972. A survey of parasites of the bullfrog, *Rana catesbeiana* Shaw, in central east Texas. *Southwest. Nat.* 17(2):198–200.

488.   Holman, J. A. 1962a. *Tantilla nigriceps* from Kinney County, Texas. *Her-petologica* 17(4):274.

489.   ———. 1962b. A Texas Pleistocene herpetofauna. *Copeia* 1962(2): 255–61.

490.   ———. 1963. Late Pleistocene amphibians and reptiles of the Clear Creek and Ben Franklin local faunas of Texas. *J. Grad. Res. Centr.* 31(3):152–67.

491.   ———. 1964. Pleistocene amphibians and reptiles from Texas. *Herpe-tologica* 20(2):73–83.

492.   ———. 1965a. A small Pleistocene herpetofauna from Houston, Texas. *Texas J. Sci.* 17(4):418–23.

493.   ———. 1965b. Pleistocene snakes from the Seymour formation of Texas. *Copeia* 1965(1):102–104.

494.   ———. 1966a. A huge Pleistocene box turtle from Texas. *Quart. J. Flor-ida Acad. Sci.* 28(4):345–48.

495.   ———. 1966b. The Pleistocene herpetofauna of Miller's Cave, Texas. *Texas J. Sci.* 18(4):372–77.

495.01   ———. 1966. A small Miocene herpetofauna from Texas. *Quart. J. Florida Acad. Sci.* 29(4):267–75.

495.02   ———. 1968. A Pleistocene herpetofauna from Kendall County, Texas. *Quart. J. Florida Acad. Sci.* 31(3):165–72.

495.03   ———. 1969a. Pleistocene amphibians from a cave in Edwards County, Texas. *Texas J. Sci.* 21(1):63–68.

495.04   ———. 1969b. Herpetofauna of the Pleistocene Slaton local fauna of Texas. *Southwest. Nat.* 14(2):203–12.

495.05   ———. 1969c. The Pleistocene amphibians and reptiles of Texas. *Publ. Michigan St. Mus. Biol. Ser.* 4(5):163–92.

495.06   ———. 1971a. *Ophisaurus. Cat. Amer. Amphib. Rept.* 110.1–110.3.

495.07   ———. 1971b. *Ophisaurus attenuatus. Cat. Amer. Amphib. Rept.* 111.1–111.3.

495.08   ———. 1977. Amphibians and reptiles of the Gulf Coast Miocene of Texas. *Herpetologica* 33(4):391–403.

495.3   Holmback, E. 1981. Life history notes. *Crotalus atrox. Herp Rev.* 12(2):70.

495.31   ———. 1985. *Crotalus atrox* (western diamondback rattlesnake). Coloration. *Herp Rev.* 16(3):78.

495.4   Honegger, R. E. 1970. Houston toad, *Bufo houstonensis* Sanders 1953. *Red Data Book.* Vol. 3, *Amphibia and Reptilia.* IUCN, Switzerland.

495.6   Houseal, T. W., J. W. Bickham, and M. D. Springer. 1982. Geographic variation in the yellow mud turtle. *Kinosternon flavescens. Copeia* 1982(3):567–80.

495.7   Huang, T. T., S. R. Lewis, and B. S. Lucas III. 1975. Venomous snakes. Pp. 123–42 in *Dangerous plants, snakes, arthropods, and marine life in Texas,* edited by M. D. Ellis. Washington, D.C.: U.S. Dept. Health, Education and Welfare.

496.   Hubbs, C. 1962. Effects of a hurricane on the fish fauna of a coastal pool and drainage ditch. *Texas J. Sci.* 14(3):289–96.

497.   Hubbs, C., and N. E. Armstrong. 1961. Minimum developmental temperature tolerance of two anurans, *Scaphiopus couchi* and *Microhyla olivacea. Texas J. Sci.* 13(3):358–62.

497.2   Hubbs, C., and F. D. Martin. 1967. *Bufo valliceps* breeding in artificial pools. *Southwest. Nat.* 12(1):105–106.

498.   Hubbs, C., T. Wright, and O. Cuellar. 1963. Developmental temperature tolerance of central Texas populations of two anuran amphibians, *Bufo valliceps* and *Pseudacris streckeri. Southwest. Nat.* 8(3):142–49.

498.2   Hudson, R., and G. Carl. 1983. Life history notes: *Coluber constrictor flaviventris.* Coloration. *Herp Rev.* 14(1):19.

498.21   ————. 1985. *Crotalus horridus* (timber rattlesnake). Coloration. *Herp Rev.* 16(1):28–29.

499.   Hughes, N. 1962. The number and form of chromosomes in the genus *Scaphiopus. Texas J. Sci.* 14(2):225–28.

500.   ————. 1963. Notes on two partial albino (?) toads, *Scaphiopus bombifrons. Herpetologica* 19(2):139–40.

501.   ————. 1965. Comparison of frontoparietal bones of *Scaphiopus bombifrons* and *S. hammondi* as evidence of interspecific hybridization. *Herptologica* 21(3):196–201.

502.   Hughes, R. C., J. R. Baker, and C. B. Dawson. 1941. The tapeworms of reptiles. Part I. *Amer. Midl. Nat.* 25(2):454–68.

503.   Hughes, R. C., J. W. Higginbotham, and J. W. Clary. 1942. The trematodes of reptiles. Part 1, systematic section. *Amer. Midl. Nat.* 27(1):109–34.

504.   Huheey, J. E. 1959. Distribution and variation in the glossy water snake, *Natrix rigida* (Say). *Copeia* 1959(4):303–11.

505.   Hunsaker, D., II. 1959a. Birth and litter sizes of the blue spiny lizard *Sceloporus cyanogenys. Copeia* 1959(3):260–61.

506.   ————. 1959b. Stomach contents of the American egret, *Casmerodius albus,* in Travis Co., Texas. *Texas J. Sci.* 11(4):454.

507.   Hunsaker, D., II, R. E. Alston, W. F. Blair, and B. L. Turner. 1961. A comparison of the ninhydrin positive and phenoloci substances of parotoid gland secretions of certain *Bufo* species and their hybrids. *Evolution* 15(3):352–59.

508.   Hunsaker, D., II, and D. Sellers. 1953. Notes on the possible intergradation between the colubrine snakes *Arizona elegans blanchardi* Klauber and *Arizona elegans elegans* Kennicott in Texas. *Texas J. Sci.* 5(2):268–69.

509.   Hurter, J., and J. K. Strecker. 1909. Amphibians and reptiles of Arkansas. *Trans. Acad. Sci. St. Louis* 18:11–27.

509.2   Ideker, J. 1974. *Storeria dekayi texana* from the caprock of Northwest Texas. *Tex. J. Sci.* 25(1–4):87.

509.21   ———. 1979. Adult *Cybister fimbriolatus* are predaceous (Coleoptera: Dytiscidae). *Coleopterists Bull.* 33(1):41–44.

509.22   ———. 1979. Geographical distribution. *Nerodia rhombifera*. *Herp Rev.* 10(2):60.

509.3   Ingram, W., III, and W. W. Tanner. 1971. A taxonomic study of *Crotaphytus collaris* between the Rio Grande and Colorado rivers. *Brigham Young Univ. Sci. Bull. Bio. Ser.* 13(2):1–29.

509.5   Irby, L. R., and R. H. Cutting. 1970. Comparative cranial osteology of *Storeria dekayi texana* and *Virginia striatula* (Serpentes: colubridae). *TASCA* 24(2):7–14.

510.   Irwin, L. N. 1965. Diel activity and social interaction of the lizard *Uta stansburiana stejnegeri*. *Copeia* 1965(1):99–101.

510.3   Iverson, J. B. 1977. *Kinosternon subrubrum*. *Cat. Amer. Amphib. Rept.* 193.1–193.4.

510.31   ———. 1978. Distribution problems of the genus *Kinosternon* in the American southwest. *Copeia* 1978(3):476–79.

510.32   ———. 1979a. A taxonomic reappraisal of the yellow mud turtle, *Kinosternon flavescens* (Testudines: Kinosternidae). *Copeia* 1979(2):212–25.

510.33   ———. 1979b. *Sternotherus carinatus*. *Cat. Amer. Amphib. Rept.* 226.1–226.2.

510.5   ———. 1981. Biosystematics of the *Kinosternon hirtipes* species group (Testudines: Kinosternidae). *Tulane Stud. Zool. Bot.* 23(1):1–74.

510.51   ———. 1985. Geographic variation in sexual dimorphism in the mud turtle *Kinosternon hirtipes*. *Copeia* 1985(2):388–93.

511.   Jackson, A. W. 1952. The effect of temperature, humidity, and barometric pressure on the rate of call in *Acris crepitans* Baird in Brazos County, Texas. *Herpetologica* 8(2):18–20.

511.2   Jackson, M. K., and H. Reno. 1975. Comparative skin structure of some fossorial and subfossorial leptotyphloid and colubrid snakes. *Herpetologica* 31(3):350–59.

511.4   Jacob, J. S. 1977. An evaluation of the possibility of hybridization between the rattlesnakes *Crotalus atrox* and *C. scutulatus*, in the southwestern United States. *Southwest. Nat.* 22(4):469–85.

511.5   Jacob, J. S., and H. S. McDonald. 1976. Diving bradycardia in four spe-
         cies of North American aquatic snakes. *Comp. Biochem. Physiol.* (A)
         53(1):69–72.

512.   Jacobs, B., and E. O. Morrison. 1966. Ectopic lung fluke. *Southwest.
         Nat.* 11(3):412.

513.   James, P. 1966. The Mexican burrowing toad, *Rhinophrynus dorsalis*, an
         addition to the vertebrate fauna of the United States. *Texas J. Sci.*
         18(3):272–76.

514.   Jameson, D. L. 1950a. The development of *Eleutherodactylus latrans*.
         Copeia 1950(1):44–46.

515.   ———. 1950b. The breeding and development of Strecker's chorus frog
         in central Texas. *Copeia* 1950(1):61.

516.   ———. 1954. Social patterns in the leptodactylid frogs *Syrrhophus* and
         Eleutherodactylus. *Copeia* 1954(1):36–38.

517.   ———. 1955. The population dynamics of the cliff frog, *Syrrhophus mar-
         nocki*. *Amer. Midl. Nat.* 54(2):342–81.

518.   ———. 1956a. Duplicate feeding habits in snakes. *Copeia* 1956(1):
         54–55.

519.   ———. 1956b. Survival of some central Texas frogs under natural condi-
         tions. *Copeia* 1956(1):55–57.

520.   ———. 1957. Extension of the range of the Davis Mountain rat snake.
         Herpetologica 13(1):80.

521.   Jameson, D. L., and A. G. Flury. 1949. Reptiles and amphibians of the
         Sierra Vieja. *Texas J. Sci.* 1(2):54–79.

522.   Jameson, D. L., and A. M. Jameson, Jr. 1956. Food habits and toxicity of
         the venom of the night snake. *Herpetologica* 12(3):240.

522.1   Jameson, D. L., and R. C. Richmond. 1971. Parallelism and conver-
         gence in the evolution of size and shape in Holartic *Hyla*. *Evolution*
         25(3):497–508.

523.   Johnson, C. 1959. Genetic incompatibility in the call races of *Hyla ver-
         sicolor* LeConte in Texas. *Copeia* 1959(4):327–35.

524.   ———. 1960. Reproductive cycle in females of the greater earless liz-
         ard, *Holbrookia texana*. *Copeia* 1960(4):297–300.

525.   ———. 1963. Additional evidence of sterility between call types in the
         Hyla versicolor complex. *Copeia* 1963(1):139–43.

526.   ———. 1966. Species recognition in the *Hyla versicolor* complex. *Texas J. Sci.* 18(4):361–64.

526.2   Johnson, C. R., W. G. Voight, and E. N. Smith. 1978. Thermoregulation in crocodilians. III. Thermal preferenda, voluntary maxima, and heating and cooling rates in the American alligator, *Alligator mississippiensis. Zool. J. Linn. Soc.* 62(2):179–88.

527.   Johnson, J. E., Jr. 1948. Copperhead in a tree. *Herpetologica* 4(6):214.

528.   Johnson, L., Jr., D. A. Suhm, C. D. Tunnell. 1962. Salvage archeology of Canyon Reservoir: The Wunderlich, Footbridge, and Oblate Sites. *Bull. Texas Mem. Mus.* 5.

529.   Jones, J. P. 1926. The proper name for *Sceloporus consobrinus* Baird and Girard. *Occ. Papers Mus. Zool. Univ. Michigan* 172:1–3.

529.1   Jones, M. P. 1977. Rulemaking actions May–June 6, 1977. Proposed rulemakings. Houston Toad. *Endangered Spec. Tech. Bull.* 2(6):4.

529.2   Jones, S. M., and G. W. Ferguson. 1980. The effect of paint marking on mortality in a Texas population of *Sceloporus undulatus. Copeia* 1980(4):850–54.

529.3   Judd, F. W. 1974a. Intraspecific variation in blood properties of the keeled earless lizard, *Holbrookia propinqua. Herpetologica* 30(1):99–102.

529.31   ———. 1974b. The ecology of the keeled earless lizard, *Holbrookia propinqua. Diss. Abst. Int.* B35(1):599–600.

529.32   ———. 1975. Activity and thermal ecology of the keeled earless lizard, *Holbrookia propinqua. Herpetologica* 31(2):137–50.

529.33   ———. 1976a. Food and feeding behavior of the keeled earless lizard *Holbrookia propinqua. Southwest. Nat.* 21(1):17–25.

529.34   ———. 1976b. Demography of a barrier island population of the keeled earless lizard *Holbrookia propinqua. Occ. Papers Mus. Texas Tech. Univ.* 44:1–45.

529.35   ———. 1977. Toxicity of monosodium methanearsonate herbicide to Couch's spadefoot toad, *Scaphiopus couchi. Herpetologica* 33(1):44–46.

529.4   Judd, F. W., and J. C. McQueen. 1980. Incubation, hatching, and growth of the tortoise, *Gopherus berlandieri. J. Herp.* 14(4):377–80.

529.41   ———. 1982. Notes on the longevity of *Gopherus berlandieri* (Testudinidae). *Southwest. Nat.* 27(2):230–32.

529.45 Judd, F. W., and F. L. Rose. 1977. Aspects of the thermal biology of the Texas tortoise, *Gopherus berlandieri* (Reptilia, Testudines, Testudinidae). *J. Herp.* 11(2):147–53.

529.46 ———. 1983. Population structure, density, and movements of the Texas tortoise *Gopherus berlandieri*. *Southwest. Nat.* 28(4):387–98.

529.48 Judd, F. W., and R. K. Ross. 1978. Year-to-year variation in clutch size of island and mainland populations of *Holbrookia propinqua* (Reptilia; Lacertilia; Iguanidae). *J. Herp.* 12(2):203–207.

529.49 Judd, F. W., F. L. Rose, and J. C. McQueen. 1980. Population structure, size relationships, and growth of the Texas tortoise, *Gopherus berlandieri*. Abstract, p. 186 in *Desert Tortoise Council Proc. 1979 symposium*, edited by E. St. Amant, S. Allan, and R. Kirwan.

529.5   Karges, J. P. 1978. Texas amphibians and reptiles: Some new distributional records, part I. *Herp Rev.* 9(4):143–45.

529.51 ———. 1979. Texas amphibians and reptiles: Some new distributional records, part II. *Herp Rev.* 10(4):119–21.

529.52 ———. 1981. Texas amphibians and reptiles: Some new distributional records, part III. *Herp Rev.* 12(2):68–69.

529.53 ———. 1982. Texas amphibians and reptiles: Some new distributional records, part IV. *Herp Rev.* 13(1):27.

530.   Kassing, E. F. 1961. A life history study of the Great Plains ground snake, *Sonora episcopa episcopa* (Kennicott). *Texas J. Sci.* 13(2):185–203.

531.   Kauffeld, C. F. 1948. Notes on a hook-nosed snake from Texas. *Copeia* 1948(4):301.

532.   ———. 1957. *Snakes and snake hunting*. Garden City, N.Y.: Hanover House.

533.   Kellogg, R. 1932. Mexican tailless amphibians in the United States National Museum. *Bull. United States Natl. Mus.* 160:1–224.

534.   Kennedy, J. P. 1956a. An arboreal nest of the five-lined skink, *Eumeces fasciatus*, in eastern Texas. *Southwest. Nat.* 1(3):138–39.

535.   ———. 1956b. Food habits of the rusty lizard, *Sceloporus olivaceus* Smith. *Texas J. Sci.* 8(3):328–49.

536.   ———. 1958. Notes on a breeding congress of *Pseudacris clarki* and *Pseudacris nigrita* in Harris County, Texas. *Herpetologica* 14(2):192.

537.   ———. 1959a. A minimum egg complement for the western mud snake, *Farancia abacura reinwardti*. *Copeia* 1959(1):71.

538. ———. 1959b. Sleeping habits of the eastern fence lizard, *Sceloporus undulatus hyacinthinus* (Sauria, Iguanidae). *Southwest. Nat.* 3:90–93.

539. ———. 1960. Parturition of the blue spiny lizard, *Sceloporus cyanogenys* Cope. *Southwest. Nat.* 5(1):44–45.

540. ———. 1961. Eggs of the eastern hog nose snake, *Heterodon platyrhinos*. *Texas J. Sci.* 13(4):416–22.

541. ———. 1962. Spawning season and experimental hybridization of the Houston toad, *Bufo houstonensis*. *Herpetologica* 17(4):239–45.

542. ———. 1964a. Natural history notes on some snakes of eastern Texas. *Texas J. Sci.* 16(2):210–15.

543. ———. 1964b. Experimental hybridization of the green treefrog, *Hyla cinerea* Schneider (Hylidae). *Zoologica* 49(4):211–19.

543.01 ———. 1968. Reproductive success in *Sceloporus undulatus*. *J. Herp.* 2(3–4):179.

543.02 ———. 1973. *Sceloporus olivaceus*. *Cat. Amer. Amphib. Rept.* 143.1–143.4.

543.1 Kenney, J. W., and F. L. Rose. 1974. Oxygen requirements and activity rhythms of the tiger salamander, *Ambystoma tigrinum* (Amphibia: Caudata). *Herpetologica* 30(4):333–37.

544. Kennicott, R. 1860. Descriptions of new species of North American serpents in the Museum of the Smithsonian Institution, Washington. *Proc. Acad. Nat. Sci. Philadelphia* 12:328–38.

545. ———. 1861. On three new forms of rattlesnakes. *Proc. Acad. Nat. Sci. Philadelphia* 13:206–208.

545.1 Keown, G. 1972. Geographical distribution. *Hemidactylus turcicus*. *Herp Rev.* 4(5):170.

545.2 Kerfoot, W. C. 1968. Geographical variability of the lizard, *Sceloporus graciosus* Baird and Girard, in the eastern part of its range. *Copeia* 1968(1):139–52.

545.3 Kessler, W. W., and D. A. Ingold. 1977. Studies on immunity to *Clostridium botulinum* toxins in the western diamondback rattlesnake. *Bull. Chicago Herp. Soc.* 12(2):47–52.

545.4 Kiester, A. R. 1971. Species density of North American amphibians and reptiles. *Syst. Zool.* 20(2):127–37.

545.5 Killebrew, F. C. 1975. Mitotic chromosomes of turtles III. The kinosternids. *Herpetologica* 31(4):398–403.

545.51 ———. 1977a. Mitotic chromosomes of turtles. IV. The Emydidae. *Texas J. Sci.* 29(3–4):245–53.

545.52 ———. 1977b. Mitotic chromosomes of turtles. V. The Chelyridae. *Southwest. Nat.* 21(4):547–48.

545.53 ———. 1980. Geographical distribution. *Cnemidophorus tesselatus. Herp Rev.* 11(2):38.

545.56 Killebrew, F. C., and T. L. James. 1983. *Crotalus viridis viridis* (Prairie Rattlesnake). Coloration. *Herp Rev.* 14(3):74.

545.57 ———. 1984. *Arizona elegans elegans* (Kansas Glossy Snake). Coloration. *Herp Rev.* 15(2):49.

545.59 Killebrew, F. C., T. L. James, and J. Bertl. 1984. Geographic distribution. *Graptemys versa. Herp Rev.* 15(3):77.

545.6 Killebrew, F. C., and R. R. McKown. 1978. Mitotic chromosomes of *Gopherus berlandieri* and *Kinixys belliana belliana* (Testudines, Testudinidae). *Southwest. Nat.* 23(1):162–64.

545.61 Killebrew, F. C., and M. Rhea. 1980. Geographical distribution. *Regina grahami. Herp Rev.* 11(2):39.

545.62 Killebrew, F. C., and R. C. Stone, Jr. 1978. An unusual color pattern in Couch's spadefoot, *Scaphiopus couchi* (Anura: Pelobatidae). *Texas J. Sci.* 30(4):389.

545.7 King, F. W. 1969. Texas blind salamander *Typhlomolge rathbuni* Stejneger. *Animal Kingdon* 72(2):33.

545.8 King, K. A. 1975. Unusual food item of the western diamondback rattlesnake (*Crotalus atrox*). *Southwest. Nat.* 20(3):416–17.

546. Kingman, R. H. 1932. A comparative study of the skull in the genus *Eumeces* of the Scincidae (a preliminary paper). *Univ. Kansas Sci. Bull.* 20(15):273–95.

547. Kirn, A. J. 1949. Cannibalism among *Rana pipiens berlandieri*, and possibly by *Rana catesbeiana*, near Somerset, Texas. *Herpetologica* 5(4):84.

548. Kirn, A. J., W. L. Burger, and H. M. Smith. 1949. The subspecies of *Tantilla gracilis. Amer. Midl. Nat.* 42(1):238–51.

549. Klauber, L. M. 1930. Differential characteristics of southwestern rattlesnakes allied to *Crotalus atrox. Bull. San Diego Zool. Soc.* 6:1–72.

550. ———. 1936. A key to the rattlesnakes with summary of characteristics. *Trans. San Diego Soc. Nat. Hist.* 8(20):185–276.

551. ———. 1937. A statistical study of the rattlesnakes. IV. The growth of the rattlesnake. *Occ. Papers San Diego Soc. Nat. Hist.* 3:1–56.

552. ———. 1938. A statistical study of the rattlesnakes. V. Head dimensions. *Occ. Papers San Diego Soc. Nat. Hist.* 4:1–53.

553. ———. 1939a. A statistical study of the rattlesnakes. VI. Fangs. *Occ. Papers San Diego Soc. Nat. Hist.* 5:1–61.

554. ———. 1939b. A new subspecies of the western worm snake. *Trans. San Diego Soc. Nat. Hist.* 9:67–68.

555. ———. 1940a. The worm snakes of the genus *Leptotyphlops* in the United States and northern Mexico. *Trans. San Diego Soc. Nat. Hist.* 9:87–162.

556. ———. 1940b. The lyre snakes (genus *Trimorphodon*) of the United States. *Trans. San Diego Soc. Nat. Hist.* 9:163–94.

557. ———. 1941a. The long-nosed snakes of the genus *Rhinocheilus*. *Trans. San Diego Soc. Nat. Hist.* 9:289–332.

558. ———. 1941b. Reviews and comments: Variations and relationships in the snakes of the genus *Pituophis* by O. G. Stull. Bull. United States Natl. Mus. 175. *Copeia* 1941(1):57–60.

559. ———. 1943. The correlation of variability within and between rattle-snake populations. *Copeia* 1943(2):115–18.

560. ———. 1945. The geckos of the genus *Coleonyx* with descriptions of new subspecies. *Trans. San Diego Soc. Nat. Hist.* 10:133–216.

561. ———. 1946. The glossy snake, *Arizona*, with descriptions of new subspecies. *Trans. San Diego Soc. Nat. Hist.* 10:311–98.

562. ———. 1947. Classification and ranges of the gopher snakes of the genus *Pituophis* in the western United States. *Bull. San Diego Zool. Soc.* 22:1–81.

563. ———. 1952. Taxonomic studies of the rattlesnakes of mainland Mexico. *Bull. San Diego Zool. Soc.* 26:1–143.

564. ———. 1956. *Rattlesnakes, their habits, life histories, and influence on mankind.* 2 vols. Berkeley: University of California Press.

565. Klein, T. A., Jr., 1949. A record litter of *Thamnophis sirtalis proximus*. *Herpetologica* 5(1):17.

566. ———. 1951a. Notes on the feeding habits of *Crotaphytus reticulatus*. *Herpetologica* 7(4):200.

567.   ———. 1951b. A new method of collecting *Holbrookia texana*. *Herpetologica* 7(4):200.

568.   Kluge, A. G. 1962. Comparative osteology of the eublepharid lizard genus *Coleonyx* Gray. *J. Morphol.* 110(3):299–332.

568.01   ———. 1975. Phylogenetic relationships and evolutionary trends in eublepharine lizards *Coleonyx*. *Copeia* 1975(1):24–25.

569.   Knight, M. T., G. J. Barbay, and E. O. Morrison. 1965. Incidence of infection by lung-fluke (*Haematoleochus*) of the bullfrog, *Rana catesbeiana*, in Jefferson County, Texas. *Southwest. Nat.* 10(2):141–42.

570.   Knopf, G. N. 1962. Paedogenesis and metamorphic variation in *Ambystoma tigrinum mavortium*. *Southwest. Nat.* 7(1):75–76.

571.   ———. 1963. Sexual, geographic, and individual variation in three Texas populations of the lizard, *Uta stansburiana*. *Amer. Midl. Nat.* 70(1):74–89.

572.   Knopf, G. N., and D. W. Tinkle. 1961. The distribution and habits of *Sistrurus catenatus* in northwest Texas. *Herpetologica* 17(2):126–31.

573.   Knowlton, G. F. 1948. Some insect food of *Sceloporus poinsettii* B. and G. *Herpetologica* 4(4):151–52.

573.05   Kocher, T. D., and R. D. Sage. 1986. Further genetic analyses of a hybrid zone between leopard frogs (*Rana pipiens* complex) in central Texas. *Evolution* 40(1):21–34.

573.1   Kofron, C. P., and J. R. Dixon. 1980. Observations on aquatic colubrid snakes in Texas. *Southwest. Nat.* 25(1):107–109.

573.21   Kraus, F., and G. W. Schuett. 1980a. Geographical distribution. *Crotalus scutulatus scutulatus*. *Herp Rev.* 11(3):81.

573.22   ———. 1980b. Geographical distribution. *Crotalus viridis viridis*. *Herp Rev.* 11(3):81.

573.23   ———. 1980c. Geographical distribution. *Masticophis flagellum testaceus*. *Herp Rev.* 11(3):81.

573.24   ———. 1980d. Geographical distribution. *Sistrurus catenatus edwardsi*. *Herp Rev.* 11(3):81.

573.25   ———. 1981. An intergrade *Lampropeltis triangulum* from west Texas. *Herp Rev.* 12(2):53.

573.3   Kroll, J. C. 1971. Combat behavior in male Great Plains ground snakes (*Sonora episcopa episcopa*). *Texas J. Sci.* 23(2):300.

573.31 ———. 1972. Review of amphibians and reptiles in Texas: Taxonomic synopsis, bibliography and county distributional maps by Gerald G. Raun and Fredrick R. Gehlbach. *Dallas Mus. Nat. Hist. Bull.* 2. 7" × 10". 61pp+140 county distribution maps. 1972 (paper). *Southwest. Nat.* 17(2):218–19.

573.32 ———. 1976. Feeding adaptations of hognose snakes. *Southwest. Nat.* 20(4):537–57.

573.33 ———. 1973. Comparative physiological ecology of eastern and western hognose snakes. *Heterodon platyrhinos* and *H. nasicus*. *Diss. Abst. Int.* B34(3):1069.

573.34 ———. 1977. Self-wounding while death feigning by western hognose snakes (*Heterodon nasicus*). *Copeia* 1977(2):372–73.

573.4 Kroll, J. C., and T. K. Paley. 1973. Marbled salamander. *Texas Parks and Wildlife* 31(11):23.

573.5 Kroll, J. C., and H. W. Reno. 1971. A reexamination of the cloacal sacs and gland of the blind snake, *Leptotyphlops dulcis* (Reptilia: Leptotyphlopidae). *J. Morphol.* 133:273–80.

573.55 Lambert, S., and G. M. Ferguson. 1985. Blood ejection frequency by *Phrynosoma cornutum* (Iguanidae). *Southwest. Nat.* 30(3):616–17.

573.6 Lamoureaux, W. E. 1981. An aberrant pattern variant or alias "blond suboc" of the Trans-Pecos region, *Elaphe subocularis* (Brown). *Occ. Papers Dallas Herp. Soc.* 1981(1):9–13.

573.7 Landry, L. A. 1973. Distribution: *Cemophora coccinea lineri*. *HISS News-J.* 1(3):98.

573.8 Langston, W., Jr. 1974. Nonmammalian Comanchean tetrapods. *Geoscience and Man* 8:77–102.

574. Lardie, R. L. 1963. A length record for *Trionyx spinifer emoryi*. *Herpetologica* 19(2):150.

575. ———. 1965a. Eggs and young of *Rhinocheilus lecontei tessellatus*. *Copeia* 1965(3):366.

576. ———. 1965b. Pugnacious behavior in the soft-shell *Trionyx spinifer pallidus* and implications of territoriality. *Herpetologica* 20(4):281–84.

576.01 ———. 1975a. Courtship and mating behavior in the yellow mud turtle, *Kinosternon flavescens flavescens*. *J. Herp.* 9(2):223–27.

576.02 ———. 1975b. Observations on reproduction in *Kinosternon*. *J. Herp.* 9(2):260–64.

576.03 ———. 1976. Eggs of the Great Plains Ground Snake, *Sonora episcopa episcopa* from Texas and Oklahoma. *Bull. Oklahoma Herp. Soc.* 1(2):19.

576.04 ———. 1976. Louisiana milk snake from Parker County, Texas. *Bull. Oklahoma Herp. Soc.* 1(3):36.

576.05 ———. 1979. Eggs and young of the plain's yellow mud turtle. *Bull. Oklahoma Herp. Soc.* 4(2–3):24–30.

576.06 ———. 1980. Winter activity of *Chrysemys scripta elegans* (Wied-Neuwied) in north central Texas. *Bull. Oklahoma Herp. Soc.* 4(4): 72–76.

576.2 Larsen, K. R., and W. W. Tanner. 1974. Numeric analysis of the genus *Sceloporus* with special reference to cranial osteology. *Great Basin Nat.* 34(1):1–41.

577. La Rue, G. R. 1917. Two new larval trematodes from *Thamnophis marcianus* and *Thamnophis eques*. *Occ. Papers Mus. Zool. Univ. Michigan* 35:1–12.

578. Laughlin, H. E., and B. J. Wilks. 1962. The use of sodium pentobarbital in population studies of poisonous snakes. *Texas J. Sci.* 14(2):188–91.

579. Lawrence, J. F. 1955. Range extension of the whiptailed lizard *Cnemidophorus neomexicanus*. *Copeia* 1955(2):142.

579.2 Lawson, D. A. 1975. Pterosaur from the latest Cretaceous of west Texas: Discovery of the largest flying creature. *Science* 187 (4180):947–48.

580. Leary, T. R. 1957. A schooling of leatherback turtles, *Dermochelys coriacea coriacea*, on the Texas coast. *Copeia* 1957(3):232.

581. Lee, S. H. 1955. The mode of egg dispersal in *Physaloptera phrynosoma* Ortlepp (Nematoda, Spiruroidea) a gastric nematode of Texas horned toads, *Phrynosoma cornutum*. *J. Parasit.* 41(1):70–74.

582. Legler, J. M. 1959. A new tortoise, genus *Gopherus*, from north central Mexico. *Univ. Kansas Publ. Mus. Nat. Hist.* 11(5):335–43.

583. ———. 1960a. Natural history of the ornate box turtle, *Terrapene ornata ornata* Agassiz. *Univ. Kansas Publ. Mus. Nat. Hist.* 11(10): 527–669.

584. ———. 1960b. A new subspecies of slider turtle (*Pseudemys scripta*) from Coahuila, Mexico. *Univ. Kansas Publ. Mus. Nat. Hist.* 13(3): 73–84.

585. ———. 1960c. Remarks on the natural history of the Big Bend slider, *Pseudemys scripta gaigeae* Hartweg. *Herpetologica* 16(2):139–40.

585.2   Leon, P., and J. Kezer. 1974. The chromosomes of *Siren intermedia net-tingi* (Goin) and their significance to comparative salamander kary-ology. *Herpetologica* 30(1):1–11.

586.   Leviton, A. E. 1953. Catalogue of the amphibian and reptile types in Natural History Museum of Stanford University. *Herpetologica* 8(4): 121–32.

587.   Leviton, A. E., and B. H. Banta. 1956. Catalogue of the amphibian and reptile types in the Natural History Museum of Stanford University, suppl. 1. *Herpetologica* 12(3):213–19.

587.1   Lewis, H. L., and F. L. Rose. 1969. Effects of fat body fatty acids on ovarian and liver metabolism of *Ambystoma tigrinum*. *Comp. Bio-chem. Physiol.* 30:1055–60.

587.5   Lewis, M. R. 1974. Recent county records and range extensions in south central Texas. *Herp Rev.* 5(1):21.

588.   Lewis, T. H. 1951. The biology of *Leiolopisma laterale* (Say). *Amer. Midl. Nat.* 45(1):232–40.

588.01   Lewis, T. W., and J. R. Dixon. 1976. Geographical distribution, *Cemo-phora coccinea copei*. *Herp Rev.* 7(4):178.

588.2   Licht, L. E. 1967a. Initial appearance of the parotoid gland in three spe-cies of toads (genus *Bufo*). *Herpetologica* 23(2):115–18.

588.21   ———. 1967b. Growth inhibition in crowded tadpoles: Intraspecific and interspecific effects. *Ecology* 48(5):736–45.

588.22   ———. 1968. Unpalatability and toxicity of toad eggs. *Herpetologica* 24(2):93–98.

588.3   Licht, L. E., and B. Low. 1968. Cardiac response of snakes after inges-tion of toad parotoid venom. *Copeia* 1968(3):547–51.

588.35   Lieb, C. S. 1971. A study of the variation in *Elaphe obsoleta* of Texas. *TASCA* 26(1):3–6.

588.36   ———. 1985a. Systematics and distribution of the skinks allied to *Eu-meces tetragrammus* (Sauria: Scincidae). *Nat. Hist. Mus. Los Angeles Co., Contr. Sci.* 357:1–19.

588.37   ———. 1985b. Review: *Snakes of Texas*, by Alan Tennant. *Southwest. Nat.* 30(4):621–22.

588.39   Lieb, C. S., and V. J. Roessling. 1983. Distributional records for central and southern Texas. *Herp Rev.* 14(2):54.

588.4   Liner, E. A. 1982. Life history notes: *Regina grahami*. Coloration. *Herp Rev.* 13(2):48.

588.45 Liner, E. A., and A. H. Chaney. 1973. Life history: *Micrurus fulvius tenere. Herp Rev.* 1(6):186.

588.6 Little, J., and S. Hopkins. 1968. *Neoechinorhynchus constrictus* sp. n. An acanthocephalan from Texas turtles. *Proc. Helminthol. Soc. Washington.* 35:46–49.

589. Littlejohn, M. J. 1959. Artificial hybridization within the Pelobatidae and Microhylidae. *Texas J. Sci.* 11(1):57–59.

590. ———. 1960. Call discrimination and potential reproductive isolation in *Pseudacris triseriata* females from Oklahoma. *Copeia* 1960(4): 370–71.

591. ———. 1961a. Mating call discrimination by females of the spotted chorus frog (*Pseudacris clarki*). *Texas J. Sci.* 13(1):49–50.

592. ———. 1961b. Artificial hybridization between some hylid frogs of the United States. *Texas J. Sci.* 13(2):176–84.

593. Littlejohn, M. J., M. J. Fouquette, Jr., and C. Johnson. 1960. Call discrimination by female frogs of the *Hyla versicolor* complex. *Copeia* 1960(1):47–49.

594. Littlejohn, M. J., and T. C. Michaud. 1959. Mating call discrimination by females of Strecker's chorus frog (*Pseudacris streckeri*). *Texas J. Sci.* 11(1):86–92.

594.1 Littlejohn, M. J., and R. S. Oldham. 1968. *Rana pipiens* complex: Mating call structure and taxonomy. *Science* 162(3857):1003.

595. Livezey, R. L. 1948. Distributional records of amphibians in east Texas. *Copeia* 1948(1):67–68.

596. ———. 1949. An aberrant pattern of *Agkistrodon mokeson austrinus. Herpetologica* 5(4):93.

597. ———. 1950a. The eggs of *Acris gryllus crepitans* Baird. *Herpetologica* 6(5):139–40.

598. ———. 1950b. An intergrade population of the Texas subspecies of *Desmognathus fuscus. Amer. Midl. Nat.* 43(3):600–604.

599. ———. 1951. *Natrix rigida* from Tyler County, Texas. *Herpetologica* 7(2):60.

600. ———. 1952. Observations on *Pseudacris nigrita triseriata* (Wied) in Texas. *Amer. Midl. Nat.* 47(2):372–81.

601. Livezey, R. L., and H. M. Johnson. 1948. *Rana grylio* in Texas. *Herpetologica* 45(5):164.

602.   Livezey, R. L., and A. H. Wright. 1947. A synoptic key to the salientian eggs of the Unites States. *Amer. Midl. Nat.* 47(1):179–222.

602.2   Logan, L. E., and C. C. Black. 1979. The Quaternary vertebrate fauna of Upper Sloth Cave, Guadalupe Mountains National Park, Texas. *Natl. Park Serv. Trans. Proc. Ser.* (4):141–58.

602.5   Long, D. R. 1985. Lipid utilization during reproduction in female *Kinosternon flavescens*. *Herpetologica* 41(1):58–65.

603.   Long, R. L. 1961. A record of the red-bellied snake from Texas. *Herpetologica* 17(3):208–209.

603.2   Longley, G. 1977. Status of *Typhlomolge* (= *Eurycea*) *rathbuni*, the Texas blind salamander. USFWS End. Spec. Rept. 2:ix–76.

604.   Loomis, R. B., and D. A. Crossley. 1963. New species and new records of chiggers (Acarina: Trombiculidae) from Texas. *Acarologia* 5(3):371–85.

605.   Lord, R. D., Jr., and W. B. Davis. 1955. A taxonomic study of the relationship between *Pseudacris nigrita triseriata* Wied and *Pseudacris clarki* Baird. *Herpetologica* 12(2):115–20.

606.   Lowe, C. H., Jr. 1955. The evolutionary relationships of the narrow-lined skinks of the inland southwest, *Eumeces taylori*, *E. gaigei*, and *E. multivirgatus*. *Herpetologica* 11(3):233–35.

607.   ———. 1956. A new species and a new subspecies of whiptailed lizards (genus *Cnemidophorus*) of the inland southwest. *Bull. Chicago Acad. Sci.* 10(9):137–50.

608.   ———. 1966. The prairie lined racerunner. *J. Arizona Acad. Sci.* 4(1):44–45.

609.   Lowe, C. H., Jr., and J. W. Wright. 1966. Evolution of parthenogenic species of *Cnemidophorus* (whiptail lizards) in western North America. *J. Arizona Acad. Sci.* 4(2):81–87.

609.5   Lundelius, E. 1972. Fossil vertebrates from the Late Pleistocene Ingleside fauna, San Patricio County, Texas. *Univ. Texas Bur. Econ. Geol. Rept. Invest.* 77:1–74.

610.   Lynch, J. D. 1964. Additional hylid and leptodactylid remains from the Pleistocene of Texas and Florida. *Herpetologica* 20(2):141–42.

611.   ———. 1966. Additional treefrogs (Hylidae) from the North American Pleistocene. *Ann. Carnegie Mus.* 38:265–71.

611.2   Mahmovd, I. Y., and J. Klicka. 1972. Seasonal gonadal changes in kinosternid turtles. *J. Herp.* 6(3–4):183–89.

612. Malnate, E. 1939. A study of the yellow-lipped snake, *Rhadinaea flavilata* (Cope). *Zoologica* 24(3):359–66.

612.2 Mares, M. A. 1971. Coprophagy in the Texas tortoise, *Gopherus berlandieri*. *Texas J. Sci.* 23(2):300.

612.3 Marion, W. R., and D. R. Blankenship. 1974. Distribution: *Drymobius margaritiferus margaritiferus*. *Herp. Rev.* 5(1):21.

612.4 Marker, R. G. 1979. The kingsnakes: An annotated checklist. *Bull. Chicago Herp. Soc.* 14(4):101–16.

613. Marr, J. C. 1944. Notes on amphibians and reptiles from the central United States. *Amer. Midl. Nat.* 32(2):478–90.

613.2 Martin, J. H., and R. M. Bagby. 1972. Temperature frequency relationships of the rattlesnake rattle. *Copeia* 1972(3):482–85.

614. Martin, P. S., and B. E. Harrell. 1957. The Pleistocene history of temperate biotas in Mexico and eastern United States. *Ecology* 38(3):469–80.

614.11 Martin, R. F. 1972. Arciferal dextrality and sinistrality in anuran pectoral girdles. *Copeia* 1972(2):376–81.

614.12 ———. 1973a. Reproduction in the tree lizard (*Urosaurus ornatus*) in central Texas: Drought conditions. *Herpetologica* 29(1):27–32.

614.13 ———. 1973b. Osteology of North American *Bufo:* The *americanus, cognatus* and *boreas* species groups. *Herpetologica* 29(4):375–87.

614.14 ———. 1977. Variation in reproductive productivity of range margin tree lizards (*Urosaurus ornatus*). *Copeia* 1977(1):83–92.

614.15 ———. 1978. Clutch weight/total body weight ratios of lizards (Reptilia; Lacertilia; Iguanidae): Preservative induced variation. *J. Herp.* 12(2):248–51.

614.2 Martin, W. F., and R. B. Huey. 1971. The function of the epiglottis in sound production (hissing) of *Pituophis melanoleucus*. *Copeia* 1971(4):752–54.

614.4 Martof, B. S. 1973. *Siren intermedia. Cat. Amer. Amphib. Rept.* 127.1–127.3.

614.41 ———. 1974a. *Siren. Cat. Amer. Amphib. Rept.* 152.1–152.2.

614.42 ———. 1974b. Sirenidae. *Cat. Amer. Amphib. Rept.* 151.1–151.2.

614.43 ———. 1975. *Hyla squirella* Bosc. *Cat. Amer. Amphib. Rept.* 168.1–168.2.

614.6   Marvel, B. 1972. A feeding observation on the yellow-bellied water snake, *Natrix e. flavigaster*. *Bull. Maryland Herp. Soc.* 8(2):52.

615.   Marx, H. 1958. Catalogue of type specimens of reptiles and amphibians in the Chicago Natural History Museum. *Fieldiana Zool.* 36(4):411–96.

616.   Maslin, T. P., R. G. Beidleman, and C. H. Lowe, Jr. 1958. The status of the lizard *Cnemidophorus perplexus* Baird and Girard (Teiidae). *Proc. United States Nat. Mus.* 108:331–45.

616.1   Mather, C. M. 1970. Some aspects of the life history of the ground skink, *Lygosoma laterale*. *Texas J. Sci.* 21(4):429–38.

616.11   ———. 1977. Comparative ecology of two lizards (*Sceloporus variabilis* and *Sceloporus undulatus*) in an area of sympatry. *Diss. Abst. Int.* B37(8):3756.

616.12   ———. 1978. A case of limb regeneration in *Sceloporus variabilis* (Reptilia; Lacertilia; Iguanidae). *J. Herp.* 12(2):263.

616.13   ———. 1979. Incidence of mites on *Sceloporus variabilis* and *Sceloporus undulatus* (Sauria: Iguanidae) in South Texas. *Texas J. Sci.* 31(1):103.

616.14   ———. 1982. Record of a turtle eaten by a catfish. *Bull. Oklahoma Herp. Soc.* 7(1):5.

616.2   Mather, C. M., and J. R. Dixon. 1976. Geographic records of some Texas amphibians and reptiles. *Herp Rev.* 7(3):127.

616.5   Mathewson, J. J. 1979. Enterobacteriaceae isolated from iguanid lizards of west-central Texas. *Applied Environ. Microbiol.* 38(3):402–405.

617.   Mattiessen, P. 1959. *Wildlife in America*. New York: Viking Press.

617.5   Maxson, R. D., and L. R. Maxson. 1978. Resolution of diploid-tetraploid tree frogs. *Science* 202(4365):336.

617.7   Mays, S. R., and P. S. Freed. 1985. Life history notes. *Bufo houstonensis*. Coloration. *Herp Rev.* 16(4):108–109.

618.   McAlister, W. 1954. Natural history notes on the barking frog. *Herpetologica* 10(3):197–99.

619.   ———. 1959. The vocal structures and method of call production in the genus *Scaphiopus* Holbrook. *Texas J. Sci.* 11(1):60–77.

620.   ———. 1961a. The mechanics of sound production in North American *Bufo*. *Copeia* 1961(1):86–95.

621.   ———. 1961b. Artificial hybridization between *Rana a. areolata* and *Rana p. pipiens* from Texas. *Texas J. Sci.* 13(4):423–26.

622. ———. 1962. Variation in *Rana pipiens* Schreber in Texas. *Amer. Midl. Nat.* 67(2):334–63.

622.1 McAllister, C. T. 1982. Geographic distribution: *Chrysemys concinna. Herp Rev.* 13(3):80.

622.11 ———. 1983. *Crotaphytus collaris collaris* (Eastern Collared Lizard). Hibernacula. *Herp Rev.* 14(3):73–74.

622.12 ———. 1984a. Geographic distribution. *Nerodia rhombifera rhombifera. Herp Rev.* 15(1):21.

622.13 ———. 1984b. *Crotaphytus collaris collaris* (eastern collared lizard). Reproduction. *Herp Rev.* 15(2):48.

622.14 ———. 1984c. Geographic distribution. *Pituophis melanoleucus sayi. Herp Rev.* 15(3):78.

622.15 ———. 1984d. Geographic distribution. *Sonora semiannualata. Herp Rev.* 15(3):78.

622.16 ———. 1985a. Geographic distribution. *Cnemidophorus tesselatus. Herp Rev.* 16(2):60.

622.17 McAllister, C. T., and E. A. McAllister. 1984. Geographic distribution. *Acris crepitans blanchardi. Herp Rev.* 15(1):20.

622.18 ———. 1985. Geographic distribution. *Pseudacris streckeri. Herp Rev.* 16(3):83.

622.19 McAllister, C. T., and S. P. Tabor. 1985a. Geographic distribution. *Cnemidophorus sexlineatus viridis. Herp Rev.* 16(3):83.

622.2 ———. 1985b. Geographic distribution. *Nerodia rhombifera rhombifera. Herp Rev.* 16(3):84.

622.21 ———. 1985c. Life history notes. *Gastrophryne olivacea.* Coexistence. *Herp Rev.* 16(4):109.

622.22 ———. 1985d. Geographic distribution. *Gastrophryne olivacea. Herp Rev.* 16(4):114–15.

622.23 ———. 1985e. Geographic distribution. *Hypsiglena torquata. Herp Rev.* 16(4):115–16.

622.231 McAllister, C. T., S. E. Trauth, and J. E. Ubelaker. 1986. Nematode parasites of the parthenogenetic whiptail lizard *Cnemidophorus laredoensis* (Sauria: Teiidae) from South Texas. *Proc. Helminthol. Soc. Washington* 53(1):138–39.

622.232 McAllister, C. T., and R. Ward. 1986a. New distributional records of Texas herpetofauna. *Tex. J. Sci.* 38(1):65–69.

622.233 ———. 1986b. More distributional records of amphibians and reptiles from Texas. *Herp Rev.* 17(1):28–30.

622.24 McAllister, C. T., R. Ward, and J. R. Glidewell. 1983. New distributional records for selected amphibians and reptiles of Texas. *Herp Rev.* 14(2):52–53.

622.5   McAllister, C. T., and M. C. Wooten. 1981. Geographic distribution. *Cnemidophorus gularis. Herp Rev.* 12(3):84.

622.51 ———. 1982. Geographic distribution. *Acris crepitans blanchardi. Herp Rev.* 13(1):24.

622.52 McAllister, C. T., M. C. Wooten, and T. L. King. 1981. Geographic distribution. *Salvadora grahamiae lineata. Herp Rev.* 12(2):66.

623.   McCallion, J. 1944. Notes on *Natrix harteri* in captivity. *Copeia* 1944 (1):63.

624.   ———. 1945. Notes on Texas reptiles. *Herpetologica* 2(7–8):197–98.

624.1   McCarley, H. 1970. *Rana areolata* in southern Oklahoma–northern Texas. *Southwest. Nat.* 15(2):266–67.

624.11 ———. 1975. *Rana grylio* in the coastal prairie of Texas. *Southwest. Nat.* 20(3):420.

625.   McCarley, H., and M. J. Cundiff. 1965. Range extensions for some East Texas amphibians. *Southwest. Nat.* 10(4):311–12.

625.2   McClung, G. D., and T. C. Maxwell. 1976. New locality for *Agkistrodon contortrix pictigaster* (Crotalidae) in Texas. *Texas J. Sci.* 27(3):405–406.

625.4   McClure, W. L. 1969. A new record of *Opheodrys vernalis blanchardi* in Texas. *Southwest. Nat.* 14(1):129.

625.41 ———. 1974. The Houston toad Sanders. *Texas Highway Dept. Environmental Brief* No. 74-12-02.

625.5   McClure, W. L., and W. W. Milstead. 1967. *Terrapene carolina triunguis* from the Late Pleistocene of southeast Texas. *Herpetologica* 23(4):321–22.

626.   McConkey, E. H. 1954. A systematic study of the North American lizards of the genus *Ophisaurus. Amer. Midl. Nat.* 51(1):133–69.

626.5   McCord, J. S. 1986. Geographical distribution: *Rana catesbeiana. Herp Rev.* 17(1):26.

627.   McCoy, C. J. 1961. Additional records of *Ficimia cana* from Mexico and Texas. *Herpetologica* 17(3):215.

627.1 ———. 1970. *Hemidactylus turcicus. Cat. Amer. Amphib. Rept.* 87.1–87.2.

628. McCoy, C. J., and F. R. Gehlbach. 1967. Cloacal hemorrhage and the defense display of the colubrid snake *Rhinocheilus lecontei. Texas J. Sci.* 19(4):349.

629. McCoy, C. J., and G. A. Hoddenbach. 1966. Geographic variation in ovarian cycles and clutch size in *Cnemidophorus tigris* (Teiidae). *Science* 154:1671.

629.2 McCoy, C. J., and W. L. Minckley. 1969. *Sistrurus catenatus* (Reptilia: Crotalidae) from the Cuatro Cienegas Basin, Coahuila, Mexico. *Herpetologica* 25(2):152–53.

630. McCoy, C. J., and N. D. Richmond. 1966. Herpetological type-specimens in Carnegie Museum. *Ann. Carnegie Mus.* 38(10):233–64.

630.1 McCranie, J. R. 1980. *Drymarchon. Cat. Amer. Amphib. Rept.* 267.1–267.4.

630.15 McCrystal, H. K., R. H. Dean, and J. R. Dixon. 1984. *Lampropeltis triangulum annulata* (Mexican Milk Snake). Size. *Herp Rev.* 15(1):19.

630.16 ———. 1985. Range extension for the whiptail lizard *Cnemidophorus laredoensis* (Teiidae). *Tex. J. Sci.* 36(4):283–84.

630.2 McCullen, R. E., and G. G. Raun. 1971. Notes on the distribution of some reptiles and amphibians in northeastern Texas. *Southwest. Nat.* 16(2):220.

631 McKenzie, D., and J. R. Reddell. 1964. The caves of Bell and Coryell counties. *Texas Speleo. Survey* 2(4):1–63.

631.1 McKinney, C. O. 1969. Experimental hybridization in three populations of the lizard *Uta stansburiana. Copeia* 1969(2):289–92.

631.2 McKinney, C. O., and R. E. Ballinger. 1966. Snake predators of lizards in western Texas. *Southwest. Nat.* 11(3):410–12.

632 McKinney, C. O., F. R. Kay, and R. A. Anderson. 1973. A new all-female species of the genus *Cnemidophorus. Herpetologica* 29(4):361–66.

632.1 McKinstry, D. M. 1978. Evidence of toxic saliva in some colubrid snakes of the United States. *Toxicon* 16:523–34.

632.2 McMickle, T. J. 1970. A study to determine the presence of encephalitis in reptiles in Harris County, Texas. *TASCA* 24(3):11–12, 16.

632.3 McNaughton, G. 1976. Geographic distribution: *Lampropeltis triangulum amura. Herp Rev.* 7(3):124.

633. Meacham, W. R. 1962. Factors affecting secondary intergradation between two allopatric populations in the *Bufo woodhousei* complex. *Amer. Midl. Nat.* 67(2):282–304.

633.5 Means, D. B. 1974. The status of *Desmognathus brimleyorum* Stejneger and an analysis of the genus *Desmongnathus* (Amphibia: Urodela) in Florida. *Bull. Florida St. Mus.* 18(1):1–100.

634. Mearns, E. A. 1907. Mammals of the Mexican boundary of the United States part I. Families Didelphidae to Muridae. *Bull. United States Natl. Mus.* 56.

635. Mecham, J. S. 1954. Geographic variation in the green frog, *Rana clamitans. Texas J. Sci.* 6(1):1–25.

636. ———. 1956. The relationship between the ring-neck snakes *Diadophis regalis* and *D. punctatus. Copeia* 1956(1):51–52.

637. ———. 1957a. The taxonomic status of some southwestern skinks of the *multivirgatus* group *Copeia* 1957(2):111–23.

638. ———. 1957b. Some hybrid combinations between Strecker's chorus frog, *Pseudacris streckeri,* and certain related forms. *Texas J. Sci.* 9(8):337–45.

639. ———. 1959a. Some Pleistocene amphibians and reptiles from Friesenhahn Cave, Texas. *Southwest. Nat.* 3:17–27.

640. ———. 1959b. Experimental evidence of the relationship of two allopatric chorus frogs of the genus *Pseudacris. Texas J. Sci.* 11(3):343–47.

641. ———. 1961. Isolating mechanisms in anuran amphibians. Pp. 24–61 in *Vertebrate speciation,* edited by W. F. Blair. Austin: University of Texas Press.

642. ———. 1965. Genetic relationships and reproductive isolation in southeastern frogs of the genera *Pseudacris* and *Hyla. Amer. Midl. Nat.* 74(2):269–308.

642.01 ———. 1967a. *Notophthalmus viridescens.* Rafinesque. *Cat. Amer. Amphib. Rept.* 53.1–53.4.

642.02 ———. 1967b. Polymorphic *Eumeces multivirgatus* from the Texas high plains. *Southwest. Nat.* 12(1):104–105.

642.03 ———. 1968a. On the relationships between *Notophthalmus meridionalis* and *Notophthalmus kallerti. J. Herp.* 2(3–4):121–27.

642.04 ———. 1968b. *Notophthalmus meridionalis* (Cope). *Cat. Amer. Amphib. Rept.* 74.1–74.2.

642.05 ———. 1971. Vocalizations of the leopard frog, *Rana pipiens*, and three related Mexican species. *Copeia* 1971(3):505–16.

642.06 ———. 1979. The biogeographical relationships of the amphibians and reptiles of the Guadalupe Mountains. *Natl. Park Serv. Trans. Proc. Ser.* (4):169–79.

642.07 ———. 1980. *Eumeces multivirgatus. Cat. Amer. Amphib. Rept.* 241.1– 241.2.

642.08 ———. 1982. New distributional information for some snakes in western Texas. *Texas J. Sci.* 34(2):191.

642.2 Mecham, J. S., et al. 1973. A new species of leopard frog (*Rana pipiens* complex) from the plains of the central United States. *Occ. Papers Mus. Texas Tech. Univ.* 18:1–11.

643. Mecham, J. S., and W. W. Milstead. 1949. *Lampropeltis alterna* from Pecos County, Texas. *Herpetologica* 5(6):140.

643.2 Medellin-Leal, F. 1982. The Chihuahuan desert. Pp. 317–81 in *Reference handbook on the deserts of North America*, edited by G. L. Bender. Westport, Conn.: Greenwood Press.

643.5 Medica, P. A. 1975. *Rhinocheilus* Baird and Girard. *Cat. Amer. Amphib. Rept.* 175.1–175.4.

643.51 ———. 1980. Locality records of *Rhinocheilus lecontei* in the United States and Mexico. *Herp Rev.* 11(2):42.

643.6 Merkord, G. W. 1975. Range extension and new county records of some Texas amphibians and reptiles. *Herp Rev.* 6(3):79.

643.7 Michael, E. D. 1969. A longevity record for a non-captive *Anolis carolinensis. Herpetologica* 25(4):318.

643.71 ———. 1971. Snake visits to an earthen tank in south Texas. *J. Herp.* 5(3–4) 195–96.

643.72 ———. 1972. Growth rates in *Anolis carolinensis. Copeia* 1972(3): 575–77.

643.8 Michael, E. D., and T. F. Bailey. 1972. Hibernation sites of *Anolis carolinensis* and *Sceloporus undulatus. Texas J. Sci.* 24(3):351–53.

644. Michaud, T. C. 1962. Call discrimination by females of the chorus frogs, *Pseudacris clarki* and *Pseudacris nigrita. Copeia* 1962(1):213–15.

644.1 Miller, D. 1977. The gray-banded kingsnake. *Chihuahuan Desert Disc.* 2:9.

644.11   ———. 1979a. A life history study of the gray-banded kingsnake, *Lampropeltis mexicana alterna*, in Texas. *Chihuahuan Desert Res. Inst. Contr.* 87:1–48.

644.12   ———. 1979b. The Trans-Pecos copperhead. *Chihuahuan Desert Disc.* 6:3.

644.13   ———. 1979c. Whatever became of the Big Bend gecko? *Chihuahuan Desert Disc.* 4:5.

644.14   ———. 1980. Trans-Pecos ratsnake: Handle with (loving) care. *Chihuahuan Desert Disc.* 8:7.

644.15   ———. 1983. The Texas alligator lizard. *Chihuahuan Desert Disc.* 6:3.

645.   Milne, L. J. 1938. Mating of *Phrynosoma cornutum*. *Copeia* 1938(4): 200–201.

646.   Milstead, W. W. 1951. A new locality record for the Texas neotenic salamander, *Eurycea latitans*. *Herpetologica* 7(2):57–58.

647.   ———. 1953a. Geographic variation in the garter snake, *Thamnophis cyrtopsis*. *Texas J. Sci.* 5(3):348–79.

648.   ———. 1953b. Ecological distribution of the lizards of the La Mota Mountain region of Trans-Pecos. *Texas J. Sci.* 5(4):403–15.

649.   ———. 1956. Fossil turtles of Friesenhahn Cave, Texas, with the description of a new species of *Testudo*. *Copeia* 1956(3):162–71.

650.   ———. 1957a. A reconsideration of the nomenclature of the small whiptail lizards, *Cnemidophorus*, of southwestern Texas. *Copeia* 1957(3): 228–29.

651.   ———. 1957b. Some aspects of competition in natural populations of whiptail lizards (genus *Cnemidophorus*). *Texas J. Sci.* 9(4):410–47.

652.   ———. 1957c. Observations on the natural history of four species of whiptail lizards, *Cnemidophorus* (Sauria: Teiidae) in Trans-Pecos Texas. *Southwest. Nat.* 2(2–3):105–21.

653.   ———. 1958. A list of the arthropods found in the stomachs of whiptail lizards from four stations in southwestern Texas. *Texas J. Sci.* 10(4): 443–46.

654.   ———. 1959. Drift-fence trapping of lizards on the Black Gap Wildlife Management Area of southwestern Texas. *Texas J. Sci.* 11(2):150–57.

655.   ———. 1960a. Supplementary notes on the herpetofauna of the Stockton Plateau. *Texas J. Sci.* 12(3–4):228–31.

656.   ———. 1960b. Relict species of the Chihuahuan desert. *Southwest. Nat.* 5(2):75–88.

657.   ———. 1961a. Observations of the activities of small animals (Reptilia and Mammalia) on a quadrant in southwest Texas. *Amer. Midl. Nat.* 65(1):127–38.

658.   ———. 1961b. Competitive relations in lizard populations. Pp. 460–89 in *Vertebrate speciation,* edited by W. F. Blair. Austin: University of Texas Press.

659.   ———. 1965a. Changes in competing populations of whiptail lizards (*Cnemidophorus*) in southwestern Texas. *Amer. Midl. Nat.* 73(1): 75–80.

660.   ———. 1965b. Notes on some poorly known fossils of box turtles (*Terrapene*). *Copeia* 1965(4):513–14.

661.   ———. 1967. Fossil box turtles (Terrapene) from central North America, and box turtles of eastern Mexico. *Copeia* 1967(1):168.

661.1   ———. 1969. Studies on the evolution of box turtles (genus *Terrapene*). *Bull. Florida St. Mus.* 14(1):1–113.

661.2   ———. 1970. Late summer behavior of the lizards *Sceloporus merriami* and *Urosaurus ornatus* in the field. *Herpetologica* 26(3):343–54.

661.4   ———. 1973. A re-study of a lizard population after twenty years. *Yearbook Amer. Philos. Soc.* 1973:337–38.

661.5   ———. 1977(1978). The Black Gap whiptail lizards after twenty years. Pp. 523–32 in *Transactions of the symposium on the biological resources of the Chihuahuan desert region, United States and Mexico,* edited by R. W. Wauer, and D. H. Riskind. Natl. Park Ser. Trans. Proc. Ser. 3.

662.   Milstead, W. W., J. S. Mecham, and H. McClintock. 1950. The amphibians and reptiles of the Stockton Plateau in northern Terrell County, Texas. *Texas J. Sci.* 2(4):543–62.

662.1   Milstead, W. W., and D. W. Tinkle. 1969. Interrelationships of feeding habits in a population of lizards in southwestern Texas. *Amer. Midl. Nat.* 81:491–99.

663.   Minton, J. E. 1949. Coral snake preyed upon by a bullfrog. *Copeia* 1949(4):288.

664.   Minton, S. A. 1956. A new snake of the genus *Tantilla* from west Texas. *Fieldiana Zool.* 34:449–52.

665.   ———. 1959. Observations on amphibians and reptiles of the Big Bend region of Texas. *Southwest. Nat.* 3:28–54.

665.5   Mitchell, J. C. 1979. The concept of phenology and its application to the study of amphibian and reptile life histories. *Herp Rev.* 10(2):51–54.

666.   Mitchell, J. D. 1903. The poisonous snakes of Texas, with notes on their habits. *Trans. Texas. Acad. Sci.* 5(2):19–48.

667.   Mitchell, R. W., and J. R. Reddell. 1965. *Eurycea tridentifera*, a new species of troglobitic salamander from Texas and a reclassification of *Typhlomolge rathbuni. Texas J. Sci.* 17(1):12–27.

667.1   Mitchell, R. W., and R. E. Smith. 1972. Some aspects of the osteology and evolution of the neotenic spring and cave salamanders (*Eurycea*, Plethodontidae) of central Texas. *Texas J. Sci.* 23(3):343–62.

668.   Mitchell, R. W., and D. W. Tinkle. 1960. Another Texas record for the Louisiana pine snake, *Pituophis melanoleucus ruthveni* Stull. *Herpetologica* 16(2):143–44.

669.   Mittleman, M. B. 1940. Two new lizards of the genus *Uta. Herpetologica* 2(2):33–38.

670.   ———. 1942. A summary of the iguanid genus *Urosaurus. Bull. Mus. Comp. Zool.* 91:103–81.

671.   ———. 1947. American Caudata. I. Geographic variation in *Manculus quadridigitatus. Herpetologica* 3(6):209–24.

672.   ———. 1949. Geographic variation in Marcy's garter snake, *Thamnophis marcianus* (Baird and Girard). *Bull. Chicago Acad. Sci.* 8:235–49.

672.1   ———. 1967. *Manculus* Cope. *Cat. Amer. Amphib. Rept.* 44.1–44.2.

673.   Mittleman, M. B., and B. C. Brown. 1947. Notes on *Gopherus berlandieri* (Agassiz). *Copeia* 1947(3):211.

674.   ———. 1948. The alligator in Texas. *Herpetologica* 4(6):195–96.

675.   Mittleman, M. B., and J. T. Geir. 1942. Notes on leopard frogs. *Proc. New England Zool. Club* 20:7–15.

676.   Mohr, C. E. 1939. I explore caves. *Nat. Hist.* 43(4):190–204.

677.   ———. 1948a. How fast do bats fly? *Bull. Natl. Speleo. Soc.* 10:108.

678.   ———. 1948b. Tracing an underground stream: A digest of an article by Edward Uhlenhuth. *Bull. Natl. Speleo. Soc.* 10:109–11.

679.   ———. 1948c. Unique animals inhabit subterranean Texas. *Bull. Natl. Speleo. Soc.* 10:15–21, 88.

680.   ———. 1958. Creatures of darkness. *Illus. Library Nat. Sci.* 1:606–17.

681.   Moll, E. O., and K. L. Williams. 1963. The musk turtle *Sternothaerus odoratus* from Mexico. *Copeia* 1963(1):157.

681.1   Montanucci, R. R. 1969. Remarks upon the *Crotaphytus-Gambelia* controversy (Sauria: Iguanidae). *Herpetologica* 25(4):308–14.

681.11   ———. 1971. Ecological and distributional data on *Crotaphytus reticulatus* (Sauria: Iguanidae). *Herpetologica* 27(2):183–97.

681.12   ———. 1974. Convergence, polymorphism, or introgressive hybridization? An analysis of interaction between *Crotaphytus collaris* and *G. reticulatus* (Sauria: Iguanidae). *Copeia* 1974(1):87–101.

681.13   ———. 1976. *Crotaphytus reticulatus* Baird. *Cat. Amer. Amphib. Rept.* 185.1–185.2.

681.14   ———. 1981. Habitat separation between *Phrynosoma douglassi* and *P. orbiculare* (Lacertilia: Iguanidae). *Copeia* 1981(1):147–53.

681.15   Montanucci, R. R., R. W. Axtell, and H. C. Dessaur. 1975. Evolutionary divergence among collared lizards (*Crotaphytus*), with comments on the status of *Gambelia*. *Herpetologica* 31(3):336–47.

681.3   Moodie, K. B., and T. R. Van Devender. 1979. Extinction and extirpation in the herpetofauna of the southern high plains with emphasis on *Geochelone wilsoni* (Testudinidae). *Herpetologica* 35(3):198–206.

682.   Moore, G. W., and G. G. Nicholas. 1964. *Speleology: The study of caves*. Boston: D. C. Health and Co.

683.   Moore, J. A. 1944. Geographic variation in *Rana pipiens* Schreber in eastern North America. *Bull. Amer. Mus. Nat. Hist.* 82:345–70.

683.1   Moore, R. H. 1976. Reproduction habits and growth of *Bufo speciosus* on Mustang Island, Texas, with notes on the ecology and reproduction of other anurans. *Texas J. Sci.* 27(1):173–78.

683.2   Morafka, D. J. 1977. A biogeographical analysis of the Chihuahuan desert through its herpetofauna. *Biogeographica* 9:1–313.

683.21   ———. 1977(1978). Is there a Chihuahuan desert? A quantitative evaluation through a herpetofaunal perspective. Pp. 437–54 in *Transactions of the symposium on the biological resources of the Chihuahuan desert region, United States and Mexico*, edited by R. W. Wauer and D. H. Riskind. Natl. Park Ser. Trans. Proc. Ser. (3).

683.3   Morris, M. A. 1978. Geographical distribution. *Cnemidophorus scalaris septemvittatus*. *Herp Rev.* 9(3):108.

684.   Morris, P. A. 1944. They hop and crawl. Lancaster, Pa.: Jaques Cattell Press.

685.   ———. 1948. *Boy's book of snakes*. New York: Ronald Press.

686.   Morrison, E. O. 1961. A new locality record for the warty gecko. *Texas J. Sci.* 13(3):357.

687.   Mosaur, W. 1932. The amphibians and reptiles of the Guadalupe Mountains of New Mexico and Texas. *Occ. Papers Mus. Zool. Univ. Michigan* 246:1–18.

687.5   Mueller, A. J. 1985. Vertebrate use of nontidal wetlands on Galveston Island, Texas. *Tex. J. Sci.* 37(2–3):215–25.

688.   Mulaik, S. 1935a. A *Sonora* from the lower Big Bend of Texas. *Copeia* 1935(1):43.

689.   ———. 1935b. Tail regeneration in *Coleonyx brevis* Stejneger. *Copeia* 1935(3):155–56.

690.   ———. 1936. An ovoviviparous *Sceloporus* from Texas. *Copeia* 1936(1):72.

691.   ———. 1937. Notes on *Leptodactylus labialis* (Cope). *Copeia* 1937(1):72–73.

692.   ———. 1938. Notes on *Mustela frenata frenata. J. Mamm.* 19(1):104–105.

693.   ———. 1945. New mites in the family Caeculidae. *Univ. Utah Biol. Ser.* 8(6):1–23.

694.   Mulaik, S., and D. Mulaik. 1941a. Variation in *Sonora taylori. Copeia* 1941(4):263.

695.   ———. 1941b. *Elaphe bairdi* from Kerr County, Texas. *Copeia* 1941(4):263–64.

696.   ———. 1942. A neglected species of *Coluber. Copeia* 1942(1):13–15.

697.   ———. 1943. Observations on *Ficimia streckeri* Taylor. *Amer. Midl. Nat.* 29(3):796–97.

698.   ———. 1945. *Lampropeltis triangulum annulata* from Kerr County, Texas. *Copeia* 1945(1):49.

699.   Mulaik, S., and D. Sollberger. 1938. Notes on the eggs and habits of *Hypopachus cuneus. Copeia* 1938(2):90.

699.01   Mulvany, P. S. 1983. Blind snakes of the United States, their natural history with a discussion of climate and physiography as limiting factors to their range. *Bull. Oklahoma Herp. Soc.* 8(1):2–45.

699.1   Murphy, J. B. 1979. Herpetology at the Dallas Zoo. *Herp Rev.* 10(4): 111–12.

699.2   Murphy, J. B., B. W. Tyron, and B. J. Brecke. 1978. An inventory of reproductive and social behavior in captive gray-banded kingsnakes, *Lampropeltis mexicana alterna* (Brown). *Herpetologica* 34(1):84–93.

699.3   Murphy, J. C. 1976. The natural history of the box turtle. *Bull. Chicago Herp. Soc.* 11(1–4):2–45.

699.4   ———. 1980. The lyre snakes. *Bull. Chicago Herp. Soc.* 15(1):24–28.

699.5   Murphy, R. W., and R. C. Drewes. 1976. Comments on the occurrence of *Smilisca baudini* (Dumeril and Bibron) (Amphibia: Hylidae) in Bexar County, Texas. *Texas J. Sci.* 17(3):406–407.

700.   Murray, L. T. 1939. Annotated list of amphibians and reptiles from the Chisos Mountains. *Contrib. Baylor Univ. Mus.* 24:4–16.

701.   Myers, C. W. 1967. The pine woods snake, *Rhadinaea flavilata*. *Bull. Florida St. Mus.* 11(2):47–97.

701.1   Myers, S. 1982. Geographic distribution. *Chrysemys concinna. Herp Rev.* 13(1):24.

701.11   ———. 1983a. Geographic distribution. *Chrysemys scripta elegans. Herp Rev.* 14(3):83.

701.12   ———. 1983b. Geographic distribution. *Leiolopisma laterale. Herp Rev.* 14(3):84.

701.2   Neck, R. W. 1977. Cutaneous myiasis in *Gopherus berlandieri* (Reptilia; Testudines; Testudinidae). *J. Herp.* 11(1):96–98.

701.21   ———. 1978. Occurrence of marine turtles in the lower Rio Grande of south Texas (Reptilia; Testudines). *J. Herp.* 12(3):422–27.

701.22   ———. 1980a. Geographical distribution. *Ambystoma texanum. Herp Rev.* 11(2):36.

701.23   ———. 1980b. Geographical distribution. *Gastrophryne olivacea. Herp Rev.* 11(2):36.

701.24   ———. 1980c. Geographical distribution. *Bufo woodhousei woodhousei. Herp Rev.* 11(2):36.

701.25   ———. 1980d. Geographical distribution. *Pseudacris clarki. Herp Rev.* 11(2):38.

701.26   ———. 1980e. Geographical distribution. *Rana catesbeiana. Herp Rev.* 11(2):38.

701.27   ———. 1980f. Geographical distribution. *Terrapene o. ornata. Herp Rev.* 11(2):38.

701.28   ———. 1981. Probable native populations of bullfrog, *Rana catesbeiana*, in south Texas. *Herp Rev.* 12(2):68.

701.29   ———. 1982. Geographical distribution. *Cnemidophorus gularis gularis. Herp Rev.* 13(3):80.

701.3   ———. 1983. Origin of *Rana catesbeiana* populations in the Rio Grande delta of Texas. *Herp Rev.* 14(2):55.

701.4   Neck, R. W., D. H. Riskind, and K. Peterson. 1979. Geographical distribution *Gerrhonotus liocephalus infernalis. Herp Rev.* 10(4):118.

701.5   Neill, W. E., and J. C. Grubb. 1971. Arboreal habits of *Bufo valliceps* in central Texas. *Copeia* 1971(2):347–48.

702.   Neill, W. T. 1949a. The status of *Hyla flavigula. Copeia* 1949(1):.78.

703.   ———. 1949b. A new subspecies of rat snake (genus *Elaphe*), and notes on related forms. *Herpetologica* 5, Suppl. 2:1–12.

704.   ———. 1951. The taxonomy of North American soft-shelled turtles, genus *Amyda. Publ. Res. Div. Ross Allen's Rept. Inst.* 1:1–24.

704.2   Nelson, C. E. 1972a. Systematic studies of the North American microhylid genus *Gastrophryne. J. Herp.* 6(2):111–37.

704.21   ———. 1972b. *Gastrophryne carolinensis. Cat. Amer. Amphib. Rept.* 120.1–120.4.

704.22   ———. 1972c. *Gastrophryne olivacea. Cat. Amer. Amphib. Rept.* 122.1–122.4.

704.23   ———. 1973a. *Gastrophryne. Cat. Amer. Amphib. Rept.* 134.1–134.2.

704.24   ———. 1973b. Mating calls of the Microhylinae: Descriptions and phylogenetic and ecological considerations. *Herpetologica* 29(2):163–76.

704.25   ———. 1974. Further studies on the systematics of *Hypopachus* (Anura: Microhylidae). *Herpetologica* 30(3):250–74.

705.   Netting, M. G. 1936. *Rhadinaea flavilata* (Cope) in Texas. *Copeia* 1936(2):114.

706.   Netting, M. G., and C. J. Goin. 1946. *Acris* in Mexico and Trans-Pecos Texas. *Copeia* 1946(3):253.

707.   Newman, H. H., and J. T. Patterson. 1909. Field studies of the behavior of the lizard *Sceloporus spinosus floridanus. Bull. Univ. Texas Sci. Ser.* 15:1–24.

708.   Nicholas, B. G. 1960. Checklist of macroscopic troglobitic organisms of the United States. *Amer. Midl. Nat.* 64(1):123–60.

709.   Noble, G. K. 1925. An outline of the relation of ontogeny to phylogeny within the Amphibia, I. *Amer. Mus. Novitates* 165:1–10.

710.   Noble, G. K., and B. C. Marshall. 1932. The validity of *Siren intermedia* LeConte, with observations on its life history. *Amer. Mus. Novitates* 532:1–16.

711.   Norman, W. W. 1900. Remarks on the San Marcos salamander, *Typhlomolge rathbuni* Stejneger. *Amer. Nat.* 34:179–83.

712.   O'Brien, G. P., H. K. Smith, and J. R. Meyer. 1965. An activity study of a radio-isotope-tagged lizard, *Sceloporus undulatus hyacinthinus* (Sauria: Iguanidae). *Southwest. Nat.* 10(3):179–87.

712.1   Odum, R. A. 1985. Natural history notes. *Pseudemys scripta elegans.* Deformity. *Herp Rev.* 16(4):113.

712.2   Oldham, R. S. 1974. Mate attraction by vocalization in members of the *Rana pipiens* complex. *Copeia* 1974(4):982–84.

712.3   ———. 1976. Chorus maintenance in breeding populations of *Rana pipiens* complex. *Texas J. Sci.* 27(2):323–25.

713.   Oliver, J. A. 1955. *North American amphibians and reptiles.* Princeton, N.J.: D. Van Nostrand Co.

714.   Olson, R. E. 1967. Peripheral range extensions and some new records of Texas amphibians and reptiles. *Texas J. Sci.* 19(1):99–106.

714.1   ———. 1973. Variation in the canyon lizard, *Sceloporus merriami* Stejneger. *Herpetologica* 29(2):116–21.

714.11 ———. 1975. *Ficimia streckeri* in south Texas. *Texas J. Sci.* 16(3–4):614–15.

714.12 ———. 1976. Weight regimes in the tortoise *Gopherus berlandieri. Texas J. Sci.* 17(2):321–23.

714.13 ———. 1977. Evidence for the species status of Baird's ratsnake. *Texas J. Sci.* 29(1):79–84.

714.14 ———. 1979. *Sceloporus merriami. Cat. Amer. Amphib. Rept.* 227.1–227.2.

715.   Ortenburger, A. I. 1922. Some cases of albinism in snakes. *Copeia* 1922(2):90.

716.   ———. 1923. A note on the genera *Coluber* and *Masticophis,* and a description of new species of *Masticophis. Occ. Papers Mus. Zool. Univ. Michigan* 139:1–14.

717.   ———. 1928. The whipsnakes and racers genera *Masticophis* and *Coluber. Mem. Univ. Michigan Mus.* 1:1–247.

718.   Orton, G. L. 1951. An example of interspecific mating in toads. *Copeia* 1951(1):78.

718.1   Osten, L. W. 1977. A protostegid (sea turtle) from the Taylor Formation of Texas. *Texas J. Sci.* 29(3–4):289–92.

718.2   Pace, A. E. 1974. Systematic and biological studies of the leopard frogs (*Rana pipiens* complex) of the United States. *Misc. Publ. Mus. Zool. Univ. Michigan* 48:1–40.

718.3   Palmer, W. M. 1978. *Sistrurus miliarius. Cat. Amer. Amphib. Rept.* 220.1–220.2.

718.4   Parker, E. D., Jr. 1979a. Phenotypic consequences of parthenogenesis in *Cnemidophorus* lizards. I. Variability in parthenogenetic and sexual populations. *Evolution* 33(4):1150–66.

718.41 ———. 1979b. Phenotypic consequences of parthenogenesis in *Cnemidophorus* lizards. II. Similarity of *C. tesselatus* to its sexual parental species. *Evolution* 33(4):1167–79.

718.5   Parker, E. D., Jr., and R. K. Selander. 1976. The organization of genetic diversity in the parthenogenetic lizard *Cnemidophorus tesselatus. Genetics* 84(4):791–805.

719.   Parker, H. W. 1934. *A monograph of the frogs of the family Microhylidae.* London: British Museum.

719.1   Parker, O. S., and R. H. McCoy. 1977. Some blood values of the western diamondback rattlesnake (*Crotalus atrox*) from south Texas. *J. Wildlife Diseases* 13(3):269–72.

719.2   Parker, W. S. 1973. Notes on reproduction of some lizards from Arizona, New Mexico, Texas, and Utah. *Herpetologica* 29(3):258–64.

720.   Parks, H. B., F. Archibald, and M. Caldwell. 1939. Amphibians and reptiles of the East Texas pine belt. *Tech. Bull. Stephen F. Austin State Teachers College* 1(6):1–4.

720.2   Parmley, D. 1982. Food items of roadrunners from Palo Pinto County, north central Texas. *Texas J. Sci.* 34(1):94–95.

720.22 ———. 1986. An annotated key to isolated trunk vertebrae of *Elaphe* (Colubridae) species occurring in Texas. *Tex. J. Sci.* 38(1) 41–44.

720.27 Parmley, D., and C. Mulford. 1985. An instance of a largemouth bass, *Micropterus salmoides*, feeding on a water snake, *Nerodia erythrogaster transversa. Texas J. Sci.* 37(4):389.

720.4   Parrish, W. C. 1978. Paleoenvironmental analysis of a lower Permian bonebed and adjacent sediments, Wichita County, Texas. *Paleogeogr. Paleoclimat. Paleoecol.* 24(3):209–37.

721.   Patton, T. H. 1963. Fossil vertebrates from Miller's cave. Llano County, Texas. *Bull. Texas Mem. Mus.* 7:1–41.

722.   Paxon, D. W. 1962. An observation of eggs in a tortoise shell. *Herpetologica* 17(4):278–79.

722.1   Perez, J. C., W. C. Haws, and C. H. Hatch. 1978. Resistance of woodrats (*Neotoma micropus*) to *Crotalus atrox* venom. *Toxicon* 16(2):198–200.

722.2   Perez, J. C., et al. 1978. Resistance of warm-blooded animals to snake venoms. *Toxicon* 16(4):375–83.

722.3   Perez, J. C., S. Pichyangkul, and V. Garcia. 1979. The resistance of three species of warm-blooded animals to western diamondback rattlesnake (*Crotalus atrox*) venom. *Toxicon* 17(6):601–607.

723.   Perkins, C. B. 1940. A key to the snakes of the United States. *Bull. Zool. Soc. San Diego* 16:5–61.

724.   Peters, J. A. 1951. Studies on the lizard *Holbrookia texana* (Troschel) with descriptions of two new subspecies. *Occ. Papers Mus. Zool. Univ. Michigan.* 537:1–20.

725.   ————. 1952. Catalogue of type specimens in the herpetological collections of the University of Michigan of Zoology. *Occ. Papers Mus. Zool. Univ. Michigan.* 539:1–55.

725.1   ————. 1968. Houston Toad–*Bufo houstonensis* Sanders (Endangered). Sheet RA-10, in *Rare and endangered fish and wildlife of the United States.* USDI/BSF Resource Pub. 34.

725.2   Peters, U. W. 1978. Einige Bemerkungen über die Pflege und Langlebigkeit verschiedener *Graptemys*-Arten. Aquarium *Aqua Terra* 12(108):272–74.

725.4   Peterson, K. H. 1980. Cophrophagy in *Thamnophis s. sirtalis. Herp Rev.* 11(1):9.

726.   Peterson, R. L. 1950. Amphibians and reptiles of Brazos County, Texas. *Amer. Midl. Nat.* 43(1):157–64.

727.   Pettus, D. 1958. Water relationships in *Natrix sipedon. Copeia* 1958(3):207–11.

728.   ————. 1963. Salinity and subspeciation in *Natrix sipedon. Copeia* 1963(3):499–504.

729.   Phelan, R. L., and B. H. Brattstrom. 1955. Geographic variation in *Sceloporus magister. Herpetologica* 11(1):1–14.

730.   Phillips, H. W., and W. A. Thornton. 1949. The summer resident birds of the Sierra Vieja range in southwestern Texas. *Texas J. Sci.* 1(4): 101–31.

730.2   Pianka, E. 1970. Comparative autecology of the lizard *Cnemidophorus tigris* in different parts of its geographic range. *Ecology* 51(4):703–20.

730.2   Pianka, E., and W. S. Parker. 1975. Ecology of the horned lizards: A review with special reference to *Phrynosoma platyrhinos. Copeia* 1975(1):141–62.

731.   Piatt, J. 1934. The systematic status of *Eleutherodactylus latrans. Amer. Midl. Nat.* 15(1):89–91.

732.   ———. 1935. A comparative study of the hyobranchial apparatus and throat musculature in the Plethodontidae. *J. Morph.* 57:213–52.

732.1   Pierce, B. A., and J. B. Mitton. 1980. Patterns of allozyme variation in *Ambystoma tigrinum mavortium* and *A. t. nebulosum. Copeia* 1980(4): 594–605.

732.2   Pierce, B. A., J. B. Mitton, and F. L. Rose. 1981. Allozyme variation among large, small and cannibal morphs of the tiger salamander inhabiting the Llano Estacado of west Texas. *Copeia* 1981(3):590–95.

732.21   Pierce, B. A., et al. 1983. Head shape and size in cannibal and noncannibal larvae of the tiger salamander from west Texas. *Copeia* 1984(4): 1006–12.

732.3   Pierce, J. R. 1968. Isolation and differentiation in the canyon tree frog, *Hyla arenicolor. Diss. Abst. Int.* B29:2244–45.

732.31   ———. 1975. Genetic compatibility of *Hyla arenicolor* with other species in the family Hylidae. *Texas J. Sci.* 16(3–4):431–41.

732.32   ———. 1976. Distribution of two mating call types of the plains spadefoot, *Scaphiopus bombifrons*, in southwestern United States. *Southwest. Nat.* 20:578–82.

732.33   Pierce, J. R., and Dennis B. Ralin. 1972. Vocalization and behavior of the males of the three species in the *Hyla versicolor* complex. *Herpetologica* 28(4):329–37.

732.4   Pietruszka, R. D. 1981. Use of scutellation for distinguishing sexes in bisexual species of *Cnemidophorus. Herpetologica* 37(4):244–49.

732.5   Pilch, J., Jr. 1981. Life history notes. *Chrysemys concinna texana. Herp Rev.* 12(3):81.

732.6   Platt, D. R. 1969. Natural history of the hognose snakes *Heterodon platyrhinos* and *heterodon nasicus*. *Univ. Kansas Publ. Mus. Nat. Hist.* 18(4):253–420.

732.7   Platz, J. E. 1972. Sympatric interaction between two forms of leopard frog (*Rana pipiens* complex) in Texas. *Copeia* 1972(2):232–40.

732.71   ———. 1981. Suture Zone Dynamics: Texas populations of *Rana berlandieri* and *R. blairi*. *Copeia* 1981(3):733–34.

733.   Pope, C. H. 1937. *Snakes alive and how they live.* New York: Viking Press.

734.   ———. 1939. *Turtles of the United States and Canada.* New York: Alfred A. Knopf.

735.   ———. 1955. *The reptile world.* New York: Alfred A. Knopf.

736.   Pope, P. H. 1919. Some notes on the amphibians of Houston, Texas. *Copeia* 1919(2):93–98.

736.1   Porras, L. 1982. Life history notes. *Tantilla rubra cucullata. Herp Rev.* 13(1):18–19.

736.2   Porras, L., and J. Beraducci. 1980. Newsnotes. Dicephalic *Kinosternon. Herp Rev.* 11(2):35.

737.   Porter, K. R. 1964a. Distribution and taxonomic status of seven species of mexican *Bufo. Herpetologica* 19(4):229–47.

738.   ———. 1964a. Morphological and mating call comparisons in the *Bufo valliceps* complex. *Amer. Midl. Nat.* 81(1):232–45.

738.1   ———. 1970. *Bufo valliceps. Cat. Amer. Amphib. Rept.* 94.1–94.4.

738.3   Potter, F. E., Jr., and S. S. Sweet. 1981. Genetic boundaries in Texas cave salamanders, and a redescription of *Typhlomolge robusta* (Amphibia: Plethodonitidae). *Copeia* 1981(1):64–75.

739.   Potter, G. E., and S. O. Brown. 1941. Color changes in *Phrynosoma cornutum. Proc. Trans. Texas Acad. Sci.* 4(1):7 (abstract).

740.   ———. 1942. Effect of sex and gonadotropic hormones on the development of the gonads in *Phrynosoma cornutum* during reproductive and nonreproductive phases. *Proc. Trans. Texas Acad. Sci.* 25:55–56.

741.   Potter, G. E., and H. B. Glass. 1931a. A study of respiration in hibernating horned lizards, *Phrynosoma cornutum. Anat. Rec.* 51(1):suppl. 2.

742.   ———. 1931b. A study of respiration in hibernating horned lizards. *Copeia* 1931(3):128–31.

743.   Potter, G. E., and E. L. Rabb. 1955. Thyroxin induced metamorphosis in a neotenic salamander, *Eurycea nana* Bishop. *Texas A&M Coll. Zool. Ser.* 1(1):11.

744.   Pratt, H. S. 1923. *A manual of land and fresh water vertebrate animals of the United States.* Philadelphia: P. Blakiston's Sons and Co.

74.   ———. 1935. *A manual of land and fresh water vertebrate animals of the United States.* 2nd ed. Philadelphia: P. Blakiston's Sons and Co.

746.   Preston, J. R., and W. L. Pratt, Jr. 1962. An eastward range extension of *Uta stansburiana stejnegeri. Herpetologica* 18(1):53.

746.1   Preston, R. 1966(1965). Turtles of the Gilliland faunule from the Pleistocene of Knox County, Texas. *Papers Michigan Acad. Sci., Arts, Letters* 51:221–39.

746.2   Price, A. H. 1980a. *Crotalus molossus. Cat. Amer. Amphib. Rept.* 242.1–242.2.

746.3   ———. 1980b. Geographical distribution. *Hemidactylus turcicus. Herp Rev.* 11(2):39.

746.4   Price, A. H., and J. L. LaPointe. 1981. Structure-functional aspects of the scent gland in *Lampropeltis getulus splendida. Copeia* 1981(1):138–46.

746.5   Pritchard, P. C. 1980. *Dermochelys coriacea. Cat. Amer. Amphib. Rept.* 238.1–238.4.

747.   Pritchett, A. H. 1903. Some experiments in feeding lizards with protectively colored insects. *Biol. Bull.* 5:271–87.

747.1   Punzo, F. 1974a. A qualitative and quantitative study of the food items of the yellow mud turtle, *Kinosternon flavescens* Agassiz. *J. Herp.* 8(3):269–71.

747.11   ———. 1974b. An analysis of the stomach contents of gecko *Coleonyx brevis. Copeia* 1974(3):779–80.

747.12   ———. 1976. Analysis of the pH and electrolyte components found in the blood plasma of several species of west Texas reptiles. *J. Herp.* 10(1):49–52.

747.13   ———. 1982a. Tail autonomy and running speed in the lizards *cophosaurus texanus* and *Uma notata. J. Herp.* 16(3):329–31.

747.14   ———. 1982b. Clutch and egg size in several species of lizards from the desert southwest. *J. Herp.* 16(4):414–17.

748.   Pyburn, W. F. 1955. Species discrimination in two sympatric lizards, *Sceloporus olivaceus* and *S. poinsetti. Texas J. Sci.* 7(2):312–15.

749.　　———. 1958. Size and movement of a local population of cricket frogs (*Acris crepitans*). *Texas J. Sci.* 10(3):325–42.

750.　　———. 1960. Hybridization between *Hyla versicolor* and *H. Femoralis*. *Copeia* 1960(1):55–56.

751.　　———. 1961a. The inheritance and distribution of vertebral stripe color in the cricket frog. Pp. 235–60 in *Vertebrate speciation*, edited by W. F. Blair. Austin: University of Texas Press.

752.　　———. 1961b. Inheritance of the green vertebral stripe in *Acris crepitans*. *Southwest. Nat.* 6(3–4):164–67.

753.　　Pyburn, W. F., and J. P. Kennedy. 1960. Artificial hybridization of the gray treefrog, *Hyla versicolor* (Hylidae). *Amer. Midl. Nat.* 64(1):216–23.

753.11　Quinn, H. R. 1979. Reproduction and growth of the Texas coral snake (*Micrurus fulvius tenere*). *Copeia* 1979(3):453–63.

753.12　———. 1980. Captive propagation of endangered Houston toads. *Herp Rev.* 11(4):109.

753.13　———. 1981. Life history notes. *Crotalus lepidus lepidus*. *Herp Rev.* 12(3):79–80.

753.3　Rabalais, S. C., and N. N. Rabalais. 1980. The occurrence of sea turtles on the south Texas coast. *Contr. Mar. Sci.* 23:123–29.

753.35.　Rael, E. D., R. A. Knight, and H. Zepeda. 1984. Electrophoretic variants of Mojave rattlesnake (*Crotalus scutulatus scutulatus*) venoms and migration differences of Mojave toxin. *Toxicon* 22(6):980–85.

753.4　Rakowitz, V. A., R. R. Fleet, and F. L. Rainwater. 1983. New distributional records of Texas amphibians and reptiles. *Herp Rev.* 14(3):85–89.

753.5　Ralin, D. B. 1968. Ecological and reproductive differentiation in the cryptic species of the *Hyla versicolor* complex (Hylidae). *Southwest. Nat.* 13(3):283–99.

753.51　———. 1978. Resolution of diploid-tetraploid tree frogs. *Science* 202(4365):335–36.

753.6　Ralin, D. B., and J. S. Rogers. 1972. Aspects of tolerance to desiccation in *Acris crepitans* and *Pseudacris streckeri*. *Copeia* 1972(3):519–25.

753.61　———. 1979. A morphological analysis of a North American diploid-tetraploid complex of treefrogs (Amphibia: Anura: Hylidae). *J. Herp.* 13(3):261–69.

753.64 Ralin, D. B., M. A. Romano, and C. W. Kilpatrick. 1983. The tetraploid treefrog *Hyla versicolor:* Evidence for a single origin from the diploid *H. chrysoscelis. Herpetologica* 39(3):212–25.

754. Ramsey, L. W. 1946. Captive specimens of *Tropidoclonion lineatum. Herpetologica* 3(4):112.

755. ———. 1947. Feeding behavior of *Tropidoclonion lineatum. Herpetologica* 4(1):15–18.

756. ———. 1948a. Hibernation of *Holbrookia texana. Herpetologica* 4(6): 223.

757. ———. 1948b. Combat dance and range extension of *Agkistrodon piscivorus leucostoma. Herpetologica* 4(6):228.

758. ———. 1949. Hibernation and the effect of a flood on *Holbrookia texana. Herpetologica* 5(6):125–26.

759. ———. 1951. New localities for several Texas snakes. *Herpetologica* 7(4):176.

760. ———. 1953. The lined snake *Tropidoclonion lineatum* (Hallowell). *Herpetologica* 9(1):7–24.

761. ———. 1954. A possible range extension for *Natrix grahami. Herpetologica* 10(3):188.

762. ———. 1956. Nesting of Texas horned lizards. *Herpetologica* 12(3): 239–40.

763. Ramsey, L. W., and E. T. Donlon. 1949. The young of the lizard *Sceloporus poinsetti. Copeia* 1949(3):229.

764. Ramsey, L. W., and J. W. Forsyth. 1950. Breeding dates for *Ambystoma texanum. Herpetologica* 6(3):70.

764.5 Ramirez, S. A., and R. E. Huff. 1967. A cytological study of parthenogenetically activated eggs of *Rana pipiens. Texas J. Sci.* 19(1):41–56.

765. Raun, G. G. 1959. Terrestrial and aquatic vertebrates of a moist, relict area in central Texas. *Texas J. Sci.* 11(2):158–71.

766. ———. 1962. Observations on behavior of newborn hog-nosed snakes, *Heterodon p. platyrhinos. Texas J. Sci.* 14(1):3–6.

767. ———. 1965a. Western limits of distribution of the stinkpot, *Sternothaerus odoratus,* in Texas. *Herpetologica* 21(1):69–71.

768. ———. 1965b. A guide to Texas snakes. *Texas Mem. Mus. Notes,* no. 9.

769.   ———. 1966a. The distribution of whipsnakes (*Masticophis taeniatus*) in Texas. *Texas J. Sci.* 18(2):226–27.

770.   ———. 1966b. A population of woodrats (*Neotoma micropus*) in southern Texas. *Bull. Texas Mem. Mus.* 11.

770.1   ———. 1974. The Scarlet Snake (*Cemophora coccinea*) in Texas. *J. Herp.* 8(2):186–87.

770.2   Raun, G. G., and L. J. Eck. 1967. Vertebrate remains from four archeological sites in the Amistad Reservoir Area, Val Verde County, Texas. *Texas J. Sci.* 19(2):138–50.

770.3   Raun, G. G., and F. R. Gehlbach. 1972. Amphibians and reptiles in Texas. *Dallas Mus. Nat. Hist. Bull.* 2:1–61.

771.   Raun, G. G., and B. J. Wilks. 1964. Natural history of *Baiomys taylori* in southern Texas and competition with *Sigmodon hispidus* in a mixed population. *Texas J. Sci.* 16(1):28–49.

771.3   Raymond, L. R., and L. M. Hardy. 1983. Taxonomic status of the corn snake *Elaphe guttata* Linnaeus (Colubridae), in Louisiana and east Texas. *Southwest. Nat.* 28(1):105–107.

772.   Reddell, J. R. 1961. The caves of Uvalde County. Part I. *Texas Speleo. Survey* 1(3):1–34.

773.   ———. 1963. The caves of Val Verde County. *Texas Speleo. Survey* 1(7):1–53.

774.   ———. 1964. The caves of Comal County. *Texas Speleo. Survey* 2(2):1–60.

775.   ———. 1967. A checklist of the cave fauna of Texas. III. Vertebrata. *Texas J. Sci.* 19(2):184–226.

775.1   ———. 1970. A checklist of the cave fauna of Texas. VI. Additional records of Vertebrata. *Tex J. Sci.* 22(2–3):139–58.

776.   Reddell, J. R., and J. H. Estes. 1962. The caves of San Saba County. Part I. *Texas Speleo. Survey* 1(6):1–42.

777.   Reddell, J. R., and R. C. Finch. 1963. The caves of Williamson County. *Texas Speleo. Soc.* 2(1):1–61.

778.   Reddell, J. R., and O. Knox. 1962. The caves of Bexar County. Part I. *Texas Speleo. Soc.* 1(4):1–38.

778.1   Reddell, J. R., and R. W. Mitchell. 1969. *A checklist and annotated bibliography of the subterranean aquatic fauna of Texas*. Texas Technological College, Water Resources Center, Lubbock, Texas. Spec. Rep. No. 24. 1969:1–48.

779.   Reddell, J. R., and W. H. Russell. 1961. The caves of Travis County. *Texas Speleo Survey* 1(1):1–31.

780.   Reddell, J. R., and A. R. Smith. 1965. The caves of Edwards County. *Texas Speleo. Survey* 2(5–6):1–70.

781.   Reese, A. M. 1915. *The alligator and its allies.* New York: G. P. Putnam's Sons.

782.   Reese, R. W., and I. L. Firschein. 1950. Herpetological results of the University of Illinois field expedition, spring 1949. II. Amphibia. *Trans. Kansas Acad. Sci.* 53:44–54.

783.   Reeve, W. L. 1952. Taxonomy and distribution of the horned lizard genus *Phrynosoma. Univ. Kansas Sci. Bull.* 34(14):817–960.

784.   Reid, J. R., and T. E. Lott. 1963. Feeding of *Leptotyphlops dulcis dulcis* (Baird and Girard). *Herpetologica* 19(2):141–42.

784.1   Reno, H. W., F. R. Gehlbach, and R. A. Turner. 1972. Skin and Aestivational cocoon of the aquatic amphibian *Siren intermedia* LeConte. *Copeia* 1972(4):625–31.

784.5   Reynolds, S. L., and M. E. Seidel. 1983. Morphological homogeneity in the turtle *Sternotherus odoratus* (Kinosternidae) throughout its range. *J. Herp.* 17(2):113–20.

785.   Richardson, C. H. 1912. The distribution of *Hyla arenicolor* Cope, with notes on its habits and variation. *Amer. Nat.* 46:605–11.

785.2   Ridlehuber, K. T., and N. J. Silvy. 1981. Texas rat snake feeds on Mexican freetail bat and wood duck eggs. *Southwest. Nat.* 26(1):70–71.

786.   Riemer, W. J., et al., eds. 1963 et seq. *Catalogue of American amphibians and reptiles.* New York: American Soc. Ichthyol. and Herpetol.

786.1   Rogers, J. S. 1972. Discriminant function analysis of morphological relationships within the *Bufo cognatus* species group. *Copeia* 1972(2): 381–83.

786.11   ———. 1973. Protein polymorphism, genic heterozygosity and divergence in the toads *Bufo cognatus* and *B. speciosus. Copeia* 1973(2): 322–30.

786.12   ———. 1976. Species density and taxonomic diversity of Texas amphibians and reptiles. *Syst. Zool.* 25(1):26–40.

786.2   Rogers, K. C. 1975. Herpetofauna of Beck Ranch local fauna (Upper Pliocene: Blancan). *Diss. Abst. Int.* B36(3):1095.

786.21 ———. 1976. Herpetofauna of the Beck Ranch local fauna (Upper Pliocene: Blancan) of Texas. *Publ. Mus. Michigan St. Univ. (Paleont. Ser.)* 1(5):163–200.

786.3 Rose, F. L. 1959. Albinism in *Thamnophis sauritus. Herpetologica* 15(4):233.

786.31 ———. 1969. Desiccation rates and temperature relationships of *Terrapene ornata* following scute removal. *Southwest. Nat.* 14(1):67–72.

786.32 ———. 1976a. Sex ratios of larval and transformed *Ambystoma tigrinum* Green inhabiting the Llano Estacado of west Texas. *Copeia* 1976(3):455–61.

786.33 ———. 1976b. Tumorous growths of the tiger salamander, *Ambystoma tigrinum*, associated with treated sewage effluent. *Prog. Exp. Tumor Res.* 20:251–62.

786.4 Rose, F. L., and D. Armentrout. 1974. Population estimates of *Ambystoma tigrinum* inhabiting two playa lakes. *J. Anim. Ecol.* 43:671–79.

786.41 ———. 1976. Adaptive strategies of *Ambystoma tigrinum* Green inhabiting the Llano Estacado of west Texas. *J. Anim. Ecol.* 45(3):713–29.

786.42 Rose, F. L., D. Armentrout, and P. Roper. 1971. Physiological responses of paedogenic *Ambystoma tigrinum* to acute anoxia. *Herpetologica* 27(2):101–107.

786.43 Rose, F. L., and Clyde D. Barbour. 1968. Ecology and reproductive cycles of the introduced gecko, *Hemidactylus turcicus*, in the southern United States. *Amer. Midl. Nat.* 79(1):159–68.

786.44 Rose, F. L., and R. B. Drotman. 1967. Anaerobiosis in a frog, *Rana pipiens. J. Exp. Zool.* 166(3):427–32.

786.45 Rose, F. L., and J. C. Harshbarger. 1977. Neoplastic and possibly related skin lesions in neotenic tiger salamanders from a sewage lagoon. *Science* 196(4287):315–17.

786.46 Rose, F. L., and F. W. Judd. 1975. Activity and home range size of the Texas tortoise, *Gopherus berlandieri*, in south Texas. *Herpetologica* 31(4):448–56.

786.47 ———. 1980. Home range estimates of *Gopherus berlandieri*. Abstract, p. 187 in *Desert Tortoise Council Proc.*, 1979 symposium, edited by E. St. Amant, S. Allen, and R. Kirwin.

786.5 Rose, F. L., and H. L. Lewis. 1968. Changes in weight and free fatty acid concentration of fat bodies of paedogenic *Ambystoma tigrinum* during vitellogenesis. *Comp. Biochem. Physiol.* 26:149–54.

786.6 Ross, C. A., and C. D. Roberts. 1979. Scalation of the American alligator. USDI, FWS, Special Report 225:1–8.

786.7   Ross, R. K., and F. W. Judd. Comparison of lipid cycles of *Holbrookia propinqua* from Padre Island and mainland Texas. *J. Herp.* 16(1): 53–60.

786.8   Rosskopf, W. J., Jr., and R. W. Woerpel. 1981. Response to medical treatment in a critically ill Texas tortoise *Gopherus berlandieri. Bull. Chicago Herp. Soc.* 16(4): 95–99.

787.   Rossman, D. A. 1963a. The colubrid snake genus *Thamnophis:* A revision of the *sauritus* group. *Bull. Florida St. Mus.* 7(3): 99–178.

788.   ——. 1963b. Relationships and taxonomic status of the North American natricine snake genera *Liodytes, Regina,* and *Clonophis. Occ. Papers Mus. Zool. Louisiana St. Univ.* 29: 1–29.

788.1   ——. 1970. *Thamnophis proximus. Cat. Amer. Amphib. Rept.* 98.1– 98.3.

788.11   ——. 1971. Systematics of the neotropical populations of *Thamnophis marcianus* (Serpentes: Colubridae). *Occ. Papers Mus. Zool. Louisiana St. Univ.* 41: 1–13.

788.2   Rossman, D. A., and R. Erwin. 1980. Geographic variation in the snake *Storeria occipitomaculata* (Storer) (Serpentes: Colubridae) in southeastern United States. *Brimleyana* 4: 95–102.

789.   Roze, J. A. 1967. A check list of the new world venomous coral snakes (Elapidae), with descriptions of new forms. *Amer. Mus. Novitates* 2287: 1–60.

789.1   ——. 1974. *Micruroides. Cat. Amer. Amphib. Rept.* 163.1–163.4

790.   Ruick, J. D., Jr. 1948. Collecting coral snakes, *Micrurus fulvius tenere* in Texas. *Herpetologica* 4(6): 215–16.

790.5   Russell, F. E. 1980. Snake venom poisoning in the United States. *Ann. Rev. Med.* 31: 247–59.

791.   Ruthven, A. G. 1908. Variations and genetic relationships of the garter snakes. *Bull. United States Nat. Mus.* 61: 1–198.

792.   Sabath, H. 1960a. *Sceloporus g. graciosus* in southern New Mexico and Texas. *Herpetologica* 16(1): 22.

793.   ——. 1960b. Eggs and young of several Texas reptiles. *Herpetologica* 16(1): 72.

793.5   Sabath, M. C., and L. E. Sabath. 1969. Morphological intergradation in Gulf coastal brown snakes, *Storeria dekayi* and *Storeria tropica. Amer. Midl. Nat.* 81(1): 148–55.

794.   Sabath, M. C., and R. Worthington. 1959. Eggs and young of certain Texas reptiles. *Herpetologica* 15(1):31–32.

794.2   Sage, R. D., and R. L. Selander. 1979. Hybridization between species of the *Rana pipiens* complex in central Texas. *Evolution* 33(4):1069–88.

794.31   Salthe, S. N. 1969. Geographic variation of the lactate dehydrogenases of *Rana pipiens* and *Rana palustris. Biochem. Gen.* 2(4):271–303.

794.32.   ———. 1973a. Amphiumidae. *Cat. Amer. Amphib. Rept.* 147.1–147.4.

794.33   ———. 1973b. *Amphiuma tridactylum. Cat. Amer. Amphib. Rept.* 149.1–149.3.

795.   Sanders, C. L., Jr. 1963. Habitat preferences of the white-tailed deer and several exotic ungulates in south Texas. *Ecology* 44(4):803–16.

796.   Sanders, O. 1948. *Necturus* and *Amphiuma* in Texas. *Herpetologica* 4(5):167.

797.   ———. 1953. A new species of toad, with a discussion of morphology of the bufonid skull. *Herpetologica* 9(1):25–47.

797.1   ———. 1978. *Bufo woodhousei* in central Texas. *Bull. Maryland Herp. Soc.* 14(2):55–66.

798.   Sanders, O., and J. C. Cross. 1964. Relationships between certain North American toads as shown by cytological studies. *Herpetologica* 19(4): 248–55.

799.   Sanders, O., and H. M. Smith. 1949. Some noteworthy records of amphibians from Texas. *Trans. Kansas Acad. Sci.* 52:28–29.

800.   ———. 1951. Geographic variations in toads of the *debilis* group of *Bufo. Field and Lab.* 19(4):141–60.

801.   Sanger, D. B. 1931. An adventure with snakes. *Bull. Antivenin Inst. Amer.* 5(2):34–35.

801.5   Sattler, P. W. 1980. Genetic relationships among selected species of North American *Scaphiopus. Copeia* 1980(4):605–10.

802.   Savage, J. M. 1954. A revision of the toads of the *Bufo debilis* complex. *Texas J. Sci.* 6(1):83–112.

802.1   Savitzky, A. H., and J. T. Collins. 1971a. *Tantilla gracilis*, a snake new to the fauna of Mexico. *J. Herp.* 5(1–2):86–87.

802.11   ———. 1971b. The ground snake *Sonora episcopa episcopa* in Coahuila, Mexico. *J. Herp.* 5(1–2):87–88.

802.2   Saxon, J. G. 1968. Sexual behavior of a male checkered whiptail lizard, *Cnemidophorus tesselatus* (Say). *Southwest. Nat.* 13(4):454–55.

802.21   ———. 1971. The biology of the lizard, *Cnemidophorus tesselatus* and effects of pesticides upon the population in the Presidio Basin, Texas. *Diss. Abst. Int.* B37(5):3079-B.

802.22   Saxon, J. G., H. G. Applegate, and J. M. Inglis. 1967. Male *Cnemidophorus tesselatus* Say from Presidio, Texas. *Texas J. Sci.* 19(2):233–34.

802.3   Schaaf, R. T., Jr., and P. W. Smith. 1970. Geographic variation in the pickerel frog. *Herpetologica* 26(2):240–54.

802.31   ———. 1971. *Rana palustris. Cat. Amer. Amphib. Rept.* 117.1–117.3.

802.4   Schall, J. J. 1977a. Comparative ecology of sympatric parthenogenetic and bisexual species of *Cnemidophorus. Diss. Abst. Int.* B37(8):3757–58.

802.41   ———. 1977b. Thermal ecology of five sympatric species of *Cnemidophorus* (Saura: Teiidae). *Herpetologica* 33(3):261–72.

802.42   ———. 1978. Reproductive strategies in sympatric whiptail lizards (*Cnemidophorus*): Two parthenogenetic and three bisexual species. *Copeia* 1978(1):108–16.

803.   Schmidt, K. P. 1920. *Bufo fowleri* in Louisiana and Texas. *Copeia* 1920(1):84–85.

804.   ———. 1921. A new name for subspecies of *Uta stansburiana* Baird and Girard. *Amer. Mus. Novitates* 15:1–2.

805.   ———. 1922. A review of the North American genus of lizards, *Holbrookia. Bull. Amer. Mus. Nat. Hist.* 46:709–25.

806.   ———. 1925. Note on *Elaphe subocularis* (Brown). *Copeia* 1925(1):87–88.

807.   ———. 1932. Stomach contents of some American coral snakes, with the description of a new species of *Geophis. Copeia* 1932(1):6–9.

808.   ———. 1940. Notes on Texas snakes of the genus *Salvadora. Field Mus. Nat. Hist. Zool. Ser.* 24(12):143–50.

809.   ———. 1953. *A check list of North American amphibians and reptiles.* Chicago: University of Chicago Press.

810.   Schmidt, K. P., and D. D. Davis. 1941. *Field book of snakes of the United States and Canada.* New York: G. P. Putnam's Sons.

811.   Schmidt, K. P., and T. F. Smith. 1944. Amphibians and reptiles of the Big Bend region of Texas. *Field Mus. Nat. Hist. Zool. Ser.* 29:75–96.

811.1   Schrank, G. D., and R. E. Ballinger. 1973. Male reproductive cycles in two species of lizards (*Cophosaurus texanus* and *Cnemidophorus gularis*). *Herpetologica* 29(3):289–93.

811.14   Schreber, H. 1882. Beitrag zur Naturgeschichte der Frosche. Der Naturforscher. Halle: Johann Jacob Gebaur. 18:1–268.

811.2   Schuett, G. W. 1982. A copperhead (*Agkistrodon contortrix*) brood produced from autumn copulations. *Copeia* 1982(3):700–702.

811.3   Schuett, G. W., and F. Kraus. 1980a. Geographic distribution. *Crotalus viridus viridus*. *Herp Rev.* 11(3):81.

811.31   ———. 1980b. Geographic distribution. *Sistrurus catenatus edwardsi*. *Herp Rev.* 11(3):81.

811.32   ———. 1982. Life history notes. *Agkistrodon contortrix pictigaster*. *Herp Rev.* 13(1):17.

812.   Schwartz, A. 1956. Geographic variation in the chicken turtle *Deirochelys reticularia* Latreille. *Fieldiana Zool.* 34:461–503.

813.   Schwartz, A., and W. A. Babis. 1949. Extension of the range of *Crotalus lepidus klauberi*. *Copeia* 1949(1):74.

814.   Scroggin, J. B., and W. B. Davis. 1956. Food habits of the Texas dwarf siren. *Herpetologica* 12(3):231–37.

815.   Scudday, J. F. 1965a. Another *Lampropeltis alterna* in Brewster County, Texas. *Southwest. Nat.* 10(1):77–78.

816.   ———. 1965b. *Eleutherodactylus latrans* in Terrell County, Texas. *Southwest. Nat.* 10(1):78.

816.1   ———. 1967. Additional notes on distribution of *Crotaphytus wislizeni* in Texas. *Texas J. Sci.* 19(4):396–97.

816.11   ———. 1973. A new species of lizard of the *Cnemidophorus tesselatus* group from Texas. *J. Herp.* 7(4):363–71.

816.12   ———. 1977(1978). Some recent changes in the herpetofauna of the northern Chihuahuan desert. Pp. 513–22 in *Transactions of the symposium on the biological resources of the Chihuahuan desert region, United States and Mexico*, edited by R. H. Wauer and D. H. Riskind. Natl. Park Ser. Trans. Proc. Ser. (3).

816.2   Scudday, J. F., and J. R. Dixon. 1973. Diet and feeding behavior of teiid lizards from Trans-Pecos, Texas. *Southwest. Nat.* 18(3):279–89.

816.3   Scudday, J. F., and L. F. Scudday. 1975. A preliminary survey of the vertebrate fauna of the upper Canadian Breaks area. Pp. 59–67 in *Cana-*

dian Breaks, a natural area survey. Austin: Div. Nat. Resources and Environ., University of Texas.

816.4   Seidel, M. E. 1978. *Kinosternon flavescens. Cat. Amer. Amphib. Rept.* 216.1–216.4.

816.5   Seifert, W. S. 1978a. Geographic distribution. *Hylactophryne augusti latrans. Herp Rev.* 9(2):61.

816.51   ———. 1978b. Geographic distribution. *Eumeces anthracinus pluvialis. Herp Rev.* 9(2):61.

816.52   ———. 1978c. Geographic distribution. *Gerrhonotus liocephalus infernalis. Herp Rev.* 9(2):61–62.

816.53   ———. 1978d. Geographic distribution. *Salvadora grahamiae lineata. Herp Rev.* 9(2):62.

816.54   ———. 1980a. Geographic distribution. *Rana areolata areaolata. Herp. Rev.* 11(4):115.

816.55   ———. 1980b. Geographic distribution. *Cemophora coccinea copei. Herp Rev.* 11(4):116.

816.6   Seifert, W. S., and R. W. Murphy. 1972. Additional specimens of *Coleonyx reticulatus* (Davis and Dixon) from the Black Gap Wildlife Management Area, Texas. *Herpetologica* 28(1):24–26.

816.7   Seifert, W. S., F. Rainwater, and T. Kasper. 1973. Significant range extension with field and lab notes for the reticulated gecko, *Coleonyx reticulatus* Davis and Dixon. *Southwest. Nat.* 18(1):101–103.

816.8   Seifert, W. S., and D. Wuerch. 1978. Geographic distribution. *Desmognathus auriculatus. Herp Rev.* 9(3):106.

817.   Selander, R. K., et al. 1962. Vertebrates from the barrier islands of Tamaulipas Mexico. *Univ. Kansas Publ. Mus. Nat. Hist.* 12(7):309–45.

817.1   Selcer, K. W., and R. A. Bloom. 1984. *Cyrtodactylus scaber* (Gekkonidae): A new gecko to the fauna of the United States. *Southwest. Nat.* 29(4):499–500.

817.2   Selcer, K. W., and F. W. Judd. 1982. Variation in the reproductive ecology of *Holbrookia propinqua* (Sauria: Iguanidae). *Texas J. Sci.* 34(2):125–35.

818.   Semken, H. A., Jr. 1961. Fossil vertebrates from Longhorn Cavern, Burnet County, Texas. *Texas J. Sci.* 13(3):290–310.

818.1   Sever, D. M. 1985. Sexually dimorphic glands of *Eurycea nana, Eurycea neotenes* and *Typhlomolge rathbuni* (Amphibia: Plethodonitidae). *Herpetologica* 41(1):71–84.

819. Shannon, F. A., and H. M. Smith. 1949. Herpetological results of the University of Illinois field expedition, spring 1949. I. Introduction, Testudines, Serpentes. *Trans. Kansas Acad. Sci.* 52:494–509.

820. Shields, L. M, and R. G. Lindborg. 1956. Records of the spineless soft-shelled turtle and the snapping turtle from New Mexico. *Copeia* 1956(2):120–21.

820.1 Sites, J. W. 1980. Chromosomal, allozyme and morphological variation in three cytotypes of the *Sceloporus grammicus* complex. *Diss. Abst. Int.* B41(4):1980:1181.

820.11 ———. 1982. Morphological variation within and among three chromosome races of *Sceloporus grammicus* (Sauria: Iguanidae) in the north-central part of its range. *Copeia* 1982(4):920–41.

820.12 ———. 1983. Chromosome evolution in the iguanid lizard *Sceloporus grammicus*. I. Chromosome polymorphisms. *Evolution* 37(1):38–53.

820.16 Sites, J. W., and D. A. Boyce. 1985. A test for allozyme selection in *Sceloporus grammicus* (Sauria: Iguanidae). *Southwest. Nat.* 30(1):41–51.

820.2 Sites, J. W., and J. R. Dixon. A new subspecies of the iguanid lizard, *Sceloporus grammicus*, from northeastern Mexico, with comments on its evolutionary implications and the status of S. *g. disparilis. J. Herp.* 15(1):59–69.

820.21 ———. 1982. Geographic variation in *Sceloporus variabilis* and its relationship to S. *teapensis* (Sauria: Iguanidae). *Copeia* 1982(1):14–27.

820.22 Sites, J. W., and I. F. Greenbaum. 1983. Chromosome evolution in the iguanid lizard *Sceloporus grammicus*. 2. Allozyme variation. *Evolution* 37(1):54–65.

820.3 Sitou-Hsian, Mao, and H. C. Dessauer. 1972. Selectively neutral mutations, transferrins and evolution of onatricine snakes. *Comp. Biochem. Physiol.* 40A:669–80.

821. Slaughter, B. H. 1966. The Moore Pit local fauna: Pleistocene of Texas. J. Paleontol. 40(1):78–91.

821.1 Slaughter, B. H., and W. L. McClure. 1965. The Sims Bayou local fauna: Pleistocene of Houston, Texas. *Texas J. Sci.* 17(1):404–17.

821.2 Slaughter, B. H., et al. 1962. The Hill-Shuler local faunas of the upper Trinity River, Dallas and Denton counties, Texas. *Bur. Econ. Geol. Texas, Rept. Invest.* 48:viii–75.

821.3 Slevin, J. R. 1928. The amphibians of western North America. *Occ. Papers California Acad. Sci.* 16:1–152.

822.   Smith, A. R., and J. R. Reddell. 1965. The caves of Kinney County. *Texas Speleo. Survey* 2(7):1–34.

822.01   Smith, D. B., and H. L. Gregory. 1983. *Elaphe subocularis*. Coloration. *Herp Rev.* 14(2):47.

822.02   Smith, D. D. 1983a. *Crotaphytus collaris* (Collared Lizard). Reproduction. *Herp Rev.* 14(2):46.

822.03   ———. 1983b. Geographic distribution. *Nerodia harteri harteri*. *Herp Rev.* 14(3):84–85.

822.08   Smith, D. D., et al. 1985. *Crotalus molossus* (Blacktail Rattlesnake). Anomaly. *Herp Rev.* 16(3):78–79.

822.1   Smith, E. N. 1979. Behavioral and physiological thermoregulation of crocodilians. *Amer. Zool.* 19:239–47.

822.11   ———. 1980. The alligator population of the Welder Wildlife Refuge from 1972–1978. *Welder Wildlife Foundation Symposium* 1:225–28.

822.2   Smith, E. N., and S. R. Adams. 1978. Thermoregulation of small American alligators. *Herpetologica* 34(4):406–408.

822.3   Smith, E. N., R. D. Allison, and W. E. Crowder. 1974. Bradycardia in a free ranging American alligator. *Copeia* 1974(3):770–72.

822.4   Smith, E. N., C. R. Johnson, and B. Voight. 1976. Leech infestation of the American alligator in Texas. *Copeia* 1976(4):842.

822.5   Smith, E. N., S. Robertson, and D. G. Davies. 1978. Cutaneous blood flow during heating and cooling in the American alligator. *Amer. J. Physiol.* 235(3):R160–67.

823.   Smith, H. M. 1933a. On the proper name for the brevicipitid frog *Gastrophryne texensis* (Girard). *Copeia* 1933(4):217.

824.   ———. 1933b. On the relationships of the lizards *Coleonyx brevis* and *Coleonyx variegatus*. *Trans. Kansas Acad. Sci.* 36:301–14.

825.   ———. 1934a. Descriptions of new lizards of the genus *Sceloporus* from Mexico and southern United States. *Trans. Kansas Acad. Sci.* 37:263–79.

826.   ———. 1934b. On the taxonomic status of three species of lizards of the genus *Sceloporus* from Mexico and southern United States. *Proc. Biol. Soc. Washington* 47:121–34.

827.   ———. 1936. The lizards of the *torquatus* group of the genus *Sceloporus*. *Univ. Kansas Sci. Bull.* 24(21):539–693.

828. ———. 1937a. A new subspecies of the lizard genus *Sceloporus* from Texas. *Proc. Biol. Soc. Washington* 50:83–86.

829. ———. 1937b. Notes on *Scaphiopus hurteri* Strecker. *Herpetologica* 1(4):104–108.

830. ———. 1937c. A synopsis of the *variabilis* group of the lizard genus *Sceloporus*, with descriptions of new subspecies. *Occ. Papers Mus. Zool. Univ. Michigan.* 358:1–14.

831. ———. 1938a. Remarks on the status of the subspecies of *Sceloporus undulatus*, with descriptions of new species and subspecies of the *undulatus* group. *Occ. Papers Mus. Zool. Univ. Michigan* 387:1–17.

832. ———. 1938b. A review of the snake genus *Farancia*. *Copeia* 1938(3):110–17.

833. ———. 1938c. Additions to the herpetofauna of Mexico. *Copeia* 1938(3):149–50.

834. ———. 1938d. Notes on the snakes of the genus *Salvadora*. *Univ. Kansas Sci. Bull.* 25(12):229–37.

835. ———. 1939. The Mexican and Central American lizards of the genus *Sceloporus*. *Field Mus. Nat. Hist. Zool. Ser.* 26:1–397.

836. ———. 1941a. A review of the subspecies of the indigo snake (*Drymarchon corais*). *J. Washington Acad. Sci.* 31(11):466–81.

837. ———. 1941b. Notes on the snake genus *Trimorphodon*. *Proc. United States Natl. Mus.* 91:149–68.

838. ———. 1942a. Mexican herpetological miscellany. *Proc. United States Natl. Mus.* 92:349–95.

839. ———. 1942b. Remarks on the Mexican king snakes of the *triangulum* group. *Proc. Rochester Acad. Sci.* 8:196–207.

840. ———. 1942c. A resume of Mexican snakes of the genus *Tantilla*. *Zoologica* 27(7):33–42.

841. ———. 1942d. The synonymy of the garter snakes (*Thamnophis*), with notes on Mexican and Central American species. *Zoologica* 27(3–4):97–123.

842. ———. 1942e. A new name for a United States skink. *Proc. New England Zool. Club* 21:93–95.

843. ———. 1944. Snakes of the Hoogstral expeditions to northern Mexico. *Field Mus. Nat. Hist. Zool. Ser.* 29:139–52.

844.   ———. 1946a. *Handbook of lizards.* Ithaca, N.Y.: Comstock Publ. Co.

845.   ———. 1946b. The status of *Sceloporus floridanus* Baird. *Univ. Kansas Sci. Bull.* 31:103–106.

846.   ———. 1946c. Neoteny in Texas salamanders. *Proc. Trans. Texas Acad. Sci.* 30:59–60 (abstract).

847.   ———. 1946d. The map turtles of Texas. *Proc. Trans. Texas Acad. Sci.* 30:60 (abstract).

848.   ———. 1946e. The systematic status of *Eumeces pluvialis* Cope, and noteworthy records of other amphibians and reptiles from Kansas and Oklahoma. *Univ. Kansas Publ. Mus. Nat. Hist.* 1(2):85–89.

849.   ———. 1947a. Herpetological papers in some Texas journals. *Herpetologica* 3(5):179–82.

850.   ———. 1947b. *Pseudacris clarkii* and *P. n. triseriata* in Texas. *Herpetologica* 3(5):183–84.

851.   ———. 1947c. Subspecies of the Sonoran toad (*Bufo compactilis* Wiegmann). *Herpetologica* 4(1):7–13.

852.   ———. 1951. The identity of the ophidian name *Coluber eques* Reuss. *Copeia* 1951(2):138–40.

853.   ———. 1953. Case history of a snake with an irregurgitable artificial egg. *Herpetologica* 9(2):93–95.

854.   Smith, H. M., and B. C. Brown. 1946a. The identity of certain specific names in *Thamnophis. Herpetologica* 3(3):71–72.

855.   ———. 1946b. *Rana palustris* (LeConte) in Texas. *Herpetologica* 3(3):73.

856.   ———. 1947. The Texas subspecies of the tree frog, *Hyla versicolor. Proc. Biol. Soc. Washington* 60:47–50.

857.   Smith, H. M., and S. O. Brown. 1946. A hitherto neglected integumentary gland in the Texas tortoise. *Proc. Trans. Texas Acad. Sci.* 30:59 (abstract).

858.   Smith, H. M., and H. K. Buechner. 1947. The influence of the Balcones Escarpment on the distribution of amphibians and reptiles in Texas. *Bull. Chicago Acad. Sci.* 8(1):1–16.

859.   Smith, H. M., and W. L. Burger. 1947. The banded water snake, *Natrix sipedon fasciata,* in Texas. *Chicago Acad. Sci. Nat. Hist. Misc.* 11:1.

860.   ———. 1949. The identity of *Ameiva tessellata* Say. *Bull. Chicago Acad. Sci.* 8(13):277–84.

861. Smith, H. M., and B. F. Glass, 1947. A new musk turtle from the south-eastern United States. *J. Washington Acad. Sci.* 37(1):22–24.

862. Smith, H. M., and J. P. Kennedy. 1951. *Pituophis melanoleucus ruthveni* in eastern Texas and its bearing on the status of *P. catenifer*. *Herpetologica* 7(3):93–96.

862.5 Smith, H. M., and A. J. Kohler. 1977. A survey of herpetological introductions in the United States and Canada. *Trans. Kansas Acad. Sci.* 80(1–2):1–24.

863. Smith, H. M., and F. E. Potter, Jr. 1946. A third neotenic salamander of the genus *Eurycea* from Texas. *Herpetologica* 3(4):105–109.

864. Smith, H. M., and L. W. Ramsey. 1952. A new turtle from Texas. *Wassman J. Biol.* 10(1) 45–54.

865. Smith, H. M., and O. Sanders. 1952a. Distributional data on Texas amphibians and reptiles. *Texas J. Sci.* 4(2):204–19.

866. ———. 1952b. *Terrapene carolina major* in Arkansas. *Herpetologica* 8(3):93.

867. Smith, H. M., and J. A. Slater. 1949. The southern races of *Eumeces septentrionalis*. *Trans. Kansas Acad. Sci.* 52:438–48.

867.5 Smith, H. M., and R. B. Smith. 1979. *Coluber chiametla* Shaw, 1802 (Reptilia, Serpentes): Revived proposal for suppression under the plenary powers Z.N. (S.) 1704. *Bull. Zool. Nomencl.* 35(3):184–86.

868. Smith, H. M, and E. H. Taylor. 1941. A review of the snakes of the genus *Ficimia*. *J. Washington Acad. Sci.* 31(8):356–68.

869. ———. 1945. An annotated checklist and key to the snakes of Mexico. *United States Natl. Mus. Bull.* 187:1–239.

870. ———. 1948. An annotated checklist and key to the amphibia of Mexico. *United States Natl. Mus. Bull.* 194:1–118.

871. ———. 1950a. Type localities of Mexican reptiles and amphibians. *Univ. Kansas Sci. Bull.* 33:313–79.

872. ———. 1950b. An annotated checklist and key to the reptiles of Mexico exclusive of the snakes. *United States. Natl. Bull.* 199:1–253.

872.5 Smith, H. M., and J. E. Werler. 1969. The status of the northern red black-headed snake, *Tantilla diabola* Fouquette and Porter. *J. Herp.* 3(3–4):172–73.

873. Smith, H. M., D. A. Langebartel, and K. Williams. 1964. Herpetological type-specimens in the University of Illinois Museum of Natural History. *Illinois Biol. Monogr.* 32:1–80.

873.2   Smith, N. M., and W. W. Tanner. 1972. Two new subspecies of *Crotaphytus* (Sauria: Iguanidae). *Great Basin Nat.* 32(1):25–34.

873.22   ———. 1974. A taxonomic study of the western collared lizards, *Crotaphytus collaris* and *Crotaphytus insularis*. *Brig. Young Univ. Sci. Bull.* 19(4):1–29.

874.   Smith, P. W. 1956. Extensions of the known range of the flat-headed snake. *Herpetologica* 12(4):327.

874.5   ———. 1966. *Pseudacris streckeri*. *Cat. Amer. Amphib. Rept.* 27.1–27.2.

875.   Smith, P. W., and W. L. Burger. 1950. Herpetological results of the University of Illinois Field expedition, spring 1949. III. Sauria. *Trans. Kansas Acad. Sci.* 53:165–75.

875.5   Smith, P. W., and L. M. Page. 1972. Repeated mating of a copperhead and timber rattlesnake. *Herp Rev.* 4(2):196.

876.   Smith, P. W., and D. M. Smith. 1952. The relationship of the chorus frogs, *Pseudacris nigrita feriarum* and *Pseudacris n. triseriata*. *Amer. Midl. Nat.* 48(1):165–80.

877.   Smith, P. W., and H. M. Smith. 1952. Geographic variation in the lizard *Eumeces anthracinus*. *Univ. Kansas Sci. Bull.* 34(11):679–94.

878.   ———. 1962. The systematic and biogeographic status of two Illinois snakes. *Occ. Papers C. C. Adams Center for Ecol. Studies* 5:1–10.

878.3   Specian, R. D., and S. E. Ubelaker. 1974a. Two new species of *Pharyngogodon* Desing, 1861 (Nematoda: Oxyuridae) from lizards in west Texas. *Proc. Helminth. Soc. Washington* 41(1):46–51.

878.31   ———. 1974b. *Parathelandros texanus* n. sp. (Nematoda: Oxyuridae) from lizards in west Texas. *Trans. Amer. Microsc. Soc.* 93(3):413–15.

878.5   Stafford, D. P., F. W. Plapp, and R. R. Fleet. 1976. Snakes as indicators of environmental contamination: Relation of detoxifying enzymes and pesticide residues to species occurrence in three aquatic ecosystems. *Arch. Environ. Contam. Toxicol.* 5:15–27.

879.   Stallcup, W. B. 1959. Observations of captive hognosed snakes, *Heterodon platyrhinos* Latreille. *Field and Lab.* 27(2):80–81.

880.   ———. 1961. Notes on the vertebrate collection in the Department of Biology, Southern Methodist University. *J. Grad. Res. Center* 29(1):66–69.

881.   Stanek, V. J. 1960. *Introducing poisonous snakes*. London: Spring Brooks.

882. Stebbins, R. C. 1951. *Amphibians of western North America*. Berkeley: University of California Press.

883. ———. 1954. *Amphibians and reptiles of western North America*. New York: McGraw-Hill.

884. ———. 1958. A new alligator lizard from the Panamint Mountains. Inyo County, California. *Amer. Mus. Novitates* 1883:1–27.

885. ———. 1966. *A field guide to western reptiles and amphibians*. Boston: Houghton Mifflin Co.

885.5 Steele, J. A., and A. L. Hamilton. 1969. Notes on the natural history of *Ambystoma texanum* in Brazos County, Texas. *TASCA* 23(4):14–15.

886. Stejneger, L. 1890. Annotated list of reptiles and batrachians collected by D. C. Hart Merriam and Vernon Bailey on the San Francisco Mountain Plateau and desert of the Little Colorado, Arizona, with descriptions of new species. *North American Fauna* 3:103–18.

887. ———. 1891a. Notes on *Sceloporus variabilis* and its geographical distribution in the United States. *Proc. United States Natl. Mus.* 14:485–88.

888. ———. 1891b. Notes on some North American snakes. *Proc. United States Natl. Mus.* 14:501–505.

889. ———. 1895. The poisonous snakes of North America. *Ann. Rept. United States Natl. Mus.* 1893:337–487.

890. ———. 1896. Description of a new genus and species of blind, tailed batrachian from subterranean waters of Texas. *Proc. United States Natl. Mus.* 18:619–21.

891. ———. 1904. A new lizard from the Rio Grande Valley, Texas. *Proc. Biol. Soc. Washington* 17:17–20.

892. ———. 1910. The amphibian generic name *Engystoma* untenable. *Proc. Biol. Soc. Washington* 23:165–68.

893. ———. 1915. A new species of tailless batrachian from North America. *Proc. Biol. Soc. Washington* 28:131.

894. ———. 1916. A new lizard of the genus *Sceloporus* from Texas. *Proc. Biol. Soc. Washington* 29:227–30.

895. ———. 1925. New species and subspecies of American turtles. *J. Washington Acad. Sci.* 15:462–63.

896. ———. 1938. Restitution of the name *Ptychemys hoyi* Agassiz for a western river tortoise. *Proc. Biol. Soc. Washington* 51:173–76.

897.   ———. 1940. "Sonora" as the locality of the Graham-Clark reptile col-
           lections of 1851. *Copeia* 1940(3):204–205.

898.   ———. 1944. Notes on the American soft-shelled turtles with special
           reference to *Amyda agassizi*. *Bull. Mus. Comp. Zool.* 94(1):1–75.

899.   Stejneger, L., and T. Barbour. 1917. *A check list of North American am-
           phibians and reptiles*. Cambridge, Mass.: Harvard University Press.

900.   ———. 1923. *A check list of North American amphibians and reptiles*.
           2nd ed. Cambridge, Mass.: Harvard University Press.

901.   ———. 1933. *A check list of North American amphibians and reptiles*.
           3rd ed. Cambridge, Mass: Harvard University Press.

902.   ———. 1939. *A check list of North American amphibians and reptiles*.
           4th ed. Cambridge, Mass.: Harvard University Press.

903.   ———. 1943. *A check list of North American amphibians and reptiles*.
           5th ed. *Bull. Mus. Comp. Zool.* 93.

904.   Stephenson, J. O., and L. H. Meitzen. 1946. Behavior and food habits of
           Sennett's white-tailed hawk in Texas. *Wilson Bull.* 58(4):198–205.

904.5   Stevens, M. S. 1977. Further study of the Castolon local fauna (Arika-
           reean: Early Miocene) Big Bend National Park, Texas. *Pearce-Sellards
           Ser. Texas Mem. Mus.* 28:1–69.

904.6   Stevens, M. S., J. B. Stevens, and M. R. Dawson. 1969. New early Mio-
           cene formation and vertebrate local fauna, Big Bend National Park,
           Brewster County, Texas. *Pearce-Sellards Ser. Texas Mem. Mus.*
           15:1–53.

904.65   Stewart, B. G. 1984. *Agkistrodon contortrix laticinctus* (Broad-banded
           Copperhead) Combat. *Herp Rev.* 15(1):17.

904.7   Stewart, B. G., and F. E. Potter. 1979. Geographic distribution. *Tham-
           nophis cyrtopsis ocellatus*. *Herp Rev.* 10(4):119.

904.8   Stewart, M. M. 1983. *Rana clamitans*. *Cat. Amer. Amphib. Rept.*
           337.1–337.4.

905.   Stickel, W. H. 1938. The snakes of the genus *Sonora* in the United
           States and Lower California. *Copeia* 1938(4):182–90.

906.   ———. 1943. The Mexican snakes of the genera *Sonora* and *Chionactis*
           with notes on the status of other colubrid genera. *Proc. Biol. Soc.
           Washington* 56:109–218.

907.   Stone, W. 1903. A collection of reptiles and batrachians from Arkansas,
           Indian Territory, and western Texas. *Proc. Acad. Nat. Sci. Philadel-
           phia* 55:538–42.

908.   ————. 1911. On some collections of reptiles and batrachians from the western United States. *Proc. Acad. Nat. Sci. Philadelphia* 63:222–32.

909.   Stone, W., and J. A. G. Rehm. 1903. On the terrestrial vertebrates of portions of southern New Mexico and western Texas. *Proc. Acad. Nat. Philadelhpia* 55:16–34.

910.   Stovall, J. W., and W. N. McAnulty. 1950. The vertebrate fauna and geologic age of Trinity River terraces in Henderson County, Texas. *Amer. Midl. Nat.* 44:211–50.

910.1   Stovall, R. H. 1976. Observations on the micro and ultrastructure of visual cells of certain snakes (Reptilia: Serpentes: Colubridae). *J. Herp.* 10(4):269–75.

910.2   Stovall, R. H., and J. P. Kennedy. 1979. Pupillary responses in certain snakes (Colubridae). *Southwest. Nat.* 24(4):701–703.

911.   Strasser, F. D. 1931. An encounter between a collared lizard and rattlesnake. *Bull. Antivenin Inst. Amer.* 5(2):41.

912.   Strecker, J. K. 1902. Reptiles and batrachians of McLennan County, Texas. *Proc. Trans. Texas Acad. Sci.* 4, pt. 2 (5):95–101.

913.   ————. 1908a. The reptiles and batrachians of Victoria and Refugio counties, Texas. *Proc. Biol. Soc. Washington* 21:47–52.

914.   ————. 1908b. A preliminary annotated list of the Batrachia of Texas. *Proc. Biol. Soc. Washington* 21:53–62.

915.   ————. 1908c. The reptiles and batrachians of McLennan County, Texas. *Proc. Biol. Soc. Washington* 21:69–84.

916.   ————. 1908d. Notes on the breeding of *Phrynosoma cornutum* and other Texas lizards. *Proc. Biol. Soc. Washington* 21:165–70.

917.   ————. 1908e. Notes on the life history of *Scaphiopus couchii* Baird. *Proc. Biol. Soc. Washington* 21:199–206.

918.   ————. 1909a. Notes on the herpetology of Burnet County, Texas. *Baylor Univ. Bull.* 12(1):1–9.

919.   ————. 1909b. Reptiles and amphibians collected in Brewster County, Texas. *Baylor Univ. Bull.* 12(1):11–16.

920.   ————. 1909c. Notes on the Texas salamander (*Ambystoma texanum* Matthes). *Baylor Univ. Bull.* 12(1):17–20.

921.   ————. 1909d. Notes on the narrow-mouthed toads (*Engystoma*) and the description of a new species from southeastern Texas. *Proc. Biol. Soc. Washington* 22:115–20.

922. ———. 1910a. Notes on the fauna of a portion of the canyon region of northwestern Texas. *Baylor Univ. Bull.* 13(4–5):1–31.

923. ———. 1910b. Description of new solitary spadefoot (*Scaphiopus hurteri*) from Texas, with other herpetological notes. *Proc. Biol. Soc. Washington* 23:115–22.

924. ———. 1910c. Studies in North American batrachology. Notes on the robber frog (*Lithodytes latrans* Cope). *Trans. Acad. Sci. St. Louis* 19:73–82.

925. ———. 1915. Reptiles and amphibians of Texas. *Baylor Univ. Bull.* 18(4):1–82.

926. ———. 1922. An annotated catalogue of the amphibians and reptiles of Bexar County, Texas. *Bull. Sci. Soc. San Antonio* 4:1–31.

927. ———. 1926a. Amphibians and reptiles collected in Somervell County, Texas. *Contr. Baylor Univ. Mus.* 2:1–2.

928. ———. 1926b. Notes on the herpetology of the east Texas timber belt. I. Liberty County amphibians and reptiles. *Contr. Baylor Univ. Mus.* 3:1–3.

929. ———. 1926c. On the habits of southern snakes. *Contr. Baylor Univ. Mus.* 4:1–11.

930. ———. 1926d. A list of reptiles and amphibians collected by Louis Garni in the vicinity of Boerne, Texas. *Contr. Baylor Univ. Mus.* 6:3–9.

931. ———. 1926e. Ophidian freaks. *Contr. Baylor Univ. Mus.* 6:10–11.

932. ———. 1926f. Notes on the herpetology of the east Texas timber belt. 2. Henderson County amphibians and reptiles. *Contr. Baylor Univ. Mus.* 7:3–7.

933. ———. 1926g. Reptiles from Lindale, Smith County, Texas. *Contr. Baylor Univ. Mus.* 7:7.

934. ———. 1926h. On the habits and variations of *Pseudacris ornata* (Holbrook). *Contr. Baylor Univ. Mus.* 7:8–11.

935. ———. 1926i. Chapters from the life-histories of Texas reptiles and amphibians. *Contr. Baylor Univ. Mus.* 8:1–12.

936. ———. 1926j. On the origins of reptile myths. *Texas Folk-Lore Soc. Publ.* 5:70–77.

937. ———. 1926k. Reptiles of the south and southwest in folk-lore. *Texas Folk-Lore Soc. Publ.* 5:56–69.

938.　———. 1927a. Notes on the ornithology of McLennan County, Texas. *Spec. Bull. Baylor Univ. Mus.* 1:1–163.

939.　———. 1927b. Chapters from the life histories of Texas reptiles and amphibians, Part 2. *Contr. Baylor Univ. Mus.* 10:1–14.

940.　———. 1927c. Birds and snake skins. *Contr. Baylor Univ. Mus.* 11: 1–7.

941.　———. 1927d. Notes on a specimen of *Gopherus berlandieri* (Agassiz). *Copeia* 1927(3):189.

942.　———. 1927e. Observations on the food habits of Texas amphibians and reptiles. *Copeia* 1927(1):6–9.

943.　———. 1928a. Field observation on the color changes of *Anolis carolinensis*. *Contr. Baylor Univ. Mus.* 13:1–9.

944.　———. 1928b. Occurrence of the spotted night snake (*Hypsiglena ochrohynchus* Cope) in central Texas with other Bosque County herpetological notes. *Contr. Baylor Univ. Mus.* 15:2–6.

945.　———. 1928c. Amphibians and reptiles collected at Harlingen, Texas. *Contr. Baylor Univ. Mus.* 15:7–8.

946.　———. 1928d. The copperhead west of the Pecos River. *Contr. Baylor Univ. Mus.* 15:9.

947.　———. 1928e. Common English and folk names for Texas amphibians and reptiles. *Contr. Baylor Univ. Mus.* 16:1–21.

948.　———. 1928f. Doubtful Texas reptile records. *Contr. Baylor Univ. Mus.* 18:3–5.

949.　———. 1928g. The type localities of *Callisaurus ventralis ventralis* (Hallowell) and *Sceloporus occidentalis biseriatus* (Hallowell). *Contr. Baylor Univ. Mus.* 18:5.

950.　———. 1928h. The eggs of *Gopherus berlandieri*. *Contr. Baylor Univ. Mus.* 18:6.

951.　———. 1929a. Field notes on the herpetology of Wilbarger County, Texas. *Contr. Baylor Univ. Mus.* 19:1–9.

952.　———. 1929b. A preliminary list of the amphibians and reptiles of Tarrant, County, Texas. *Contr. Baylor Univ. Mus.* 19:10–15.

953.　———. 1929c. Further studies in the folk-lore of reptiles. *Baylor Univ. Contr. to Folk-lore* 1:1–16.

954.　———. 1929d. Animals and streams: A contribution to the study of Texas folk names. *Baylor Univ. Contr. to Folk-lore* 2:1–23.

955.   ———. 1929e. Dragons and other reptiles real and imaginary. *Baylor Univ. Contr. to Folk-lore* 3:1–19.

956.   ———. 1930. A catalogue of the amphibians and reptiles of Travis County, Texas. *Contr. Baylor Univ. Mus.* 23:1–16.

957.   ———. 1933. Collecting at Helotes, Bexar County, Texas. *Copeia* 1933(2):77–79.

958.   ———. 1934. Notes on *Sonora semiannulata* Baird and Girard. *Copeia* 1934(4):186–87.

959.   ———. 1935a. *Alligator mississippiensis* (Daudin) in McLennan County, Texas. *Baylor Univ. Bull.* 38(3):24–25.

960.   ———. 1935b. Notes on the pit-vipers in McLennan County, Texas. *Baylor Univ. Bull.* 38(3):26–28.

961.   ———. 1935c. Albino snakes. *Baylor Univ. Bull.* 38(3):29.

962.   ———. 1935d. *Siren lacertina* Linne in central Texas. *Baylor Univ. Bull.* 38(3):30.

963.   ———. 1935e. *Storeria occipitomaculata* (Storer) at Waco, Texas. *Baylor Univ. Bull.* 38(3):31.

964.   ———. 1935f. The reptiles of West Frio Canyon, Real County, Texas. *Baylor Univ. Bull.* 38(3):32.

965.   ———. 1935g. A list of hitherto unpublished localities for Texas amphibians and reptiles. *Baylor Univ. Bull.* 38(3):35–38.

966.   Strecker, J. K., and J. E. Johnson, Jr. 1935. Notes on the herpetology of Wilson County, Texas. *Baylor Univ. Bull.* 38(3):17–23.

967.   Strecker, J. K., and W. J. Williams. 1927. Herpetological records from the vicinity of San Marcos, Texas, with distributional data on the amphibians and reptiles of the Edwards Plateau region and central Texas. *Contr. Baylor Univ. Mus.* 12:1–16.

968.   ———. 1928. field notes of the herpetology of Bowie County, Texas. *Contr. Baylor Univ. Mus.* 17:1–19.

969.   Stull, O. G. 1940. Variations and relationships in the snakes of the genus *Pituophis*. *Bull. United States Natl. Mus.* 175:1–225.

970.   Stunkard, H. W. 1915. Notes on the trematode genus *Telorchis* with descriptions of new species. *J. Parasit.* 2(2):57–66.

971.   ———. 1916. On the anatomy and relationships of some North American trematodes. *J. Parasit.* 3(1):21–27.

972. ———. 1917. Studies on North American Polystomidae, Aspidogastricae, and Paramphistomidae. *Illinois Biol. Monogr.* 3(3):1–114.

973. ———. 1919. On the specific identity of *Heronimus chelydrae* MacCallum and *Aorchis extensus* Bakes and Parsons. *J. Parasit.* 6(1):11–18.

974. ———. 1923. Studies on North American blood flukes. *Bull. Amer. Mus. Nat. Hist.* 48:165–220.

974.5 Stuzenbaker, C. D. 1973. Alligator holes. *Texas Parks and Wildlife* 31(5): 20–22.

975. Sutton, G. W. 1922. Notes on the road-runner at Fort Worth, Texas. *Wilson Bull.* 34(1):3–20.

976. Swanson, B. 1953. Northeastward range extension for *Arizona elegans elegans* Kennicott. *Herpetologica* 9(2):78.

976.2 Sweet, S. S. 1977a. *Eurycea tridentifera. Cat. Amer. Amphib. Rept.* 199.1–199.2.

976.21 ———. 1977b. Natural metamorphosis in *Eurycea neotenes,* and the generic allocation of Texas *Eurycea* (Amphibia; Plethodontidae). *Herpetologica* 33(3):364–75.

976.22 ———. 1978. On the status of *Eurycea pterophila* (Amphibia: Plethodontidae). *Herpetologica* 34(1):101–108.

976.23 ———. 1982. A distributional analysis of epigean populations of *Eurycea neotenes* in central Texas, with comments on the origin of troglobitic populations. *Herpetologica* 38(3):430–44.

976.24 ———. 1984. Secondary contact and hybridization in the Texas cave salamanders *Eurycea neotenes* and *E. tridentifera. Copeia* 1984(2): 428–41.

977. Swingle, W. W. 1922. Experiments on the metamorphosis of neotenous amphibians. *J. Exper. Zool.* 36(4):397–421.

977.2 Switak, K. H. 1979. Leben in der Wüste Krötenechsen der Gattung *Phrynosoma* Wiegmann, 1828. Part 1: Beobachtungen in Freier Wildbahn. *Das Aquarium* 124:470–75.

977.21 ———. 1980. Frosche und Kröten die in Wüsten leben. *Das Aquarium* 138:649–56.

977.3 Szabuniewicz, M., and J. D. McCrady. 1967. A case of "Siamese" twins in the turtle (*Pseudemys scripta elegans*). *Texas J. Sci.* 19(2):232–33.

977.4 Tabor, S. P. 1985. Geographic distribution. *Sistrurus miliarius streckeri. Herp Rev.* 16(4):116.

977.41 ———. 1986a. Geographic distribution. *Rana catesbeiana. Herp Rev.* 17(1):26.

977.42 ———. 1986b. Geographic distribution. *Terrapene ornata ornata. Herp Rev.* 17(1):27–28.

977.5 Tabor, S. P., and C. T. McAllister. 1985. Geographic distribution. *Nerodia erythrogaster transversa. Herp Rev.* 16(3):84.

977.51 ———. 1986. Geographic distribution. *Pseudemys scripta elegans. Herp Rev.* 17(1):27.

978. Tamsitt, J. R. 1954. Mammals of two areas in the Big Bend region of Trans-Pecos Texas. *Texas J. Sci.* 6(1):33–61.

979. ———. Tanner, V. M. 1939. A study of the genus *Scaphiopus:* The spadefoot toads. *Great Basin Nat.* 1(1):3–26.

980. Tanner, W. W. 1944. A taxonomic study of the genus *Hypsiglena. Great Basin Nat.* 5(3–4):25–92.

981. ———. 1966. A re-evaluation of the genus *Tantilla* in the southwestern United States and northwestern Mexico. *Herpetologica* 22(2):134–52.

982. Tanner, W. W., and B. H. Banta. 1963. The systematics of *Crotaphytus wislizeni,* the leopard lizards. Part I. A redescription of *Crotaphytus wislizeni wislezeni* Baird and Girard, and a description of a new subspecies from the upper Colorado River Basin. *Great Basin Nat.* 23(3–4):129–48.

982.1 ———. 1977. The systematics of *Crotaphytus wislizenii,* the leopard lizard. Part III. The leopard lizards of the Great Basin and adjoining areas, with description of a new subspecies from the Lahontan Basin. *Great Basin Nat.* 37(2):225–40.

983. Tanner, W. W., and R. B. Loomis. 1957. A taxonomic and distributional study of the western subspecies of the milk snake, *Lampropeltis doliata. Trans. Kansas Acad. Sci.* 60:12–42.

984. Tanzer, E. C. 1965. Albinism in the Texas ratsnake, *Elaphe obsoleta lindheimeri* (Baird and Girard). *Texas J. Sci.* 17(2):237–38.

984.1 ———. 1970. Polymorphism in the *mexicana* complex of kingsnakes, with notes on their natural history. *Herpetologica* 26(4):419–28.

985. Tanzer, E. C., E. O. Morrison, and C. Hoffpauir. 1966. New locality records for amphibians and reptiles in Texas. *Southwest. Nat.* 11(1):131–37.

985.5 Taub, Aaron M. 1967. Comparative histological studies on Duvernoy's gland of colubrid snakes. *Bull. Amer. Mus. Nat. Hist.* 138(1):1–50.

986. Taylor, E. H. 1931a. The discovery of a lizard *Sceloporus torquatus cyanogenys* Cope in Texas, new to the fauna of the United States. *Proc. Biol. Soc. Washington* 44:129–32.

987. ———. 1931b. Notes on two specimens of the rare snake *Ficimia cana* and the description of a new species of *Ficimia* from Texas. *Copeia* 1931(1):4–7.

988. ———. 1932. *Leptodactylus albilabris* (Gunther): A species of toad new to the fauna of the United States. *Univ. Kansas Sci. Bull.* 20(11): 243–45.

989. ———. 1935a. A new species of the genus *Eumeces* from New Mexico. *Univ. Kansas Sci. Bull.* 22(11):219–23.

990. ———. 1935b. A taxonomic study of the cosmopolitan scincoid lizards of the genus *Eumeces* with an account of the distribution and relationships of its species. *Univ. Kansas Sci. Bull.* 23:1–643.

991. ———. 1936. Notes and comments on certain American and Mexican snakes of the genus *Tantilla* with descriptions of new species. *Trans. Kansas Acad. Sci.* 39:335–48.

992. ———. 1938a. Notes on Mexican snakes of the genus *Leptodeira*, with a proposal of a new snake genus *Pseudoleptodeira*. *Univ. Kansas Sci. Bull.* 25(15):315–44.

993. ———. 1938b. Notes on the herpetological fauna of the Mexican state of Sinaloa. *Univ. Kansas Sci. Bull.* 24(20):505–37.

994. ———. 1938c. On Mexican snakes of the genera *Trimorphodon* and *Hypsiglena*. *Univ. Kansas Sci. Bull.* 25(16):357–83.

995. ———. 1939a. On North American snakes of the genus *Leptotyphlops*. *Copeia* 1939(1):1–7.

996. ———. 1939b. Herpetological miscellany no. 1. *Univ. Kansas Sci. Bull.* 24(15):489–571.

997. ———. 1940. Palatal sesamoid bones and palatal teeth in *Cnemidophorus*, with notes on these teeth in other saurian genera. *Proc. Biol. Soc. Washington* 53:119–24.

998. ———. 1943. Mexican lizards of the genus *Eumeces*, with comments on the recent literature of the genus. *Univ. Kansas Sci. Bull.* 24(5): 269–300.

999. ———. 1944. Present location of certain herpetological and other type specimens. *Univ. Kansas Sci. Bull.* 30(11):117–87.

1000. ———. 1947. A bibliography of Mexican amphibiology. *Univ. Kansas Sci. Bull.* 34(17):543–89.

1001.   Taylor, E. H., and J. S. Wright. 1932. The toad *Bufo marinus* (Linnaeus) in Texas. *Univ. Kansas Sci. Bull.* 20(12):247–49.

1002.   Taylor, H. L. 1965. Morphological variation in selected populations of the teiid lizards *Cnemidophorus velox* and *Cnemidophorus inornatus*. *Univ. Colorado Stud. Ser. Biol.* No. 21:1–27.

1003.   Taylor, W. E. 1895. The box tortoises of North America. *Proc. United States Nat. Mus.* 17:573–88.

1003.2 Telford, S. R., Jr. 1978. Saurian malaria in Texas. *J. Parasitol.* 64(3): 553–54.

1003.25 Tennant, A. 1984. *The snakes of Texas*. Austin: Texas Monthly Press.

1003.26 ———. 1985. *A field guide to Texas Snakes*. Austin: Texas Monthly Press.

1003.3 Thomas, R. A. 1974. A checklist of Texas amphibians and reptiles. *Tech. Ser. Texas Parks & Wildlife Dept.* 17:1–15.

1003.31 ———. 1976. A checklist of Texas amphibians and reptiles. *Tech. Ser. Texas Parks & Wildlife Dept.* 17:1–16.

1003.4 Thomas, R. A., B. J. Davis, and M. R. Culbertson. 1976. Notes on variation and home-range of the Louisiana pine snake *Pituophis melanoleucus ruthveni* Stull (Reptilia: Serpentes: Colubridae). *J. Herp.* 10(3): 252–54.

1003.41 Thomas, R. A., and F. S. Hendricks. 1976. Letisimulation in *Virginia striatula* (Linnaeus). *Southwest. Nat.* 21(1):123–24.

1004.   Thompson, F. G. 1957. A new Mexican garter-snake (genus *Thamnophis*) with notes on related forms. *Occ. Papers Mus. Zool. Univ. Michigan* 584:1–10.

1004.5 Thornton, O. W., and R. A. Thomas. 1976. The status of the Houston toad, *Bufo houstonensis. Herp Rev.* 7(2):98–99.

1005.   Thornton, W. A. 1955. Interspecific hybridization in *Bufo woodhousei* and *Bufo valliceps. Evolution* 9:455–68.

1006.   ———. 1960. Population dynamics in *Bufo woodhousei* and *Bufo valliceps. Texas J. Sci.* 12(3–4):176–200.

1006.5 Thurmond, J. T. 1969. Notes on mosasaurs from Texas. *Texas J. Sci.* 21(1):69–80.

1006.51 ———. 1974. Lower vertebrate faunas of the Trinity division in north-central Texas. *Geoscience and Man* 8:103–29.

1007.   Tihen, J. A. 1948. A new *Gerrhonotus* from San Luis Potosí. *Trans. Kansas Acad. Sci.* 51:302–305.

1008.   ———. 1960. Notes on Late Cenozoic hylid and leptodactylid frogs from Kansas, Oklahoma, and Texas. *Southwest. Nat.* 5(2):66–70.

1008.1   ———. 1962a. Osteological observations on new world *Bufo*. *Amer. Midl. Nat.* 67(1):157–83.

1009.   ———. 1962b. A review of New World fossil bufonids. *Amer. Midl. Nat.* 68(1):1–50.

1009.1   ———. 1969. *Ambystoma*. *Cat. Amer. Amphib. Rept.* 75.1–75.4.

1010.   Tinkle, D. W. 1951. Peculiar behavior of indigo snakes in captivity. *Copeia* 1951(1):77–78.

1011.   ———. 1958. The systematics and ecology of the *Sternothaerus carinatus* complex (Testudinata: Chelydridae). *Tulane Stud. Zool.* 6(1):4–56.

1012.   ———. 1959. Observations on the lizards *Cnemidophorus tigris, Cnemidophorus tessellatus* and *Crotaphytus wislizeni*. *Southwest. Nat.* 4(4):195–200.

1013.   ———. 1961a. Geographic variation in reproduction, size, sex ratio, and maturity of *Sternothaerus odoratus* (Testudinata: Chelydridae). *Ecology* 42(1):68–76.

1014.   ———. 1961b. Population structure and reproduction in the lizard *Uta stansburiana stejnegeri*. *Amer. Midl. Nat.* 66(1):206–34.

1015.   ———. 1962. Reproductive potential and cycles in female *Crotalus atrox* from northwestern Texas. *Copeia* 1962(2):306–13.

1016.   ———. 1965a. Population structure and effective size of a lizard population. *Evolution* 19(4):569–73.

1017.   ———. 1965b. Effects of radiation on the natality, density and breeding structure of a natural population of lizards, *Uta stansburiana*. *Health Phys.* 11:1595–99.

1017.1   ———. 1967. Home range, density, dynamics, and structure of a Texas population of the lizard *Uta stansburiana*. Pp. 5–29 in *Lizard ecology. A symposium*, edited by W. W. Milstead. Columbia: University of Missouri Press.

1017.2   ———. 1967. The life and demography of the side-blotched lizard, *Uta stansburiana*. *Misc. Publ. Mus. Zool. Univ. Michigan*. 132:1–182.

1017.3   ———. 1972. The role of environment on the evolution of life history differences within and between lizard species. Pp. 77–100 in *A symposium on ecosystematics*, edited by R. T. Allen and F. C. James. *Univ. Arkansas Mus. Occ. Papers* 4.

1017.4   Tinkle, D. W., and R. E. Ballinger. 1972. *Sceloporus undulatus:* A study of the intraspecific comparative demography of a lizard. *Ecology* 53(4):570–84.

1018.   Tinkle, D. W., and R. Conant. 1961. The rediscovery of the water snake, *Natrix harteri,* in western Texas, with the description of a new subspecies. *Southwest. Nat.* 6(1):33–44.

1019.   Tinkle, D. W., and L. Curtis. 1951. The coal skink, *Eumeces anthracinus* Baird in Texas. *Field and Lab.* 19(2):85–86.

1020.   Tinkle, D. W., and L. N. Irwin. 1965. Lizard reproduction: Refractory period and response to warmth in *Uta stansburiana* females. *Science* 148 (3677):1613–14.

1021.   Tinkle, D. W., and G. N. Knopf. 1964. Biologically significant distribution records for amphibians and reptiles in northwest Texas. *Herpetologica* 20(1):42–47.

1022.   Tinkle, D. W., and W. C. Lawrence. 1956. Blowguns for reptile sampling. *Southwest. Nat.* 1(3):133–34.

1023.   Tinkle, D. W., D. McGregor, and S. Dana. 1962. Home range and ecology of *Uta stansburiana stejnegeri. Ecology* 43(2):223–29.

1024.   Tinkle, D. W., and R. G. Webb. 1955. A new species of *Sternothaerus* with a discussion of the *Sternothaerus carinatus* complex. *Tulane Stud. Zool.* 3(3):53–67.

1024.1   Tinkle, D. W., and D. W. Woodward. 1967. Relative movements of lizards in natural populations as determined from recapture radii. *Ecology* 48(1):166–68.

1025.   Trapido, H. 1941. A new species of *Natrix* from Texas. *Amer. Midl. Nat.* 25(3):673–80.

1026.   ———. 1942. *Thamnophis angustirostris* in Texas. *Copeia* 1942(1):54.

1027.   ———. 1944. Snakes of the genus *Storeria. Amer. Midl. Nat.* 31(1): 1–84.

1027.2   Trauth, S. E. 1983. *Cnemidophorus gularis* (Texas spotted whiptail). Hibernation. *Herp Rev.* 14(3):73.

1027.25   ———. 1985. Nests, eggs, and hatchlings of the Mediterranean gecko, *Hemidactylus turcicus* (Sauria: Gekkonidae), from Texas. *Southwest. Nat.* 30(2):309–10.

1028.   Treadwell, R. W. 1962. Extension of range of Mediterranean gecko. *Copeia* 1962(2):434–35.

1029.   ———. 1966. Distribution of the leopard lizard, *Crotaphytus wislizeni,* in Texas. *Southwest. Nat.* 11(3):412.

1029.5 Treadwell, R. W., and T. Hibbitts. 1969. *Tantilla diabola* from Val Verde County, Texas. *Texas J. Sci.* 20(3):281–82.

1030. Troschel, H. 1850. *Cophosaurus texanus,* neue Eidechsengatlung aus Texas. *Arch. f. Naturg. esch.* 16(1):388–94.

1031. True, F. W. 1881. On the North American land tortoises of the genus *Xerobates. Proc. United States Nat. Mus.* 4:434–49.

1032. ———. 1883. On the bite of the North American coral snakes (genus *Elaps*). *Amer. Nat.* 17:26–31.

1032.2 Tryon, B. W. 1976. Second generation reproduction and courtship behavior in the Trans-Pecos ratsnake, *Elaphe subocularis. Herp Rev.* 7(4):156–57.

1032.21 ———. 1979. An unusually patterned specimen of the gray-banded kingsnake, *Lampropeltis mexicana alterna* (Brown). *Herp Rev.* 10(1): 4–5.

1032.33 Tryon, B. W., and R. K. Guese. 1984. Death-feigning in the gray-banded kingsnake *Lampropeltis alterna. Herp Rev.* 15(4):108–109.

1032.4 Tryon, B. W., and H. K. McCrystal. 1982. Life history notes. *Micrurus fulvius tenere. Herp Rev.* 13(2):47–48.

1032.41 Tryon, B. W., and J. B. Murphy. 1982. Miscellaneous notes on the reproductive biology of reptiles 5. Thirteen varieties of the genus *Lampropeltis,* species *mexicana, triangulum* and *zonata. Trans. Kansas Acad. Sci.* 85(2):96–119.

1032.7 Turcotte, R. 1968. The alligator lizards. *Herpetology* 2(2):7.

1032.8 Turner, E. H. 1977. Colorful kingsnake of the Trans-Pecos. *Texas Parks and Wildlife* 35(1):10–11.

1033. Turner, F. B. 1960. Post metamorphic growth in anurans. *Amer. Midl. Nat.* 64(2):327–38.

1034. ———. 1962. The demography of frogs and toads. *Quart. Rev. Biol.* 37(4):303–14.

1034.2 Turner, F. B., R. J. Mennrich, and J. D. Weintraub. 1969. Home ranges and body size of lizards. *Ecology* 50(6):1076–81.

1035. Tutor, B. M. 1962. Nesting studies of the boat-tailed grackle. *Auk* 79: 77–84.

1036. Uhlenhuth, E. 1919. Observations on the distribution of the blind Texas cave salamander, *Typhlomolge rathbuni. Copeia* 1919(1):26–27.

1037. ———. 1921. Observations on the distribution and habits of the blind cave salamander, *Typhlomolge rathbuni. Biol. Bull.* 40:73–104.

1038.   ———. 1923. The endocrine system of *Typhlomolge rathbuni*. *Biol. Bull.* 45:303–24.

1039.   ———. 1924. The interal secretions in growth and development of amphibians. *Amer. Nat.* 55:193–221.

1040.   Ulrich, C. J. 1902. A contribution to the subterranean fauna of Texas. *Trans. Amer. Micro. Soc.* 23:83–101.

1040.5   Vaeth, R. H. 1980. Observation of ophiophagy in the western hooknose snake, *Gyalopion canum. Bull. Maryland Herp. Soc.* 16(3):94–96.

1041.   Valentine, B. D. 1963. The salamander genus *Desmognathus* in Mississippi. *Copeia* 1963(1):130–39.

1042.   Valett, B. B., and D. L. Jameson. 1961. The embryology of *Eleutherodactylus augusti latrans. Copeia* 1961(1):103–109.

1042.1   Vance, T. 1978. A field key to the whiptail lizards (genus *Cnemidophorus*) Part I: The whiptails of the United States. *Bull. Maryland Herp. Soc.* 14(1):1–9.

1042.11 ———. 1980a. New locality records of some Texas amphibians. *Bull. Chicago Herp. Soc.* 15(1):18–21.

1042.12 ———. 1980b. Notes concerning locality data of some Texas reptiles. Part I: New county records. *Bull. Chicago Herp. Soc.* 15(3):70–76.

1042.13 ———. 1981a. Geographic distribution. *Anolis c. carolinensis. Herp Rev.* 12(1):13.

1042.14 ———. 1981b. Geographic distribution. *Elaphe guttata emoryi. Herp Rev.* 12(1):14.

1042.15 ———. 1981c. Geographic distribution. *Elaphe obsoleta lindheimeri. Herp Rev.* 12(1) 14.

1042.16 ———. 1983a. A brief survey of the literature concerning sound production of *Anolis* lizards with notes on *Anolis carolinensis* Voigt. *Trans. Dallas Herp. Soc.* 1983(3):1–4.

1042.17 ———. 1983b. Morphological variation within a population of the Texas whiptail lizard (*Cnemidophorus gularis gularis*). *Trans. Dallas Herp. Soc.* 1983(6):1–6.

1042.18 ———. 1984. A note on the vocalizing ability of the Texas spotted whiptail lizard (*Cnemidophorus gularis gularis*). *Vipera* 1(7):7–9.

1042.3   Vance, T., and M. Edwards. 1980. Geographic distribution. *Storeria dekayi texana. Herp Rev.* 11(2):39.

1042.4   Vance, T., and G. Taplin. 1977. Another yellow albino amphibian. *Herp Rev.* 8(1):4–5.

1043.   Vancleave, H. J. 1916. Seasonal distribution of some Acanthocephala from fresh-water hosts. *J. Parasit.* 2(3):106–10.

1044.   Vandel, A. 1964. *Biospéléologie, la biologie des animaux cavernicoles.* Paris: Gauthier—Villians.

1045.   Van Denburgh, J. 1922a. A fourth specimen of a rare snake from Texas. *Copeia* 1922(1):24.

1045.1   ———. 1922b. The reptiles of western North America. Vol. I. Lizards. *Occ. Papers California Acad. Sci.* 10(1):3–611.

1045.11   ———. 1922c. The reptiles of western North America. Vol. II. Snakes and turtles. *Occ. Papers California Acad. Sci.* 10(2):617–1028.

1045.2   Van Devender, T. R. 1967. Albinism in the eastern hog-nosed snake, *Heterodon platyrhinos platyrhinos* (Latreille). *Herpetologica* 23(1):70.

1045.21   ———. 1969. A record of albinism in the canyon tree frog *Hyla arenicolor* Cope. *Herpetologica* 25(1):69.

1045.22   ———. 1976. The desert tortoise (*Gopherus agassizi*) in the Pleistocene of the northern Chihuahuan Desert. *Herpetologica* 32(3):298–304.

1045.23   Van Devender, T. R., and K. B. Moodie. 1977. The desert tortoise in the late Pleistocene, with comments about its earlier history. *Desert Tortoise Council Sym. Proc.* 1977:41–45.

1045.3   Vandeventer, T. 1973. Open letter to the society. *Bull. Chicago Herp. Soc.* 8(3–4):27–28.

1046.   Van Tyne, J., and G. M. Sutton. 1937. The birds of Brewster County, Texas. *Misc. Publ. Mus. Zool. Univ. Michigan* 37.

1046.5   Vincent, J. W. 1982a. Phenotypic variation in *Crotalus lepidus lepidus* (Kennicott). *J. Herp.* 16(2):189–91.

1046.51   ———. 1982b. Color pattern variation in *Crotalus lepidus lepidus* (Viperidae) in southwestern Texas. *Southwest. Nat.* 27(3):263–72.

1047.   Viosca, P., Jr. 1924. A contribution to our knowledge of the water snakes. *Copeia* 1924(1):3–13.

1047.05   Vitt, L. J., and J. M. Howland. 1985. The effect of formalin fixation on weight of lizard eggs. *J. Herp.* 19(2):298–99.

1047.1   Vogt, R. C. 1981. *Graptemys versa. Cat. Amer. Amphib. Rept.* 280.1–280.2.

1047.15   Vogt, R. C., and C. J. McCoy. 1980. Status of the emydine turtle genera *Chrysemys* and *Pseudemys. Ann. Carnegie Mus.* 49(5):93–102.

1047.2   Voigt, W. G., and C. R. Johnson. 1976. Aestivation and thermoregula-
          tion in the Texas tortoise. *Gopherus berlandieri. Comp. Biochem.
          Physiol.* (A) 53(1):41–44.

1047.21   ———. 1977. Physiological control of heat exchange rates in the Texas
          tortoise, *Gopherus berlandieri. Comp. Biochem. Physiol.* (A) 56(4):
          495–98.

1048.   Voss, W. J. 1961. Rate of larval development and metamorphosis of
          the spadefoot toad, *Scaphiopus bombifrons. Southwest. Nat.* 6(3–4):
          168–74.

1048.2   Wade, J. K., A. C. Echternacht, and G. F. McCracken. 1983. Genetic
          variation and similarity in *Anolis carolinensis* (Sauria: Iguanidae).
          Copeia 1983(2):523–29.

1048.4   Wade, M., and F. L. Rose. 1972. A comparison of the hemoglobin of lar-
          val and transformed *Ambystoma tigrinum. Copeia* 1972(4):889–92.

1048.5   Wade, V. E. 1968. A range extension of the water snake, *Natrix harteri
          harteri* Trapido. *Texas J. Sci.* 20(2):194–96.

1049.   Wake, D. B. 1966. Comparative osteology and evolution of the lungless
          salamanders, family Plethodontidae. *Mem. Southern California Acad.
          Sci.* 4:1–111.

1049.2   Walker, J. M. 1980. Accessory femoral pores in a colony of the collared
          lizard, *Crotaphytus collaris,* in Texas. *J. Herp.* 14(4):417–18.

1049.9   Walker, J. M., et al. 1986. Geographical distribution, *Cnemidophorus
          laredoensis. Herp Rev.* 17(1):26–27.

1050.   Ward, J. B. 1921. A new blood fluke from turtles. *J. Parasit.* 21(3):
          144–48.

1050.01   Ward, J. P. 1978. *Terrapene ornata. Cat. Amer. Amphib. Rept.* 217.1–
          217.4.

1050.02   ———. 1984. Relationships of chrysemyd turtles of North America.
          (Testudines: Emydidae). *Sp. Publ. Mus. Texas Tech Univ.* 21:1–50.

1050.11   Ward, R. 1982a. Geographic distribution. *Scaphiopus couchi. Herp Rev.*
          13(3):80.

1050.12   ———. 1982b. Geographic distribution. *Ophisaurus attenuatus. Herp
          Rev.* 13(3):80–81.

1050.13   ———. 1982c. Geographic distribution. *Tropidoclonion lineatum. Herp
          Rev.* 13(3):82.

1050.14   ———. 1983. Geographic distribution. *Sistrurus catenatus. Herp Rev.*
          14(1):28.

1050.15 ———. 1985. Geographic distribution. *Nerodia rhombifera*. *Herp Rev.* 16(4):116.

1051. Wasserman, A. O. 1957. Factors affecting interbreeding in sympatric species of spadefoots (*Scaphiopus*). *Evolution* 11(3):320–38.

1052. ———. 1958. Relationships of allopatric populations of spadefoots (genus *Scaphiopus*). *Evolution* 13(3):311–18.

1053. ———. 1963. Further studies of hybridization in spadefoot toads. *Copeia* 1963(1):115–18.

1054. ———. 1964. Recent and summarized interspecific hybridization within the Pelobatidae. *Texas J. Sci.* 16(3):334–41.

1054.1 ———. 1968. *Scaphiopus holbrookii*. *Cat. Amer. Amphib. Rept.* 70.1–70.4.

1054.11 ———. 1970a. *Scaphiopus couchi*. *Cat. Amer. Amphib. Rept.* 85.1–85.4.

1054.12 ———. 1970b. Chromosomal studies of the Pelobatidae (Salientia) and some instances of ploidy. *Southwest. Nat.* 15(2):239–48.

1054.2 Wasserman, A. O., and J. P. Bogart. 1968. Chromosomes of two species of spadefoot toads (genus *Scaphiopus*) and their hybrid. *Copeia* 1968(2):303–306.

1055. Watkins, J. F., II, F. R. Gehlbach, and R. S. Baldridge. 1967. Ability of the blind snake *Leptotyphlops dulcis*, to follow pheromone trails of army ants, *Neivamyrmex nigrescens* and *N. opacithorax*. *Southwest. Nat.* 12(4):455.

1055.1 Watkins, J. F., II., F. R. Gehlbach, and J. C. Kroll. 1969. Attractant-repellent secretions of blind snakes (*Leptotyphlops dulcis*) and their army ant prey (*Neivamyrmex nigrescens*). *Ecology* 50(6):1098–1102.

1055.2 Watkins, J. F., II, F. R. Gehlbach, and R. W. Plsek. 1972. Behavior of blind snakes (*Leptotyphlops dulcis*) in response to army ant (*Neivamyrmex nigrescens*) raiding columns. *Texas J. Sci.* 23(4):556–57.

1055.3 Watson, J. T. 1977. Effects of hypophysectomy in the lizard *Holbrookia propinqua*. *Texas J. Sci.* 29(3–4):255–62.

1055.4 Wauer, R. H. 1978. "Head Start" for an endangered turtle. *Natl. Parks Conserv.* 52(11):16–20.

1055.41 ———. 1980. *Naturalist's Big Bend. An introduction to the trees and shrubs, wildflowers, cacti, mammals, birds, reptiles and amphibians, fish, and insects.* College Station: Texas A&M University Press.

1056.5   Weaver, W. G., Jr. 1970. Courtship and combat behavior in *Gopherus berlandieri*. *Bull. Florida St. Mus.* 15(1):1–43.

1056.   Weaver, W. G., Jr., and F. L. Rose. 1967. Systematics, fossil history, and evolution of the genus *Chrysemys*. *Tulane Stud. Zool.* 14(2):63–73.

1057.   Webb, R. G. 1956. Size of sexual maturity in the male softshell turtle, *Trionyx ferox emoryi*. *Copeia* 1956(2):121–22.

1058.   ———. 1960. Type and type locality of the Gulf Coast spiny softshell turtle, *Trionyx spinifer asper* (Agassiz). *Brevoria* 129:1–10.

1059.   ———. 1961. A new kingsnake from Mexico, with remarks on the *mexicana* group of the genus *Lampropeltis*. *Copeia* 1961(3):326–33.

1060.   ———. 1962. North American recent softshell turtles (family Trionychidae). *Univ. Kansas Publ. Mus. Nat. Hist.* 13(10):429–611.

1061.   ———. 1966. Resurrected names for Mexican populations of black-necked garter snakes, *Thamnophis cyrtopsis* (Kennicott). *Tulane Stud. Zool.* 13(2):55–70.

1061.1   ———. 1973a. *Trionyx muticus*. *Cat. Amer. Amphib. Rept.* 139.1–139.2.

1061.11   ———. 1973b. *Trionyx spiniferus*. *Cat. Amer. Amphib. Rept.* 140.1–140.4.

1061.12   ———. 1980. *Thamnophis cyrtopsis*. *Cat. Amer. Amphib. Rept.* 245.1–245.4.

1062.   Webb, R. G., and R. L. Packard. 1961. Notes of some amphibians and reptiles from eastern Texas. *Southwest. Nat.* 6(2):105–107.

1063.   Webb. W. L. 1950. Biogeographic regions of Texas and Oklahoma. *Ecology* 31(3):426–33.

1064.   Werler, J. E. 1948. *Natrix cyclopion cyclopion* in Texas. *Herpetologica* 4(4):148.

1065.   ———. 1949a. Eggs and young of several Texas and Mexican snakes. *Herpetologica* 5(2):59–60.

1066.   ———. 1949b. Reproduction of captive Texas and Mexican lizards. *Herpetologica* 5(3):67–70.

1067.   ———. 1951. Miscellaneous notes on the eggs and young of Texas and Mexican reptiles. *Zoologica* 36:34–48.

1068.   ———. 1957. The poisonous snakes of Texas and the first aid treatment of their bites. *Bull. Texas Game and Fish Comm.* 31.

1069.   ———. 1964. Poisonous snakes of Texas and first aid treatment of their bite. *Bull. Texas Parks and Wildlife Dept.* 31 (revised).

1070.   Werler, J. E., and D. M. Darling. 1950a. *Rhinocheilus lecontei tessellatus* Garman in Tamaulipas, Mexico. *Herpetologica* 6(5):112.

1071.   ———. 1950b. A case of poisoning from the bite of a coral snake, *Micrurus f. tenere* Baird and Girard. *Herpetologica* 6(7):197–99.

1071.5   West, R. 1975. Texas Monthly reporter: Low talk—the Houston toad. *Texas Monthly* 3(10):12.

1072.   Whisenhunt, M. H., Jr. 1949. An account of copulation of the western diamond rattlesnake. *Chicago Acad. Sci. Nat. Hist. Misc.* 49:1–2.

1072.1   Whitaker, J. O., Jr., D. Rubin, and J. R. Munsee. 1977. Observations on food habits of four species of spadefoot toads, genus *Scaphiopus*. *Herpetologica* 33(4):468–75.

1072.13 Whitworth, R. J., and J. K. Wangberg. 1985. Parasitization of the Texas spotted whiptail lizard (*Cnemidophorus gularis*) by a sarcophagid fly (*Blaesoxipha plintopyga*): A new host record. *Southwest. Nat.* 30(1): 163–64.

1072.2   Wiest, J. A. 1977. Anuran succession at temporary ponds in a post oak savanna region. *Herp Rev.* 8(3) suppl. 20.

1072.21 ———. 1982. Anuran succession at temporary ponds in a post oak savanna region of Texas. Pp. 39–48 in *Herpetological communities*, edited by N. J. Scott. Washington, D.C.: USDI-FWS Wildlife Res. Rept. 13.

1072.3   Wilbern, S. E., and D. A. Ingold. 1983. Sexual dimorphism in *Terrapene* shells. *Bull. Chicago Herp. Soc.* 18(2):34–36.

1073.   Wiley, G. O. 1929. Notes on the Texas rattlesnakes in captivity with special reference to the birth of a litter of young. *Bull. Antivenin Inst. Amer.* 3(1):8–14.

1073.1   Wilkins, K. T., and D. J. Schmidly. 1980. Highway mortality of vertebrates in southeastern Texas. *Texas J. Sci.* 32(4):343–50.

1074.   Wilks, B. J. 1962. The pine snake in central Texas. *Herpetologica* 18(2): 108–10.

1075.   ———. 1963. Some aspects of the ecology and population dynamics of the pocket gopher (*Geomys bursarius*) in southern Texas. *Texas J. Sci.* 15(3):241–83.

1076.   Wilks, B. J., and H. E. Laughlin. 1962. Artificial hybridization between the microhylid genera *Hypopachus* and *Gastrophryne*. *Texas J. Sci.* 14(2):183–87.

1076.1   Wilks, B. J., and G. G. Raun. 1971. Sub-recent vertebrate remains from a site in southern Texas with comments on *Microtus (Pedomys) ludovicianus. Southwest. Nat.* 16(3–4):436–39.

1076.2   Willett, R. E. 1986. Solving the riddle of the Ridleys. *Exxon USA* 25(1): 13–15.

1077.   Williams, G. G. 1951. Rat snake overpowers a red-shouldered hawk, *Buteo lineatus. Auk* 68(3):372.

1077.1   Williams, K. L. 1978. Systematics and natural history of the American milk snake, *Lampropeltis triangulum. Milwaukee Publ. Mus. Contr. Biol. Geol.* 2:1–258.

1078.   Williams, K. L., and L. D. Wilson. 1967. A review of the colubrid snake genus, *Cemophora* Cope. *Tulane Stud. Zool.* 13(4):103–24.

1079.   Williams, K. L., B. C. Brown, and L. D. Wilson. 1966. A new subspecies of the colubrid snake *Cemophora coccinea* (Blumenbach) from southern Texas. *Texas J. Sci.* 18(1):85–88.

1080.   Williams, K. L., H. M. Smith, and P. S. Chrapliwy. 1960. Turtles and lizards from northern Mexico. *Trans. Illinois Acad. Sci.* 53(1–2): 36–45.

1080.1   Williams, M. 1979. A look at the common kingsnakes of the United States. *Occ. Papers Dallas Herp. Soc.* 1:11–14.

1080.2   Williams, S. 1982. Collecting the lined snake (*Tropidoclonion lineatum*) in Dallas (June, 1979). *Herptile* 7(1):15.

1081.   Wilson, L. D. 1966. The range of the Rio Grande racer in Mexico and the status of *Coluber oaxaca* (Jan). *Herpetologica* 22(1):42–47.

1081.1   ———. 1970a. The coachwhip snake, *Masticophis flagellum* (Shaw): Taxonomy and distribution. *Tulane Stud. Zool.* 16(2):31–99.

1081.11   ———. 1970b. The racer *Coluber constrictor* (Serpentes: Colubridae) in Louisiana and eastern Texas. *Texas J. Sci.* 22(1):67–85.

1081.12   ———. 1973a. *Masticophis. Cat. Amer. Amphib. Rept.* 144.1–144.2.

1081.13   ———. 1973b. *Masticophis flagellum. Cat. Amer. Amphib. Rept.* 145.1–145.4.

1081.14   ———. 1975a. *Drymobius. Cat. Amer. Amphib. Rept.* 170.1–170.2.

1081.15   ———. 1975b. *Drymobius margaritiferus. Cat. Amer. Amphib. Rept.* 172.1–172.2.

1081.16   ———. 1978. *Coluber constrictor. Cat. Amer. Amphib. Rept.* 218.1– 218.4.

1082. Winton, W. M. 1916. Habits and behavior of the Texas horned lizard, *Phrynosoma cornutum* Harlan, I. *Copeia* 1916(36):81–84.

1083. ———. 1917. Habits and behavior of the Texas horned lizard, *Phrynosoma cornutum* Harlan, II. *Copeia* 1917(39):7–8.

1084. Wolf, B. 1934–1938. *Animalium cavernarum catalogus.* 3 vols. The· Hague: W. Junk.

1084.1 Womochel, D. R. 1977. Taphonomy and paleoecology of the Slaton local fauna (Pleistocene, Texas). *Diss. Abst. Int.* B38(6):2597.

1084.2 Wood, R. C. 1977. Evolution of the emydine turtles *Graptemys* and *Malaclemys* (Reptilia: Testudines: Emydidae). *J. Herp.* 11(4):415–21.

1085. Woodbury, A. M., and D. M. Woodbury. 1942. Studies of the rat snake, *Elaphe laeta*, with description of a new subspecies. *Proc. Biol. Soc. Washington* 55:133–42.

1085.1 Worley, M. 1970. In search of *Natrix harteri. Bull. Chicago Herp. Soc.* 5(2):41–43.

1085.2 Worthington, R. D. 1973. Remarks on the distribution of the smooth green snake, *Opheodrys vernalis blanchardi* Grobman in Texas. *Southwest. Nat.* 18(3):344–46.

1085.21 ———. 1976. Herpetofauna of the Franklin Mountains, El Paso County, Texas. Pp. 205–12 in *El Paso Geological Society Symposium on the Franklin Mountains,* edited by D. V. Lemone and E. M. P. Lovejoy. El Paso Geol. Soc. Quinn Mem. Vol.

1085.22 ———. 1980. *Elaphe subocularis. Cat. Amer. Amphib. Rept.* 268.1– 268.2.

1085.23 ———. 1982. Dry and wet year comparisons of clutch and adult body sizes of *Uta stansburiana stejnegeri. J. Herp.* 16(3):332–34.

1085.3 Worthington, R. D., and E. R. Arvizo. 1974. Western records of the Davis Mountain kingsnake, *Lampropeltis mexicana alterna*, in Texas. *Southwest. Nat.* 19(3):330–31.

1086. Worthington, R. D., and M. C. Sabath. 1966. Winter aggregations of the lizard *Urosaurus ornatus ornatus* (Baird and Girard) in Texas. *Herpetologica* 22(2):94–96.

1087. Wright, A. H. 1925. Anent the harmless coral snake. *Science* 62: 493–94.

1088. ———. 1929. Synopsis and description of North American tadpoles. *Proc. United States Natl. Mus.* 74(11):1–70.

1089. ———. 1935. Some rare amphibians and reptiles of the United States. *Proc. Natl. Acad. Sci.* 21(6):340–45.

1090.　Wright, A. H., and A. A. Wright. 1927. Notes on *Sceloporus merriami* Stejneger. *Proc. Biol. Soc. Washington* 40:57–64.

1091.　―――. 1931. Some Stejneger species photographed from life. *Copeia* 1931(3):83–85.

1092.　―――. 1938. Amphibians of Texas. *Proc. Trans. Texas Acad. Sci.* 21(2): 5–44.

1093.　―――. 1949. *Handbook of frogs and toads of the United States and Canada.* Ithaca, N.Y.: Comstock Publ. Co.

1094.　―――. 1952. List of the snakes of the United States and Canada by states and provinces. *Amer. Midl. Nat.* 48(3):574–603.

1095.　―――. 1957. *Handbook of snakes of the United States and Canada.* Ithaca, N.Y.: Comstock Publ. Co.

1095.1　―――. 1967. *Handbook of snakes of the United States and Canada.* 3rd. ed. 2 vols. Ithaca, N.Y.: Cornell University Press.

1096.　Wright, J. W. 1963. *Cnemidophorus gularis* in New Mexico. *Southwest. Nat.* 8(1):56.

1096.1　―――. 1968. Variation in three sympatric sibling species of whiptail lizards, genus *Cnemidophorus. J. Herp.* 1(1–4):1–20.

1096.11　―――. 1971. *Cnemidophorus neomexicanus. Cat. Amer. Amphib. Rept.* 109.1–109.3.

1097.　Wright, J. W., and C. H. Lowe. 1965. The rediscovery of *Cnemidophorus arizonae* Van Denburgh. *J. Arizona Acad. Sci.* 3(3):164–68.

1097.1　―――. 1967. Hybridization in nature between parthenogenetic and bisexual species of whiptail lizards (genus *Cnemidophorus). Amer. Mus. Novitates* 2286:1–36.

1097.11　―――. 1968. Weeds, polyploids, parthenogenesis, and the geographical and ecological distribution of all-female species of *Cnemidophorus. Copeia* 1968(1):128–38.

1097.2　Wright, J. W., C. Spolsky, and W. M. Brown. 1983. The origin of the parthenogenic lizard *Cnemidophorus laredoensis* inferred from mitochondrial DNA analysis. *Herpetologica* 39(4):410–16.

1098.　Yarrow, H. C. 1882. Checklist of North American Reptilia and Batrachia with catalogue of specimens in the U.S. National Museum. *Bull. United States Natl. Mus.* 24:1–249.

1099.　―――. 1883. Description of new species of reptiles in the United States National Museum. *Proc. United States Natl. Mus.* 6:152–54.

1100.   York, C. L. 1949. Notes on home range and population density of two species of heteromyid rodents in southwestern Texas. *Texas J. Sci.* 1(2):42–46.

1100.1   Zimmerman, E. G., and C. W. Kilpatrick. 1973. Karyology of North American crotaline snakes (family Viperidae) of the genera *Agkistrodon*, *Sistrurus*, and *Crotalus*. *Canadian J. Genet. Cytol.* 15(3): 389–95.

1100.2   Zug, G. R., and A. Schwartz. 1971. *Deirochelys*. *Cat. Amer. Amphib. Rept.* 107.1–107.3.

1100.21   Zug, G. R., and P. B. Zug. 1979. The marine toad, *Bufo marinus:* A natural history resume of native populations. *Smithsonian Contr. Zool.* 284:1–58.

1101.   Zweifel, R. G. 1956a. Two pelobatid frogs from the Tertiary of North America and their relationships to fossil and recent forms. *Amer. Mus. Novitates* 1762:1–45.

1102.   ———. 1956b. A survey of the frogs of the *augusti* group, genus *Eleutherodactylus*. *Amer. Mus. Novitates* 1813:1–35.

1103.   ———. 1958. The lizard *Eumeces tetragrammus* in Coahuila, Mexico. *Herpetologica* 14:175.

1104.   ———. 1959a. *Cnemidophorus tigris variolosus*, a revived subspecies of whiptail lizard from Mexico. *Southwest. Nat.* 3:94–101.

1105.   ———. 1959b. Variation in and distribution of lizards of western Mexico related to *Cnemidophorus sacki*. *Bull. Amer. Mus. Nat. Hist.* 117(2): 61–116.

1106.   ———. 1965. Variation in and distribution of the unisexual lizard, *Cnemidophorus tesselatus*. *Amer. Mus. Novitates* 2235:1–49.

1106.1   ———. 1967 *Eleutherodactylus augusti*. *Cat. Amer. Amphib. Rept.* 41.1–41.4.

1107.   Zweifel, R. G., and C. H. Lowe. 1966. The ecology of a population of *Xantusia vigilis*, the desert night lizard. *Amer. Mus. Novitates* 2247: 1–57.

1108.   Zwinenberg, A. J. 1977. Kemp's Ridley, *Lepidochelys kempii* (Garman, 1880), undoubtedly the most endangered marine turtle today, with notes on the current status of *Lepidochelys olivacea*. *Bull. Maryland Herp. Soc.* 13(3):170–92.

7
Addenda

The following are additions to the Texas herpetological literature since the formal completion of the text of this volume. These numbers do not appear in the accounts of the species to which they refer.

5.12   Altig, R., and R. Lohoeffener. 1982. *Rana grylio* Stejneger. *Cat. Amer. Amphib. Rept.* 286.1–286.2.

5.13   ————. 1983. *Rana areolata* Baird and Girard. *Cat. Amer. Amphib. Rept.* 324.1–324.4.

9.5   Arnold, P. 1983. Come back Kemp's ridley. *Science 83* 4(8):68–71.

113.72   Bloom, R. A., K. W. Selcer, and W. K. King. 1986. Status of the introduced lizard, *Cyrtodactylus scaber,* in Galveston, Texas. *Southwest. Nat.* 31(1):129–31.

213.51   Censky, E. J. 1986. *Sceloporus graciosus* Baird and Girard. *Cat. Amer. Amphib. Rept.* 386.1–386.4.

216.21   Chatterjee, S. 1984. A new ornithischian dinosaur from the Triassic of North America. *Naturwissenschaften* 71(12):630–31.

218.2   Christman, S. P. 1982. *Storeria dekayi* (Holbrook). *Cat. Amer. Amphib. Rept.* 306.1–306.4.

221.2   Clary, J. C., III, and J. K. Leong. 1984. Disease studies aid Kemp's ridley sea turtle headstart research. *Herp Rev.* 15(3):69–70.

223.21   Cole, C. J., and L. M. Hardy. 1983a. *Tantilla atriceps* (Gunther). *Cat. Amer. Amphib. Rept.* 317.1–317.2.

223.22   ————. 1983b. *Tantilla hobartsmithi* Taylor. *Cat. Amer. Amphib. Rept.* 318.1–318.2.

233.4   Cooper, W. E., Jr. 1984. Female secondary sexual coloration and sex recognition in the keeled earless lizard, *Holbrookia propinqua. Animal Behav.* 32(4):1142–50.

233.51   Cooper, W. E., Jr., C. S. Adams, and J. L. Dobie. 1983. Female color change in the keeled earless lizard, *Holbrookia propinqua:* Relationship to the reproductive cycle. *Southwest. Nat.* 28(3):275–80.

267.01   Cuellar, O. 1984. Reproduction in a parthenogenetic lizard: With a discussion of optimal clutch size and a critique of the clutch weight/body weight ratio. *Amer. Midl. Nat.* 111(2):242–58.

296.12 Dial, B. E. 1986. Tail display in two species of iguanid lizards: A test of the "predator signal" hypothesis. *Amer. Nat.* 127(1):103–11.

296.32 Dial, B. E., and L. C. Fitzpatrick. 1983. Lizard tail autotomy: Function and energetics of postautotomy tail movement in *Scincella lateralis. Science* 219(4583):391–93.

323.23 Dunham, A. E. 1983. Realized niche overlap, resource abundance, and intensity of interspecific competition, Pp. 261–80 in R. B. Huey, E. R. Pianka, and T. W. Schoener, eds., *Lizard ecology: Studies of a model organism.* Cambridge, Mass.: Harvard University Press.

353.62 Ernst, C. H., and R. B. Bury. 1982. *Malaclemys* Gray. *Cat. Amer. Amphib. Rept.* 299.1–299.4.

359.15 Ferguson, G. W., and S. F. Fox. 1984. Annual variation of survival advantage of large juvenile side blotched lizards, *Uta stansburiana:* Its causes and evolutionary significance. *Evolution* 38(2):342–49.

368.3 Fitch, H. S. 1985. Variation in clutch and litter size in New World reptiles. *Univ. Kansas Mus. Nat. Hist. Misc. Pub.* 76:1–76.

377.11 Ford, N. B., and M. L. O'Bleness. 1986. Species and sexual specificity of pheromone trails of the garter snake, *Thamnophis marcianus. J. Herp.* 20(2):259–62.

384.39. Frost, D. R. 1983. *Sonora semiannulata* Baird and Girard. *Cat. Amer. Amphib. Rept.* 333.1–333.4.

454.15 Hardy, J. D., Jr., and R. J. Borroughs. 1986. Systematic status of the spring peeper, *Hyla crucifer* (Amphibia: Hylidae). *Bull. Maryland Herp. Soc.* 22(2):68–69.

472.1 Hedges, S. B. 1986. An electrophoretic analysis of holarctic hylid frog evolution. *Syst. Zool.* 35(1):1–17.

482.55 Hillis, D. M., J. S. Frost, and D. A. Wright. 1983. Phylogeny and biogeography of the *Rana pipiens* complex: A biochemical evaluation. *Syst. Zool.* 32(2):132–43.

495.55 Houseal, T. W., and J. L. Carr. 1983. Notes on the reproduction of *Kinosternon subrubrum* (Testudines: Kinosternidae) in east Texas. *Southwest. Nat.* 28(2):237–39.

510.52 Iverson, J. B. 1985. *Kinosternon hirtipes* (Wagler). *Cat. Amer. Amphib. Rept.* 361.1–361.4.

602.51 Long, D. R. 1986. Lipid content and delayed emergence of hatchling yellow mud turtles. *Southwest. Nat.* 31(2):244–46.

613.4 Martin, N. 1986a. The sweet smell of success. *Texas Shores* 19(2):11–14.

613.41 ———. 1986b. Mission possible. *Texas Shores* 19(2):19–22.

616.25 Mather, C. M., and J. W. Sites, Jr. 1985. *Sceloporus variabilis* Weigmann. *Cat. Amer. Amphib. Rept.* 373.1–373.3.

622.161 McAllister, C. T. 1985. *Nerodia rhombifera* (Hallowell). *Cat. Amer. Amphib. Rept.* 376.1–376.4.

630.29 McDaniel, V. R. 1969. An albino *Ambystoma tigrinum mavortium* Baird. *Tex. A&I Univ. Stud.* 2(1):4–5.

630.3 McDaniel, V. R., and J. P. Karges. 1983. *Farancia abacura* (Holbrook). *Cat. Amer. Amphib. Rept.* 314.1–314.4.

630.35 McDonald, H. S. 1974. Bradycardia during death-feigning of *Heterodon platyrhinos* Latreille (Serpentes). *J. Herp.* 8(2):157–64.

630.4 McIntyre, D. C. 1977a. Reproductive habits of captive Trans-Pecos rat snakes *Elaphe subocularis*. *J. N. Ohio Assoc. Herpetol.* 3(1):20–22.

630.41 ———. 1977b. First report of double embryos in *Elaphe subocularis*. *J. N. Ohio Assoc. Herpetol.* 3(2):29.

630.42 ———. 1978. The NOAH breeder's corner. *Notes from NOAH* 6(2):9.

642.09 Mecham, J. S. 1983. *Nerodia harteri* (Trapido). *Cat. Amer. Amphib. Rept.* 330.1–330.2.

665.1 Minton, S. A. 1983. *Sistrurus catenatus* (Rafinesque). *Cat. Amer. Amphib. Rept.* 332.1–332.2.

665.51 Mitchell, J. C. 1982. *Farancia* Gray. *Cat. Amer. Amphib. Rept.* 292.1–292.2.

718.11 Owens, D. 1981. Sea turtles face extinction today. *Marine Education* 2(2):1–3.

718.12 ———. 1986. The turtle lady. *Texas Shores* 19(2):15–18.

719.21 Parker, W. S. 1982a. *Sceloporus magister* Hallowell. *Cat. Amer. Amphib. Rept.* 290.1–290.4.

719.22 ———. 1982b. *Masticophis taeniatus* (Hallowell). *Cat. Amer. Amphib. Rept.* 304.1–304.4.

720.21 Parmley, D. 1984. Herpetofauna of the Coffee Ranch local fauna (Hemphillian Land Mammal Age) of Texas. Pp. 97–106 in *Festschrift for Walter W. Dalquest*, edited by N. V. Horner. Wichita Falls, Texas: Midwestern State University.

720.23 ———. 1986. Herpetofauna of the Rancholabrean Schulze Cave Local Fauna of Texas. *J. Herp.* 20(1):1–10.

732.61 Platt, D. R. 1983. *Heterodon* Latreille. *Cat. Amer. Amphib. Rept.* 315.1–315.2.

746.31 Price, A. H. 1982. *Crotalus scutulatus* (Kennicott). *Cat. Amer. Amphib. Rept.* 291.1–291.2.

784.4 Reynolds, S. L., and M. E. Seidel. 1982. *Sternotherus odoratus* (Latreille). *Cat. Amer. Amphib. Rept.* 287.1–287.4.

786.28 Root, W. R. 1977. Subocularis eggs hatch. *Notes from NOAH* 4(4):1–2.

789.6 Roze, J. A., and G. M. Tilger. 1983. *Micrurus fulvius* (Linnaeus). *Cat. Amer. Amphib. Rept.* 316.1–316.4.

813.5 Scott, N. J., and R. W. McDiarmid. 1984. *Trimorphodon* Cope. *Cat. Amer. Amphib. Rept.* 352.1–352.2.

813.51 ———. 1984. *Trimorphodon biscutatus* (Dumeril, Bibron, and Dumeril). *Cat. Amer. Amphib. Rept.* 353.1–353.4.

819.5 Sherbrooke, W. C. 1981. *Horned lizards: Unique reptiles of western North America.* Globe, Ariz.: Southwest Parks and Monument Assoc.

885.4 Steele, G. D., et al. 1984. Human and non-human skeletal remains recovered from Sorcerer's Cave. Terrell County, Texas. *Texas J. Sci.* 36(2–3):169–84.

976.8 Swinford, G. 1971. Herpetological research at the University of Texas at El Paso. *Bull. El Paso Herp. Soc.* 2(1):7–8.

1003.45 Thomas, R. A., S. A. Nadler, and W. L. Jagers. 1984. Helminth parasites of the endangered Houston toad, *Bufo houstonensis* Sanders, 1953 (Amphibia, Bufonidae). *J. Parasit.* 70(6):1012–13.

1027.22 Trauth, S. E. 1983b. Nesting habitat and reproductive characteristics of the lizard *Cnemidophorus sexlineatus* (Lacertilia: Teiidae). *Amer. Midl. Nat.* 109(2):289–99.

1061.3 Webb, R. G., and G. M. Ferguson. 1986. Morphological variation in the Trans-Pecos rat snake (*Elaphe subocularis*). *Southwest. Nat.* 31(1):118–21.

1077.2 Williams, K. L. 1985. *Cemophora* Cope. *Cat. Amer. Amphib. Rept.* 374.1–374.4.

1081.17 Wilson, L. D. 1982. *Tantilla. Cat. Amer. Amphib. Rept.* 307.1–307.4.

1095.8 Wright, J. 1971. Account of a field trip to Arizona and Texas. *Herpetology* 5(4):9–13.

Index of Common and Scientific Names

Amphibians and Reptiles of Texas was composed into type on a Linotron 202 phototypesetter in ten point Caledonia with two points of spacing between the lines. Caledonia bold italic was selected for display. The book was designed by George Alexandres, composed by G&S Typesetters, Inc., printed offset by Thomson-Shore, Inc., and bound by John H. Dekker & Sons. The paper on which this book is printed bears acid-free characteristics for an effective life of at least three hundred years.

TEXAS A&M UNIVERSITY PRESS : COLLEGE STATION